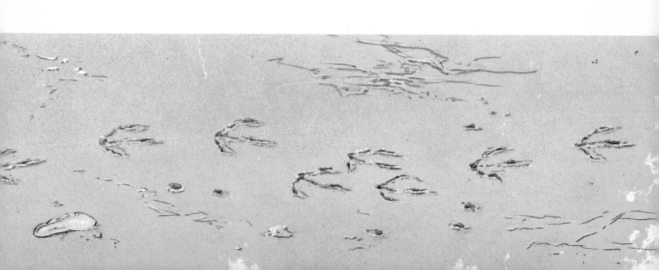

Monograph Series No. 2

published by the

Delaware Museum of Natural History

Greenville   Delaware

PHILIPPINE

BIRDS

by

John Eleuthère du Pont

With color illustrations by:

George Sandström

and

John R. Peirce

PHILIPPINE BIRDS

by

John Eleuthère duPont

Library of Congress catalog number 70-169119

Editorial production and design by *James H. Weidner Associates,* Cinnaminson, N.J. Manufactured in the United States of America at Kingsport Press, Kingsport, Tenn.

Foreword

A plan for a complete ornithological survey of the Philippines was "on the books" at the American Museum of Natural History a generation ago. The times were not propitious and it was never undertaken. My late good friend Tom Gilliard did explore portions of Luzon where he had campaigned as a soldier during World War II. Meanwhile, Jean Delacour and Ernst Mayr, then both at the American Museum, wrote their *Birds of the Philippines*. Intended as a guidebook for the thousands of troops in the Philippines, its chief drawback was the lack of illustrations in color. Nevertheless, in the absence of any modern work on Philippine birds, it was of great scientific as well as field value.

After World War II, ornithological investigations of the Philippines continued piecemeal. Several museums secured material from D. S. Rabor, who worked out of Silliman University on Negros Island and who is now affiliated with Mindanao State University. Canuto Manuel, G. Alcasid, and others did what they could, using the Philippine National Museum in Manila as a base despite the almost total destruction of the Museum there during the war. A few were able to visit and work in the Philippines from elsewhere, but usually on only one island or for brief periods. Among them were T. Gilliard, F. Salomonsen on Mindanao, A. L. Rand, and K. C. Parkes on Luzon.

It is too bad that these efforts have been so scattered, because more ornithological novelties came from the Philippines during and since World War II than from any comparable area on earth. Peruvian Amazonia and perhaps New Guinea were runners-up, but no more than that; it would be a reasonable guess that there are more new birds to be discovered on some of the remote Philippine mountains. Among those already known are several of which knowledge is fragmentary. The curious little fruit pigeon (*Ptilinopus arcanus*), described by S. D. Ripley and D. S. Rabor and known only from a single female specimen, is a good example.

Fortuitously, the time has arrived to bring together and summarize what is known of Philippine birds. John duPont has done exactly this in the present volume. A comparative newcomer to the study of Philippine ornis, he has amassed at the Delaware Museum of Natural History, which he founded, one of the finest collections of Philippine birds in existence. Of course, some specimens are absent, as they would be in any museum, but Mr. duPont has diligently sought them out in other institutions. He has also led significant expeditions in the Philippines, starting in 1958; and anyone who knows John duPont will realize that, once in the islands, he heads for the nearest mountains and jungles:

he is not one to dawdle about in the gardens of local officials.

Philippine Birds will speak for itself. It contains a colored figure, a description, and the range of most all species and races of Philippine birds. It is not a highly technical work, nor does it attempt to be erudite about what little is known of the habits and ecology of these birds.

The Philippines, notwithstanding their close association over the years with the United States, are not yet within the ken of the recently popular organized bird tours. This is unfortunate, because the rich tropical forest on which the choicer elements in the animal and plant life of these islands depend is being destroyed at an appalling rate. When timber is being slashed off and shipped, not merely to factories in the Philippines but to the United States and Japan, what can be expected? A legacy of erosion and floods will follow to haunt later generations; meanwhile the wildlife is gone forever. But while the islands remain off the beaten track of the bird tours, who will speak out against the unnatural pillage? If the present publication can help to halt such trends, even in a small way, it will be one of its most important services.

DEAN AMADON
New York

Introduction

The archipelago of the Philippines is a zoological crossroads of the southwest Pacific. Ever since its emergence from the Tethys Sea in the early Tertiary Period, its thousands of islands have been stepping stones for the invasions of land animals from Asia and Malaysia. The distributions of the birds have waxed and waned across the thousands of islands, very often forming isolated subspecies. The Philippines have been an interesting stage for the evolution of birds—one with a complex history.

The boundaries of the Philippine subregion are indistinct because of the impingement of neighboring faunas, such as the predominant Malaysian influence in Palawan and the Bornean affinities in the Sulu Archipelago and Mindanao. Zoogeographical accounts have previously been published in earlier books listed in our bibliography.

Twenty-five years have passed since the appearance of Delacour and Mayr's excellent *Birds of the Philippines*. Since that time an increase in field explorations and nomenclatorial changes has necessitated a fresh survey of this complex avian fauna. The purpose of this book is to present a ready identification guide to all the known Philippine birds, with a colored illustration of most species. The ecology and habits of these birds is sparsely known, and such a task for the future would be done best by workers who have lived in the Philippines and made field observations over a period of several seasons.

Our format is as simple as possible, with a brief description, original citations, and the Philippine occurrences accompanying the Latin and popular names. The type localities are added in parentheses at the end of each bibliographic reference.

All measurements are in millimeters and represent an average of a series. Soft-part colors have been taken from previous works and from labels; in the case of a discrepancy, the author has referred to his own field notes.

Birds known to be limited to the range listed have been designated as "Endemic."

Acknowledgments

I would like to express my deepest appreciation to Dr. Kenneth C. Parkes of the Carnegie Museum, who made available to me his most invaluable and extensive unpublished notes, and to Dr. Dean Amadon of the American Museum of Natural History. Both of these gentlemen read early versions of the text and offered invaluable suggestions in the planning and organizing of this book.

My thanks are also extended to the following persons for the loan of material, locality records, and kindnesses shown me when I visited their institutions: Mr. Rodolphe M. deSchauensee and Dr. Frank B. Gill of the Academy of Natural Sciences of Philadelphia; Dr. Charles Vaurie and Mrs. Mary K. Le Croy of the American Museum of Natural History; Dr. David W. Snow, Dr. Philip J. Burton, and Mr. Ian C. J. Galbraith of the British Museum (Natural History); Dr. Austin L. Rand and Mr. Melvin A. Traylor of the Chicago Field Museum; Dr. Oscar T. Owre of the University of Miami; Dr. Dioscoro S. Rabor of Mindanao State University; Dr. Canuto G. Manuel of the Philippine Bureau of Science; Dr. Godofredo L. Alcasid of the Philippine National Museum; Dr. S. Dillon Ripley and Dr. Richard L. Zusi of the United States National Museum; and Dr. Charles G. Sibley of the Yale Peabody Museum.

I also wish to express my thanks to artist George Sandström, who stopped other work to complete the Philippine plates where the late John R. Peirce had left off.

I am deeply indebted to my secretary, Mrs. Ann Wix, for her patience and care taken in preparing the manuscript for publication.

JOHN E. duPONT

Contents

Foreword v
Introduction vii
Acknowledgments viii
Systematic Arrangement of Families
    Podicipedidae—Grebes 1
    Procellariidae—Shearwaters 1
    Phaethontidae—Tropicbirds 3
    Pelecanidae—Pelicans 3
    Sulidae—Boobies 3
    Phalacrocoracidae—Cormorants 4
    Anhingidae—Anhingas 5
    Fregatidae—Frigatebirds 5
    Ardeidae—Herons 10
    Threskiornithidae—Ibises 22
    Ciconiidae—Storks 23
    Anatidae—Ducks 26
    Pandionidae—Ospreys 34
    Accipitridae—Hawks and Eagles 35
    Falconidae—Falcons 53
    Megapodiidae—Megapodes 54
    Phasianidae—Pheasants 55
    Turnicidae—Button-quail 57
    Gruidae—Cranes 66
    Rallidae—Rails 66
    Jacanidae—Jacanas 76
    Rostratulidae—Painted-snipe 77
    Charadriidae—Plovers 77
    Scolopacidae—Sandpipers 84
    Recurvirostridae—Stilts 102
    Phalaropodidae—Phalaropes 102
    Burhinidae—Thick-knees 103
    Glareolidae—Pratincoles 103
    Stercorariidae—Skuas 103
    Laridae—Gulls and Terns 104
    Columbidae—Pigeons and Doves 114
    Psittacidae—Parrots 139
    Cuculidae—Cuckoos 151
    Tytonidae—Barn Owls 166
    Strigidae—Owls 167
    Podargidae—Frogmouths 177

Caprimulgidae—Nightjars 178
Apodidae—Swifts 182
Hemiprocnidae—Tree Swifts 189
Trogonidae—Trogons 189
Alcedinidae—Kingfishers 190
Meropidae—Bee-eaters 206
Coraciidae—Rollers 207
Upupidae—Hoopoes 207
Bucerotidae—Hornbills 210
Capitonidae—Barbets 213
Picidae—Woodpeckers 216
Eurylaimidae—Broadbills 224
Pittidae—Pittas 224
Alaudidae—Larks 227
Hirundinidae—Swallows 232
Campephagidae—Cuckoo-shrikes 234
Dicruridae—Drongos 244
Oriolidae—Orioles 248
Corvidae—Crows 251
Paridae—Titmice 254
Sittidae—Nuthatches 257
Rhabdornithidae—Creepers 258
Timaliidae—Babblers 262
Pycnonotidae—Bulbuls 276
Irenidae—Leafbirds 286
Turdidae—Thrushes 290
Sylviidae—Old World Warblers 303
Muscicapidae—Old World Flycatchers 326
Motacillidae—Pipits 355
Artamidae—Wood-swallows 360
Laniidae—Shrikes 360
Sturnidae—Starlings 364
Nectariniidae—Sunbirds 372
Dicaeidae—Flowerpeckers 385
Zosteropidae—White-eyes 399
Incertae Sedis 408
Ploceidae—Weaverbirds 409
Estrildidae—Grass Finches, Mannikins, Waxbills 409
Fringillidae—Finches, Grosbeaks 415
Bibliography 421
Index 437

Philippine Birds

Family PODICIPEDIDAE   GREBES

COMMON DABCHICK   PLATE 1

Podiceps ruficollis philippensis (Bonnaterre, 1790)

1790   *Colymbus Philippensis* Bonnaterre, Tabl. Encyc. Meth., 1:58, (Philippines)

1948   *Podiceps ruficollis cotabato* Rand, Fieldiana: Zoology, **31**:201, (Cotabato
   Province, Mindanao)

Description: Head, neck, back, wings, upper breast, and tail tuft blackish brown; chin blackish brown; sides of face and throat chestnut; lower breast and abdomen white. Immature and nonbreeding birds differ by being duller, with the chin and sides of face buffy.

Soft Parts: Bill black; iris yellow; legs dark blue-black.

Measurements: Wing 105; tail 20; bill 21; tarsus 32.

Range: Freshwater lakes of the Philippines. (Endemic.)

BLACK-NECKED OR EARED GREBE   PLATE 1

Podiceps nigricollis nigricollis C. L. Brehm, 1831

1831   *Podiceps nigricollis* C. L. Brehm, Handb. Naturg. Vög. Deutsch., **1**:963,
   (Germany)

Description: In breeding plumage, head and neck dark gray-black; ear-tufts golden yellow; back, wings, rump, and tail tuft brown-black; breast and belly white with some rufous on the flanks. Wintering bird upperparts gray; underparts white.

Soft Parts: Bill black; iris red; feet gray-black.

Measurements: Wing 125; tail 20; bill 38; tarsus 23.

Range: Central Luzon (once); a straggler from Asia.

Family PROCELLARIIDAE   SHEARWATERS

WHITE-FACED SHEARWATER   PLATE 1

Puffinus leucomelas (Temminck, 1835)

1835   *Procellaria leucomelas* Temminck, Pl. Col., livr. 99, pl. 587, (Japan)

Description: Upperparts brown; sides of head, neck, and upperparts white; wings brown on top but white underneath; primaries tend to be darker.

Soft Parts: Bill dark brown; iris dark brown; feet pinkish.

Measurements: Wing 328; tail 139; bill 46; tarsus 51.

Range: Recorded from Luzon, Mindanao, and Negros; may breed on offshore islands.

WEDGE-TAILED SHEARWATER   PLATE 1

Puffinus pacificus chlororhynchus Lesson, 1831

1831   *Puffinus chlororhynchus* Lesson, Traité d' Orn., **8**:613, (Shark's Bay, Western
        Australia)

Description: Upperparts dark brown; underparts gray-brown.

Soft Parts: Bill rose; iris slate; feet rose.

Measurements: Wing 269; tail 125; bill 36; tarsus 45.

Range: Luzon (once); a straggler from the Pacific.

DARK-RUMPED PETREL

Pterodroma phaeopygia sandwichensis (Ridgway, 1884)

1884   *Oestrelata sandwichensis* Ridgway, in Baird, Brewer, and Ridgway's Water Bds.
        No. Am., **2**:395, (Hawaiian Islands)

Description: Upperparts dark gray; feathers of the back with light margins; underparts
white; under-wing white.

Soft Parts: Bill black; iris brown; legs and upper fourth of foot flesh color, rest of foot
blue-black.

Measurements: Wing 293; tail 145; bill 37; tarsus 35.

Range: Negros (once); a straggler from the central Pacific.

TAHITI PETREL

Pterodroma rostrata rostrata (Peale, 1848)

1848   *Procellaria rostrata* Peale, U. S. Expl. Expd., **8**:296, (Mts. of Tahiti)

Description: Upperparts blackish brown; throat and upper breast dark brown; belly and
under tail-coverts white; under-wing dark brown.

Soft Parts: Bill black; iris dark brown; legs yellowish flesh; feet black.

Measurements: Wing 285; tail 115; bill ♂38, ♀34; tarsus 47.

Range: Negros (once); a straggler from the central Pacific.

Family PHAETHONTIDAE TROPICBIRDS

WHITE-TAILED TROPICBIRD

Phaethon lepturus dorotheae Mathews, 1913

1913   *Phaethon lepturus dorotheae* Mathews, Austr. Av. Rec., **2**:7, (Queensland)

Description: All white except for stripe through eye, leading edge, and a bar on the base of the wing and the flanks, which are black.

Soft Parts: Bill yellowish, base gray; iris dark brown; legs pinkish; feet black.

Measurements: Wing 254; bill 46; tarsus 19.5.

Range: Negros (once); a straggler from the southwest Pacific.

Family PELECANIDAE PELICANS

PHILIPPINE PELICAN PLATE 2

Pelecanus philippensis Gmelin, 1789

1789   *Pelecanus philippensis* Gmelin, Syst. Nat., **1**:571, (Philippines)

Description: Almost all white; wings and tail grayer than the rest; primaries black; a brownish streak down back of neck.

Soft Parts: Bill pinkish yellow with blue spots; pouch purplish brown; iris dirty white; legs and feet light brown.

Measurements: Wing 514; tail 187; bill 311; tarsus 76.

Range: Luzon and Mindanao.

Family SULIDAE BOOBIES

BLUE-FACED BOOBY PLATE 1

Sula dactylatra personata Gould, 1846

1846   *Sula personata* Gould, Proc. Zool. Soc. London, p. 21, (Raine Island, north Queensland)

Description: All white except for wings and tail, which are dark brown. Immature—differs by having head, throat, and mantle dark brown.

Soft Parts: Bill, male brown, female pinkish; face bluish; iris yellow; feet olive-brown.

Measurements: Wing 435; tail 185; bill 102; tarsus 59.

Range: Small islands offshore from Luzon to Mindanao.

RED-FOOTED BOOBY   PLATE 1

Sula sula rubripes Gould, 1838

1838   *Sula rubripes* Gould, Syn. Bds. Austr., app. 7, (Raine Island, north Queensland)

Description: All white except for primaries, which are dark gray-brown. Immature—all brown with yellow legs.

Soft Parts: Bill blue with brown tip; face bluish; iris gray; feet red.

Measurements: Wing 395; tail 221; bill 78; tarsus 36.

Range: Small islands off Luzon, Mindanao, Negros, and Palawan.

BROWN BOOBY   PLATE 1

Sula leucogaster plotus (Foster, 1844)

1844   *Pelecanus Plotus* Foster, Descr. Anim., ed. Licht., p. 278, (New Caledonia)

Description: Head, neck, and upperparts brown; underparts white. Immature—all brown with yellow legs.

Soft Parts: Bill bluish; iris white; feet light green.

Measurements: Wing 390; tail 189; bill 99; tarsus 46.

Range: Small islands off Luzon, Mindanao, and Palawan.

Family PHALACROCORACIDAE   CORMORANTS

GREAT CORMORANT   PLATE 2

Phalacrocorax carbo sinensis (Shaw, 1801)

1801   *Pelecanus sinensis* Shaw, Nat. Misc., **13**:529, (China)

Description: All black with dull greenish gloss. Some white on head, neck, and thighs in breeding season.

Soft Parts: Bill black with a strong hook; iris emerald-green; feet black.

Measurements: Wing 348; tail 178; bill 75; tarsus 63.

Range: Northern Luzon and offshore islands.

Family ANHINGIDAE   ANHINGAS

ORIENTAL ANHINGA   PLATE 2

Anhinga rufa melanogaster Pennant, 1769

1769   *Anhinga melanogaster* Pennant, Ind. Zool., p. 13, (Ceylon and Java)

Description: Head and neck brown with a white stripe on side of neck; chin white; upper- and underparts, wings, and tail black; white flecks on wing-coverts and secondaries.

Soft Parts: Bill brown with light yellow-brown on sides; iris yellow; feet black.

Measurements: Wing 350; tail 226; bill 88; tarsus 42.

Range: Luzon, Mindanao, Mindoro, and Negros.

Family FREGATIDAE   FRIGATEBIRDS

GREATER FRIGATEBIRD   PLATE 2

Fregata minor minor (Gmelin, 1789)

1789   *Pelecanus minor* Gmelin, Syst. Nat., 1:572, (Christmas Island, Indian Ocean)

Description: Male—upperparts dark brown-black; wing-coverts buffy brown; underparts brown-black. Female—similar but has throat and breast white.

Soft Parts: Bill, male black, female red; iris dark brown; feet, male blackish brown, female pink.

Measurements: Wing 592; tail 382; bill 119; tarsus 18.

Range: Small islands in the Sulu Sea.

LESSER FRIGATEBIRD   PLATE 2

Fregata ariel ariel (G. R. Gray, 1845)

1845   *Atagen* [sic] *Ariel* G. R. Gray, Gen. Bds., **3**, pl. 185, (Raine Island, north Queensland)

Description: Male—all black with a purplish green gloss on head and neck; flanks white. Female—brown-black except for white collar, flanks, and breast.

Soft Parts: Bill gray; pouch red; iris black; feet black.

Measurements: Wing 510; tail 334; bill 68; tarsus 50.

Range: Bantayan, Cagayancillo, Luzon, Mindanao, Negros, and Palawan.

PLATE 1

A   WHITE-FACED SHEARWATER
     (Puffinus leucomelas)—page 1

B   WEDGE-TAILED SHEARWATER
     (Puffinus pacificus)—page 2

C   RED-FOOTED BOOBY
     (Sula sula)—page 4

D   BLUE-FACED BOOBY
     (Sula dactylatra)—page 3

E   BROWN BOOBY
     (Sula leucogaster)—page 4

F   BLACK-NECKED OR EARED GREBE
     (Podiceps nigricollis)—page 1

G   COMMON DABCHICK
     (Podiceps ruficollis)—page 1

PLATE 1

PLATE 2

A   GREATER FRIGATEBIRD
        (Fregata minor)—page 5

B   LESSER FRIGATEBIRD
        (Fregata ariel)—page 5

C   ORIENTAL ANHINGA
        (Anhinga rufa)—page 5

D   PHILIPPINE PELICAN
        (Pelecanus philippensis)—page 3

E   GREAT CORMORANT
        (Phalacrocorax carbo)—page 4

PLATE 2

Family ARDEIDAE   HERONS

COMMON BITTERN   PLATE 3

Botaurus stellaris stellaris (Linné, 1758)

1758   *Ardea stellaris* Linné, Syst. Nat., **1**:144, (Sweden)

Description: Upperparts light brown mottled with dark brown; chin and upper throat white; underparts buffy streaked with brown.

Soft Parts: Bill yellow-green, darker at tip; iris yellow; feet greenish.

Measurements: Wing 350; tail 110; bill 81; tarsus 110.

Range: Luzon (once); a straggler from Asia.

BLACK BITTERN   PLATE 3

Dupetor flavicollis flavicollis (Latham, 1790)

1790   *Ardea flavicollis* Latham, Ind. Orn., **2**:701, (India)

Description: Top of head and upperparts dark blue-black; chin and throat white with a dark chestnut stripe down the middle which becomes dark blue mottled with chestnut and white further down the neck as it approaches the breast; sides of neck golden yellow; breast and belly dark blue-black. Immature—browner and heavily streaked.

Soft Parts: Bill red-brown; iris light red; feet dark brown.

Measurements: Wing 216; tail 71; bill 89; tarsus 72.

Range: Cebu, Luzon, Marinduque, Mindanao, Negros, and Samar.

CHINESE LEAST BITTERN   PLATE 3

Ixobrychus sinensis sinensis (Gmelin, 1789)

1789   *Ardea Sinensis* Gmelin, Syst. Nat., **1**:642, (China)

1918   *Ixobrychus sinensis astrologus* Wetmore, Proc. Biol. Soc. Wash., **31**:83, (Laguna, Luzon)

Description: Male—top of head and crest black; mantle dark olive-green; wing-coverts light olive; primaries and tail black; sides of head and neck pale rufous; underparts white, streaked and washed with dark yellowish tan; under tail-coverts pure white. Female—streaked below. Immature—top of head streaked; heavy streaking on wing-coverts and breast.

Soft Parts: Bill, upper mandible dark brown, lower mandible light brown base with outer third olive; iris yellow; legs and feet yellow-green.

Measurements: Wing 128; tail 43; bill 56; tarsus 41.

Range: Found throughout the Philippines.

10

SCHRENCK'S LEAST BITTERN   PLATE 3

Ixobrychus eurhythmus (Swinhoe, 1873)

1873   *Ardetta eurhythma* Swinhoe, Ibis, p. 74, (Amoy, Shanghai)

Description: Top of head and crest black; sides of head and hind neck rufous; mantle, back, and rump dark chestnut; wing-coverts olive; primaries and tail gray; chin and sides of throat white; throat, breast, and belly light olive-tan with a row of blackish brown feathers that forms a streak from the chin to the belly; under tail-coverts white. Immature—heavily spotted with white above; underparts streaked.
Soft Parts: Bill dark brown; iris dirty yellow; legs and feet green.
Measurements: Wing 145; tail 41; bill 51; tarsus 45.
Range: Luzon, Mindanao, Mindoro, Negros, and Samar.

CINNAMON LEAST BITTERN   PLATE 3

Ixobrychus cinnamomeus (Gmelin, 1789)

1789   *Ardea cinnamomea* Gmelin, Syst. Nat., 1:643, (China)

Description: Male—top of head and upperparts dark cinnamon; chin and sides of throat white; breast and belly pale rufous; a row of dark brown feathers runs from the chin to the belly, forming a streak. Female—top of head dark brown; rest of upperparts rufous-brown with buffy edges to wing-coverts; underparts golden buff heavily streaked with dark brown. Immature—underparts streaked.
Soft Parts: Bill, upper mandible black, lower mandible yellow; iris yellow; tarsus yellow.
Measurements: Wing 150; tail 46; bill 53; tarsus 50.
Range: Found throughout the Philippines.

JAPANESE BITTERN   PLATE 3

Gorsachius goisagi (Temminck, 1835)

1835   *Nycticorax goisagi* Temminck, Pl. Col., livr. 98, pl. 582, (Japan)

Description: Head and crest chestnut; upperparts brown with dark vermiculations; flight feathers of wing black with rufous tips; primary coverts rufous; throat and neck buffy, a dark line down center of throat; underparts streaked black and buff. Immature—duller on head; darker and more uniform on back; wing-coverts more rufous.
Soft Parts: Bill greenish; iris yellow; feet green.
Measurements: Wing 260; tail 95; bill 43; tarsus 55.
Range: Leyte, Luzon, Mindanao, and Siquijor; a visitor from eastern Asia.

11

PLATE 3

A   COMMON BITTERN
     (Botaurus stellaris)—page 10

B   BLACK BITTERN
     (Dupetor flavicollis)—page 10

C   CHINESE LEAST BITTERN
     (Ixobrychus sinensis)—page 10

D   SCHRENCK'S LEAST BITTERN
     (Ixobrychus eurhythmus)—page 11

E   CINNAMON LEAST BITTERN
     (Ixobrychus cinnamomeus)—page 11

F   JAPANESE BITTERN
     (Gorsachius goisagi)—page 11

G   MALAY BITTERN
     (Gorsachius melanolophus)—page 18

A

B

C

D

E

F

G

SANDSTRÖM

PLATE 3

PLATE 4

A   LITTLE MANGROVE HERON
       (Butorides striatus)—page 18

B   CHINESE POND HERON
       (Ardeola bacchus)—page 19

C   CATTLE EGRET
       (Bubulcus ibis)—page 19

D   REEF EGRET
       (Egretta sacra)—page 19

E   CHINESE EGRET
       (Egretta eulophotes)—page 20

F   LITTLE EGRET
       (Egretta garzetta)—page 20

G   LESSER EGRET
       (Egretta intermedia)—page 20

H   GREATER EGRET
       (Egretta alba)—page 20

PLATE 4

PLATE 5

A   GIANT HERON
       (Ardea sumatrana)—page 21

B   GRAY HERON
       (Ardea cinerea)—page 21

C   PURPLE HERON
       (Ardea purpurea)—page 21

D   BLACK-CROWNED NIGHT HERON
       (Nycticorax nycticorax)—page 22

E   RUFOUS NIGHT HERON
       (Nycticorax caledonicus)—page 22

PLATE 5

MALAY BITTERN PLATE 3

Gorsachius melanolophus kutteri (Cabanis, 1881)

1881   *Butio Kutteri* Cabanis, Journ. f. Orn., **29**:425, (Philippines)

Description: Top of head and crest blue-black; sides of head and hind neck rufous; back, rump, and wings dark rufous with fine black streaks; primaries with white tips; tail black; chin and throat white with a row of blackish brown streaks that run down the neck; sides of neck olive-brown; breast, belly, and under tail-coverts white with buff, rufous, and black streaks.

Soft Parts: Bill, upper mandible black, lower mandible grayish green; iris yellow; feet olive-green. Immature—upperparts brown spotted with black; crest black with white spots; underparts buffy streaked with dark brown.

Measurements: Wing 256; tail 113; bill 44; tarsus 65.

Range: Found throughout the Philippines, except Palawan.

Gorsachius melanolophus rufolineatus Hachisuka, 1926

1926   *Gorsachius melanolophus rufolineatus* Hachisuka, Ibis, p. 591, (Iwahig, Palawan)

Description: Differs from *kutteri* by being darker above and with richer chestnut on neck.

Range: Palawan.

LITTLE MANGROVE HERON PLATE 4

Butorides striatus javensis (Horsfield, 1821)

1821   *Ardea Javanica* Horsfield, Trans. Linn. Soc. London, **13**:190, (western Java)

1924   *Butorides striatus carcinophilus* Oberholser, Journ. Wash. Acad. Sci., **14**:294, (Casiguran, Luzon)

Description: Top of head and crest dark purplish green; neck, back, and rump gray; tail gray with a green gloss; wings gray with a green gloss, coverts with buffy margins; ear-coverts white; malar stripe blackish; chin and throat white; breast buffy in center; sides of breast, belly, and under tail-coverts gray. Immature—upperparts brownish with buffy spots; underparts gray-white with black streaks.

Soft Parts: Bill greenish yellow; iris yellow; feet greenish.

Measurements: Wing 168; tail 73; bill 59; tarsus 41.

Range: Found throughout the Philippines.

Butorides striatus amurensis (Schrenck, 1860)

1860   *Ardea (Butorides) virescens* var. *amurensis* Schrenck, Reise Amur Lande, **1**:441, (Amurland)

Description: Differs from *javensis* by being larger and having upperparts darker and greener; sides of face whiter.

Range: Calayan, Cebu, Luzon, Mindoro, Negros, and Samar; winters in Philippines from Asia.

CHINESE POND HERON   PLATE 4

Ardeola bacchus (Bonaparte, 1855)

1855 *Buphus bacchus* Bonaparte, Consp. Av., 2:127, (Malay Peninsula)

Description: Head and neck chestnut; back black with long plumes; rump, wings, and tail white; chin white; throat chestnut; rest of underparts white. Immature—head and neck streaked; back and scapulars olive-brown.

Soft Parts: Bill, upper mandible black, lower mandible tip black with greenish yellow base; iris yellow; feet greenish.

Measurements: Wing 310; tail 68; bill 60; tarsus 56.

Range: Luzon and Negros; a straggler from eastern Asia.

CATTLE EGRET   PLATE 4

Bubulcus ibis coromandus (Boddaert, 1783)

1783 *Cancroma Coromanda* Boddaert, Table Pl., enlum., p. 54, (Coromandel)

Description: All white except for center of crown, crest, and stripe down center of neck, which are pale rusty. Nonbreeding birds not as rusty. Immature—pure white.

Soft Parts: Bill yellow; iris yellow; legs and feet yellow to reddish; immature—greenish.

Measurements: Wing 236; tail 97; bill 62; tarsus 82.

Range: Found throughout the Philippines.

REEF EGRET   PLATE 4

Egretta sacra sacra (Gmelin, 1789)

1789 *Ardea sacra* Gmelin, Syst. Nat., 1:640, (Tahiti)

Description: Forehead and crown dark blue-gray; neck dark brownish blue; elongated feathers of the back dark blue-gray; tail and wings dark brown; a white stripe from chin part way down the neck; underparts dull gray. Also an all white phase. Immature—browner.

Soft Parts: Bill blackish, lower mandible with pale base; iris yellow; legs dark green; feet black.

Measurements: Wing 262; tail 92; bill 84; tarsus 71.

Range: Found throughout the Philippines.

19

CHINESE EGRET   PLATE 4

Egretta eulophotes (Swinhoe, 1860)

1860   *Herodias eulophotes* Swinhoe, Ibis, p. 64, (Amoy, China)

Description: All white with very long plumes on the nape and back in breeding season only.

Soft Parts: Bill yellowish; iris yellow; feet greenish.

Measurements: Wing 267; tail 100; bill 91; tarsus 93.

Range: Bohol, Cebu, Panay, and Samar; a visitor from China.

LITTLE EGRET   PLATE 4

Egretta garzetta nigripes (Temminck, 1840)

1840   *Ardea nigripes* Temminck, Man. d' Orn., 4:376, (Sunda Islands)

Description: All white with long plumes on head, neck, and back in breeding season; lores naked and pinkish.

Soft Parts: Bill black; iris yellow; legs black; feet yellow.

Measurements: Wing 270; tail 102; bill 93; tarsus 103.

Range: Found throughout the Philippines.

LESSER EGRET   PLATE 4

Egretta intermedia intermedia (Wagler, 1829)

1829   *Ardea intermedia* Wagler, Isis, p. 659, (Java)

Description: All white; lores naked and greenish; long plumes on head, neck, and back in breeding season.

Soft Parts: Bill black in breeding season, otherwise yellow; iris yellow; legs and feet black.

Measurements: Wing 296; tail 121; bill 74; tarsus 109.

Range: Found throughout the Philippines.

GREATER EGRET   PLATE 4

Egretta alba modesta (J. E. Gray, 1831)

1831   *Ardea modesta* J. E. Gray, Zool. Misc., p. 19, (India)

Description: All white with long plumes on back in breeding season; naked lores yellow-green.

20

Soft Parts: Bill black in breeding season, otherwise orange; iris yellow; legs above knee yellow; tarsus and feet black.

Measurements: Wing 370; tail 154; bill 110; tarsus 131.

Range: Found throughout the Philippines.

GIANT HERON   PLATE 5

Ardea sumatrana sumatrana Raffles, 1822

1822   *Ardea Sumatrana* Raffles, Trans. Linn. Soc. London, **13**:325, (Sumatra)

Description: Upperparts gray; head and neck paler with some red; chin white; throat gray with some long whitish feathers; rest of underparts dirty white. Immature—uniformly browner; upperparts spotted with buff; underparts heavily streaked.

Soft Parts: Bill black, lower mandible yellowish at base; iris light orange; feet black.

Measurements: Wing 475; tail 196; bill 183; tarsus 154.

Range: Bantayan, Basilan, Bohol, Mindoro, Negros, and Palawan.

GRAY HERON   PLATE 5

Ardea cinerea jouyi Clark, 1907

1907   *Ardea cinerea jouyi* Clark, Proc. U. S. Nat. Mus., **32**:468, (Seoul, Korea)

Description: Top of head gray with a black crest; back of neck and upperparts gray; primaries black; chin white; throat streaked with blackish green; breast dark gray with wide white stripes; rest of underparts white. Immature—darker above and heavily streaked below.

Soft Parts: Bill yellow; iris yellow; tibia yellow; feet green; naked loral area green.

Measurements: Wing 450; tail 187; bill 133; tarsus 152.

Range: Guimaras and Luzon; an occasional visitor from eastern Asia.

PURPLE HERON   PLATE 5

Ardea purpurea manilensis Meyen, 1834

1834   *Ardea purpurea* var. *manilensis* Meyen, Nova Acta Acad. Caes. Leop. Carol., **16**, suppl. 102, (Philippines)

Description: Top of head black; sides of head and neck light chestnut with black stripes; upperparts dark gray with chestnut ends to plume feathers; breast with long gray plumes; rest of underparts dark chestnut and black.

Soft Parts: Bill, upper mandible dark brown, lower mandible yellow, brighter at base; iris yellow; tarsus brown; feet yellow.

Measurements: Wing 385; tail 148; bill 141; tarsus 125.

Range: Found throughout the Philippines.

BLACK-CROWNED NIGHT HERON PLATE 5

Nycticorax nycticorax nycticorax (Linné, 1758)

1758 *Ardea nycticorax* Linné, Syst. Nat., 1:142, (southern Europe)

Description: Forehead white; crown black with two long white feathers in the breeding season; sides of face and hind neck white; back black with a green gloss; wings and tail gray; underparts white. Immature—dull greenish brown streaked with white.

Soft Parts: Bill, upper mandible black, lower mandible pinkish, becoming greener at base; iris red; feet yellow; naked loral patch light green.

Measurements: Wing 300; tail 112; bill 72; tarsus 75.

Range: Calayan, Luzon, and Mindanao; a visitor from Asia.

RUFOUS NIGHT HERON PLATE 5

Nycticorax caledonicus manillensis Vigors, 1831

1831 *Nycticorax Manillensis* Vigors, Proc. Comm. Zool. Soc. London, p. 31, (Manila, Luzon)

1926 *Nycticorax caledonicus major* Hachisuka, Bull. Brit. Orn. Cl., 46:103, (Zamboanga, Mindanao)

Description: Head and crest dark blue-black; back dark rufous; rump, wings, and tail rufous; chin white; throat, breast, and thighs light cinnamon; belly and under tail-coverts white. Immature—heavily streaked above and below.

Soft Parts: Bill black; iris yellow; legs and feet yellowish.

Measurements: Wing 299; tail 120; bill 65; tarsus 78.

Range: Found throughout the Philippines.

Family THRESKIORNITHIDAE IBIS

WHITE IBIS PLATE 6

Threskiornis aethiopica melanocephala (Latham, 1790)

1790 *Tantalus melanocephalus* Latham, Ind. Orn., 2:709, (India)

Description: All white; upperparts tend to be grayish; naked head and neck black.

Soft Parts: Bill black; iris red; feet black.

Measurements: Wing 320; tail 138; bill 150; tarsus 100.

Range: Luzon; a straggler from Asia.

GLOSSY IBIS   PLATE 6

Plegadis falcinellus peregrinus (Bonaparte, 1855)

1855   *Ibis peregrina* Bonaparte, Consp. Av., **2**:159, (Java and Celebes)

Description: Head, neck, and mantle dark chestnut; back, rump, tail, and wings black with purplish green gloss; breast and belly chestnut.
Soft Parts: Bill olive; iris brown; feet dark green.
Measurements: Wing 280; tail 96; bill 128; tarsus 105.
Range: Luzon and Mindanao.

LESSER SPOONBILL   PLATE 6

Platalea minor Temminck and Schlegel, 1849

1849   *Platalea minor* Temminck and Schlegel, in Siebold's Faun. Jap., Aves, p. 120, (Japan)

Description: All white; naked skin on head black.
Soft Parts: Bill slate-black; iris red; feet black.
Measurements: Wing 361; tail 101; bill 178; tarsus 120.
Range: Luzon; a straggler from eastern Asia.

Family CICONIIDAE   STORKS

WHITE-NECKED STORK   PLATE 6

Ciconia episcopus episcopus (Boddaert, 1783)

1783   *Ardea Episcopus* Boddaert, Table Pl., enlum., p. 54, (Coromandel coast)
1904   *Dissoura neglecta* Finsch, Orn. Monatsb., **12**:94, (Celebes, Java, Sumbawa, Lombok, Philippines)

Description: Crown blue-black; rest of head and neck white; back, wings, and tail black glossed with green; breast black glossed with purple; belly and under tail-coverts white.
Soft Parts: Bill black with red tip; iris red; legs and feet red.
Measurements: Wing 470; tail 193; bill 131; tarsus 148.
Range: Basilan, Bohol, Calayan, Leyte, Luzon, Marinduque, Masbate, Mindanao, Mindoro, Negros, Panay, Polillo, and Samar.

PLATE 6

A   WHITE-NECKED STORK
       (Ciconia episcopus)—page 23

B   LESSER SPOONBILL
       (Platalea minor)—page 23

C   GLOSSY IBIS
       (Plegadis falcinellus)—page 23

D   EASTERN SARUS CRANE
       (Grus antigone)—page 66

E   WHITE IBIS
       (Threskiornis aethiopica)—page 22

A

B

C

D

E

PLATE 6

Family ANATIDAE   DUCKS

WANDERING WHISTLING-DUCK   PLATE 7

Dendrocygna arcuata arcuata (Horsfield, 1824)

1824   *Anas arcuata* Horsfield, Zool. Res. Java, pt. 8, pl. (64), (Java)

Description: Top of head dark brown; back, wings, and tail black; wing-coverts rufous; feathers of mantle edged dark fulvous; chin and throat dirty white; breast fulvous with black spots; belly pale cinnamon; under tail-coverts dirty white.
Soft Parts: Bill black; iris brown; feet gray-black.
Measurements: Wing 203; tail 68; bill 46; tarsus 48.
Range: Found throughout the Philippines.

SPOTTED WHISTLING-DUCK   PLATE 7

Dendrocygna guttata Schlegel, 1866

1866   *Dendrocygna guttata* Schlegel, Mus. Pays-Bas, **6**:85, (Celebes)

Description: Top of head, stripe down hind neck, back, wings, and tail dark brown; upper tail-coverts black and white; face, chin, and throat light gray; lower neck dark brown; breast and flanks fulvous with white spots; belly whitish.
Soft Parts: Bill dark red; iris dark brown; feet dark red.
Measurements: Wing 219; tail 84; bill 45; tarsus 46.
Range: Basilan and Mindanao.

SHELDRAKE   PLATE 7

Tadorna tadorna (Linné, 1758)

1758   *Anas Tadorna* Linné, Syst. Nat., **1**:122, (Sweden)

Description: Male—head and neck black with a green gloss; a white collar on lower neck and upper breast; lower breast chestnut, forming a band across upper back; back and rump white; tail black; wings multicolored (white, chestnut, and green); belly white; vent black; under tail-coverts cinnamon. Female—like male but without knob on bill and with white feathers at base of bill.
Soft Parts: Bill and knob red; iris brown; feet pink.
Measurements: Wing 324; tail 118; bill 50; tarsus 51.
Range: Winters in Philippines from Asia.

PINTAIL

PLATE 7

Anas acuta Linné, 1758

1758 *Anas acuta* Linné, Syst. Nat., 1:126, (Sweden)

Description: Male—head and neck brown with a white line on the side neck; mantle and sides gray with fine black bars; back and rump gray; tail black; wings gray with a bronze speculum; scapulars are black with light buffy edges; breast and belly white; flanks creamy; under tail-coverts black. Female—above brown with black specks; below buffy with black spots on breast; speculum greenish.

Soft Parts: Bill bluish; iris brown; feet gray.

Measurements: Wing 264; tail ♂194; bill 49; tarsus 41.

Range: Winters in Philippines from Asia.

COMMON TEAL

PLATE 7

Anas crecca crecca Linné, 1758

1758 *Anas Crecca* Linné, Syst. Nat., 1:126, (Sweden)

Description: Male—head and neck chestnut except for a green patch that extends from the eyes to the nape, edged by a yellowish line that also extends to the bill; back and flanks gray with fine black bars; tail gray; wings gray with a green speculum; scapulars black and white; breast red-brown with black flecks; belly white; under tail-coverts black. Female—brown mottled with black; belly whitish.

Soft Parts: Bill black; iris brown; feet gray.

Measurements: Wing 178; tail 68; bill 33; tarsus 29.

Range: Winters in Philippines from Asia.

SPOTBILL DUCK

PLATE 7

Anas poecilorhyncha zonorhyncha Swinhoe, 1866

1866 *Anas zonorhyncha* Swinhoe, Ibis, p. 394, (Ningpo, China)

Description: Top of head and stripe down hind neck black; a black line runs from the bill through the eyes and another from the base of the bill to the ear-coverts; rest of face, chin, and throat buff; back and tail blackish brown; wings blackish brown with a blue speculum; outer edge of the two inner tertiaries white; breast dark tan with black markings; belly black.

Soft Parts: Bill dark greenish brown with yellow tip; iris dark brown; feet dark orange.

Measurements: Wing 257; tail 131; bill 59; tarsus 46.

Range: Winters on northern islands; a visitor from Asia.

PLATE 7

A   WANDERING WHISTLING-DUCK
     (*Dendrocygna arcuata*)—page 26

B   SPOTTED WHISTLING-DUCK
     (*Dendrocygna guttata*)—page 26

C   SHELDRAKE
     (*Tadorna tadorna*), male—page 26

D   COMMON TEAL
     (*Anas crecca*), male—page 27

E   PINTAIL
     (*Anas acuta*), male—page 27

F   PHILIPPINE MALLARD
     (*Anas luzonica*)—page 30

G   SPOTBILL DUCK
     (*Anas poecilorhyncha*)—page 27

PLATE 7

PHILIPPINE MALLARD PLATE 7

Anas luzonica Fraser, 1839

1839   *Anas luzonica* Fraser, Proc. Zool. Soc. London, p. 113, (Luzon)

Description: Top of head, stripe down hind neck, and stripe from bill through eyes to nape dark brown; sides of head, chin, throat, and neck rufous; back, rump, and tail dark brown; wings gray-brown; breast and belly gray feathers with rufous tips; under tail-coverts dark brown; speculum greenish.

Soft Parts: Bill blue-black; iris brown; feet dark brown.

Measurements: Wing 253; tail 104; bill 55; tarsus 42.

Range: Found throughout the Philippines. (Endemic.)

EUROPEAN WIDGEON PLATE 8

Anas penelope Linné, 1758

1758   *Anas Penelope* Linné, Syst. Nat., 1:126, (Sweden)

Description: Forehead and crown buffy; a green patch behind eyes; rest of head and neck dark chestnut; back gray with fine black specks; tail black; wing gray with a green speculum; breast reddish purple; belly white; under tail-coverts black. Female—similar to male but with a dark gray head and breast.

Soft Parts: Bill bluish; iris brown; feet gray-blue.

Measurements: Wing 260; tail 101; bill 35; tarsus 35.

Range: Winters in the Philippines from Asia.

GARGANEY TEAL PLATE 8

Anas querquedula Linné, 1758

1758   *Anas Querquedula* Linné, Syst. Nat., 1:126, (Sweden)

Description: Male—crown black; stripe from eye part way down neck white; rest of head chestnut with white flecks; back and tail dark brown; wing gray with a green speculum bordered with two white bands; scapulars black and white; breast light brown with black flecks; belly white; flanks gray finely barred with black. Female—brown with black flecks and olive speculum.

Soft Parts: Bill dark gray; iris brown; feet dark gray.

Measurements: Wing 191; tail 65; bill 38; tarsus 25.

Range: Winters in the Philippines from Asia.

COMMON SHOVELER   PLATE 8

Anas clypeata Linné, 1758

1758 *Anas clypeata* Linné, Syst. Nat., 1:124, (Sweden)

Description: Male—head green; back black; tail black and white; wings gray with a green speculum; scapulars blue and white; breast white; belly chestnut; under tail-coverts black. Female—dull buffy brown with black flecks; green speculum; a pale eye stripe.

Soft Parts: Bill black; iris yellow; feet orange.

Measurements: Wing 233; tail 79; bill 64; tarsus 35.

Range: Winters in the Philippines from Asia.

EUROPEAN POCHARD   PLATE 8

Aythya ferina (Linné, 1758)

1758 *Anas ferina* Linné, Syst. Nat., 1:126, (Sweden)

Description: Male—head and neck chestnut; rest of upperparts light gray; tail black; breast black; belly gray. Female—mostly brown; wings and belly grayer; a light brown stripe extends from behind the eye.

Soft Parts: Bill gray-blue with a paler band in the middle; iris, male red, female brown; feet blue-gray.

Measurements: Wing 215; tail 51; bill 46; tarsus 37.

Range: Winters in the Philippines from Asia.

TUFTED DUCK   PLATE 8

Aythya fuligula (Linné, 1758)

1758 *Anas fuligula* Linné, Syst. Nat., 1:128, (Sweden)

Description: Male—head, crest, neck, and breast black with a purple gloss; back black with a few white flecks and green gloss; a white speculum in the wing; tail black; belly white; under tail-coverts black. Female—mostly dark brown; some individuals have white feathers at the base of the bill; underparts gray; under tail-coverts may be brown or white.

Soft Parts: Bill bluish; iris dark yellow; feet blue-gray.

Measurements: Wing 199; tail 50; bill 41; tarsus 31.

Range: Winters in the Philippines from Asia.

PLATE 8

A   EUROPEAN WIDGEON
        (Anas penelope), male—page 30

B   GARGANEY TEAL
        (Anas querquedula), male—page 30

C   EUROPEAN POCHARD
        (Aythya ferina), male—page 31

D   COTTON TEAL
        (Nettapus coromandelianus)—page 34

E   COMMON SHOVELER
        (Anas clypeata), male—page 31

F   GREATER SCAUP DUCK
        (Aythya marila), male—page 34

G   TUFTED DUCK
        (Aythya fuligula), male—page 31

PLATE 8

GREATER SCAUP DUCK PLATE 8

Aythya marila mariloides (Vigors, 1839)

1839 *Fuligula Mariloides* Vigors, in Beechey's Voy. "Blossom," Zool., p. 31, (Bering Sea)

Description: Male—head, neck, and breast black with a green gloss; back and wings gray barred with black; tail black; belly white; under tail-coverts black. Female—head, neck, and breast dark brown; white feathers at base of the bill; rest of upperparts gray-brown; belly white.

Soft Parts: Bill bluish; iris dark yellow; feet blue-gray.

Measurements: Wing 220; tail 58; bill 44; tarsus 36.

Range: Winters in the Philippines from Asia.

COTTON TEAL PLATE 8

Nettapus coromandelianus coromandelianus (Gmelin, 1789)

1789 *Anas coromandeliana* Gmelin, Syst. Nat., 1:522, (Coromandel, India)

Description: Male—crown and eye-ring black; rest of head and neck white; back and wing-coverts dark green; primaries black with a white band toward end; tail black; breast white with a dark green band; belly white. Female—browner than male; white areas spotted with black; a black line through eye.

Soft Parts: Bill brown; iris brown; feet black.

Measurements: Wing 160; tail 73; bill 22; tarsus 23.

Range: Luzon and northern islands.

Family PANDIONIDAE OSPREYS

OSPREY PLATE 9

Pandion haliaetus haliaetus (Linné, 1758)

1758 *Falco Haliaetus* Linné, Syst. Nat., 1:91, (Sweden)

Description: Head white with a dark brown streak from forehead to nape and from bill through eyes and down neck; back, wings, tail dark brown with purplish gloss; primaries with white bars; throat, breast, and belly white; upper breast with a few brown streaks.

Soft Parts: Bill blue-gray; iris yellow; feet greenish white.

Measurements: Wing 490; tail 210; bill 40; tarsus 61.

Range: Winters throughout the Philippines.

Pandion haliaetus melvillensis Mathews, 1912

1912 *Pandion haliaetus melvillensis* Mathews, Austr. Av. Rec., 1:34, (Melville Island)
Description: Differs from *P. h. haliaetus* by having a whiter head; also somewhat smaller (wing ♂410, ♀447).
Range: Resident throughout the Philippines.

Family ACCIPITRIDAE   HAWKS AND EAGLES

CRESTED   LIZARD   HAWK   **PLATE 9**

Aviceda jerdoni magnirostris (Kaup, 1847)

1847 *Hyptiopus magnirostris* Kaup, Isis, p. 43, (Davao, Mindanao)
1888 *Baza leucopias* Sharpe, Ibis, p. 195, (Palawan)
Description: Top of head dark brown with a black crest; back and wings dark brown with some rufous and white edges to feathers; tail dark gray with black bands; sides of face gray; throat gray with a black streak; rest of underparts buffy with dark rufous bars. Immature—head and underparts white.
Soft Parts: Bill blue-gray; iris yellow; feet greenish yellow.
Measurements: Wing 300; tail 190; bill 32; tarsus 36.
Range: Mindanao, Palawan, and Samar. (Endemic.)

BARRED   HONEY   BUZZARD   **PLATE 9**

Pernis celebensis steerei Sclater, 1919

1919 *Pernis celebensis steerei* Sclater, Bull. Brit. Orn. Cl., 40:41, (San Antonio, Negros)
Description: Head and neck buffy with dark brown spots; long black crest; upperparts dark brown with some lighter streaks; tail almost black with dark brown bars; throat buffy with black streaks; breast and belly light buff with brown bars. Immature—paler and streaking less distinct; underparts sometimes pure white.
Soft Parts: Bill black; iris yellow; feet yellow; cere yellow.
Measurements: Wing 360; tail 254; bill 28; tarsus 47.
Range: Basilan, Bohol, Luzon, Mindanao, Mindoro, Negros, and Samar. (Endemic.)

PLATE 9

A   OSPREY
    (Pandion haliaetus)—page 34

B   CRESTED LIZARD HAWK
    (Aviceda jerdoni)—page 35

C   BARRED HONEY BUZZARD
    (Pernis celebensis)—page 35

D   ASIATIC HONEY BUZZARD
    (Pernis apivorus)—page 38

E   BLACK-WINGED KITE
    (Elanus caeruleus)—page 38

F   BLACK-EARED KITE
    (Milvus migrans)—page 39

PLATE 9

ASIATIC HONEY BUZZARD

PLATE 9

Pernis apivorus philippensis Mayr, 1939

1939   *Pernis apivorus philippensis* Mayr, Orn. Monatsb., **47**:74, (Mindanao)

Description: Head and neck light buffy white, feathers having dark shafts; back, rump, and wing-coverts a mixture of light and dark brown; primaries dark brown with white tips, barred below; tail light brown with five or more dark brown bars, terminated with a white tip; lores, feathers around and behind eye blackish gray, looking somewhat like scales; underparts white, some specimens having a few dark shaft streaks on the breast.

Soft Parts: Bill black; iris yellow; feet dirty yellow.

Measurements: Wing ♂425; tail ♂278; bill ♂36; tarsus ♂49.

Range: Cebu, Leyte, Mindanao, and Negros. (Endemic.)

Pernis apivorus palawanensis Stresemann, 1940

1940   *Pernis apivorus palawanensis* Stresemann, Arkiv. Naturge., **9**:171, (Palawan)

Description: Differs from *philippensis* by having a small crest; upperparts much darker and underparts barred with dark brown; also slightly smaller.

Range: Palawan. (Endemic.)

Pernis apivorus orientalis Taczanowski, 1891

1891   *Pernis apivorus orientalis* Taczanowski, Mem. Acad. Imp. Sci. St. Petersb., **39**:50, (eastern Siberia)

Description: Differs from *philippensis* by having darker upperparts and a longer and fuller crest; underparts light brown with a few dark streaks; subterminal band on tail twice as wide.

Range: Winters in the Philippines from eastern Asia.

BLACK-WINGED   KITE

PLATE 9

Elanus caeruleus hypoleucus Gould, 1859

1859   *Elanus hypoleucus* Gould, Proc. Zool. Soc. London, p. 129, (Macassar, Celebes)

Description: Head, back, and most of wing pale blue-gray; wing-coverts black; primaries dark gray; tail light gray with white outer tail feathers; a few dark feathers around the eye; underparts white.

Soft Parts: Bill black; iris red; feet yellowish.

Measurements: Wing 298; tail 150; bill 22; tarsus 36.

Range: Found throughout the Philippines.

BLACK-EARED KITE PLATE 9

Milvus migrans lineatus (J. E. Gray, 1831)

1831 *Haliaetus lineatus* J. E. Gray, in Hardwicke's Ill. Ind. Zool., 1:18, (China)

Description: Upperparts brown streaked with black, especially on head and neck; sides of face and chin whitish streaked with black; breast dark brown with black shaft streaks; belly, thighs, and under tail-coverts buffy. Immature—upperparts have pale ends to feathers.

Soft Parts: Bill dark brown; cere yellow; iris yellowish brown; feet yellow.

Measurements: Wing ♂475; tail 350; bill 37; tarsus 59.

Range: Palawan (once); a straggler from northeast Asia.

BRAHMINY KITE PLATE 10

Haliastus indus intermedius Blyth, 1865

1865 *Haliastur intermedius* Blyth, Ibis, p. 28, (Java)

Description: Head, neck, and breast white with dark shaft streaks; back, wings, tail, and thighs chestnut; primaries black. Immature—upperparts dark brown with buffy tips to feathers; head, neck, and breast buffy, heavily streaked and washed with brown; belly buffy.

Soft Parts: Bill yellowish; iris brown; feet yellow.

Measurements: Wing 405; tail 212; bill 34; tarsus 54.

Range: Found throughout the Philippines.

WHITE-BREASTED SEA EAGLE PLATE 10

Haliaeetus leucogaster (Gmelin, 1788)

1788 *Falco leucogaster* Gmelin, Syst. Nat., 1:257, (New South Wales)

Description: Head, neck, and underparts white; back and wing-coverts dark gray-brown; primaries black; tail gray, whiter toward end. Immature—head, neck, and underparts buffy; browner on chest.

Soft Parts: Bill blue-gray; iris brown; feet light yellow.

Measurements: Wing ♂564; tail 302; bill 54; tarsus 94.

Range: Found throughout the Philippines.

PLATE 10

A   BRAHMINY KITE
    (Haliastus indus)—page 39

B   WHITE-BREASTED SEA EAGLE
    (Haliaeetus leucogaster)—page 39

C   GRAY-HEADED FISHING EAGLE
    (Ichthyophaga ichthyaetus)—page 42

D   SERPENT EAGLE
    (Spilornis holospilus)—page 42

E   MARSH HARRIER
    (Circus aeruginosus)—page 42

F   PIED HARRIER
    (Circus melanoleucus), male—page 43

40

PLATE 10

GRAY-HEADED FISHING EAGLE   PLATE 10

Ichthyophaga ichthyaetus (Horsfield, 1821)

1821   *Falco Ichthyaetus* Horsfield, Trans. Linn. Soc. London, **13**:136, (Java)

Description: Head and neck gray-brown; rest of upperparts dark brown; tail white with a blackish brown subterminal band; breast light brown; belly, thighs, and under tail-coverts white. Immature—upperparts brown with buffy edges to feathers; tail brown with a dark brown subterminal band; underparts streaked brown and white.

Soft Parts: Bill bluish gray; cere gray; iris yellow; feet yellowish.

Measurements: Wing ♂435, ♀475; tail 240; bill 55; tarsus 90.

Range: Found throughout the Philippines.

SERPENT   EAGLE   PLATE 10

Spilornis holospilus (Vigors, 1830)

1830   *Buteo holospilus* Vigors, Proc. Comm. Zool. Soc. London, p. 96, (Manila, Luzon)

1890   *Spilornis panayensis* Steere, List Bds. Mamms. Steere Expd., p. 7, (Guimaras, Panay, Negros)

1919   *Spilornis cheela palawanensis* Sclater, Bull. Brit. Orn. Cl., **40**:38, (Palawan)

Description: Head and nape dark brown; back and rump brown with white spots; wings dark brown with inconspicuous barring; tail gray-brown with three blackish brown bars; chin and throat dark rufous streaked with black; breast, belly, and thighs rufous with white spots.

Soft Parts: Bill blue-gray; iris yellow; feet yellow.

Measurements: Wing 374; tail 264; bill 34; tarsus 83.

Range: Found throughout the Philippines. (Endemic.)

MARSH   HARRIER   PLATE 10

Circus aeruginosus spilonotus Kaup, 1847

1847   *Circus spilonotus* Kaup, Isis, p. 953, (Asia)

Description: Head and neck white streaked with dark brown; back brown; tail gray barred with dark brown; wings grayish; outer primaries dark brown; underparts white; chin, throat, and upper breast streaked with light brown.

Soft Parts: Bill blackish; cere yellow; iris yellow-brown; feet yellow.

Measurements: Wing 345; tail 200; bill 26; tarsus 79.

Range: Winters in the Philippines from China.

ACCIPITRIDAE

PIED HARRIER — PLATE 10

Circus melanoleucus (Pennant, 1769)

1769 *Falco melanoleucus* Pennant, Ind. Zool., p. 2, (Ceylon)

Description: Male—head, neck, chin, throat, and back black; rump gray-white; tail gray; wings gray with a white shoulder patch; primaries black; breast and belly white. Female —top of head dark brown, rest of upperparts brown; tail rufous-brown; sides of face buffy white; underparts buffy streaked with brown.

Soft Parts: Bill black; cere yellow; iris brown; feet yellow.

Measurements: Wing 320; tail 205; bill 23; tarsus 66.

Range: Winters in the Philippines from eastern Asia.

ASIATIC SPARROW HAWK — PLATE 11

Accipiter gularis (Temminck and Schlegel, 1845)

1845 *Astur (Nisus) gularis* Temminck and Schlegel, in Siebold's Faun. Jap., Aves, p. 5, (Japan)

Description: Male—upperparts blackish gray; tail gray with black bars; chin and throat white; breast and belly rufous finely barred with dark gray; under tail-coverts white. Female—differs by having underparts white heavily barred with brown. Immature— upperparts dark brown feathers with pale edges; underparts white, streaked and barred with brown.

Soft Parts: Bill blackish; cere yellow; iris yellow-orange; feet yellow.

Measurements: Wing 175; tail 127; bill 14; tarsus 53.

Range: Winters in the Philippines from China and Japan.

PHILIPPINE SPARROW HAWK — PLATE 11

Accipiter virgatus confusus Hartert, 1910

1910 *Accipiter virgatus confusus* Hartert, Nov. Zool., 17:209, (Laguna de Bai, Luzon)

Description: Male—top of head and all upperparts blue-gray; tail dark brown with darker bars; under-wings barred; chin and throat white; breast rufous; belly and thighs white, some individuals more or less barred with rufous and gray. Female—upperparts brown; tail light brown with dark brown bars; underparts white heavily streaked with brown. Immature—similar to female but with buffy edges to feathers on upperparts and washed with buff below.

Soft Parts: Bill blue-gray; cere blue-gray; iris yellow; feet yellow.

Measurements: Wing ♂160, ♀179; tail ♂126, ♀145; bill ♂14, ♀20; tarsus ♂47, ♀54.

Range: Found throughout the Philippines, except Palawan.

43

PLATE 11

A   ASIATIC SPARROW HAWK
       (Accipiter gularis), male—page 43

B   PHILIPPINE SPARROW HAWK
       (Accipiter virgatus), male—page 43

C   CRESTED GOSHAWK
       (Accipiter trivirgatus)—page 46

D   GRAY FROG HAWK
       (Accipiter soloensis)—page 46

E   GRAY-FACED BUZZARD
       (Butastur indicus)—page 47

F   COMMON BUZZARD
       (Buteo buteo)—page 47

PLATE 11

CRESTED GOSHAWK   PLATE 11

Accipiter trivirgatus extimus Mayr, 1945

1945 *Accipiter trivirgatus extimus* Mayr, Zoologica, **30**:106, (Mindanao)

Description: Top of head and sides of face gray; rest of upperparts brownish; tail light brown with three dark brown bars; chin and throat white with a black medial stripe; breast white with rufous streaks; belly and thighs white barred with dark brown; under tail-coverts white.

Soft Parts: Bill bluish; cere yellow; iris yellow-orange; feet yellow.

Measurements: Wing ♂187, ♀206; tail ♂141, ♀172; bill 23; tarsus 48.

Range: Leyte, Mindanao, Negros, and Samar. (Endemic.)

Accipiter trivirgatus castroi Manuel and Gilliard, 1952

1952 *Accipiter trivirgatus castroi* Manuel and Gilliard, Am. Mus. Novit., 1545:3, (Anibawan, Polillo)

Description: Differs from *extimus* by having the back dark blue; underparts darker and more heavily barred; wing and tarsus tend to be somewhat longer.

Range: Polillo. (Endemic.)

Accipiter trivirgatus palawanus Mayr, 1949

1949 *Accipiter trivirgatus palawanus* Mayr, Am. Mus. Novit., 1415:5, (Taguso, Palawan)

Description: Differs from *extimus* by having the upperparts somewhat browner and the underparts with heavier barring.

Range: Palawan. (Endemic.)

GRAY FROG HAWK   PLATE 11

Accipiter soloensis (Horsfield, 1821)

1821 *Falco Soloensis* Horsfield, Trans. Linn. Soc. London, **13**:137, (Java)

Description: Upperparts dark blue-gray; tail barred with black; under-wings with no markings; chin white; breast and belly very pale rufous; thighs and under tail-coverts white. Immature—upperparts brown with buffy edges to feathers; underparts buff streaked with brown.

Soft Parts: Bill bluish; cere yellow; iris dark red-brown; feet yellow.

Measurements: Wing ♂195, ♀205; tail ♂126, ♀133; bill 17; tarsus 41.

Range: Luzon and Mindoro; a winter visitor from Asia.

GRAY-FACED BUZZARD   PLATE 11

Butastur indicus (Gmelin, 1788)

1788   *Falco indicus* Gmelin, Syst. Nat., **1**:264, (Java)

Description: Top of head, hind neck, and upper back gray with black streaks; rest of upperparts rufous-brown; tail brown with black bars; lores, chin, and throat white; breast brown with white bars; belly and thighs white. Immature—upperparts brown with buffy edges to feathers.

Soft Parts: Bill bluish; cere yellow; iris yellow; feet yellow.

Measurements: Wing ♂323, ♀330; tail ♂185, ♀195; bill 28; tarsus 58.

Range: Found throughout the Philippines; a migrant from Asia.

COMMON BUZZARD   PLATE 11

Buteo buteo japonensis (Temminck and Schlegel, 1845)

1845   *Faclo* [sic] *buteo japonensis* Temminck and Schlegel, in Siebold's Faun. Jap.,
       Aves, p. 16, (Japan)

Description: Head and hind neck brown with white streaks on crown; upperparts dark brown; upper tail-coverts white; tail brown with a white base and buffy tip barred with dark brown; chin and throat brown with white streaks; breast white heavily streaked with brown; belly buffy with dark brown bars. Immature—crown lighter and feathers of upperparts edged with buff.

Soft Parts: Bill bluish; cere yellow; iris yellow-brown; feet yellow.

Measurements: Wing ♂376, ♀400; tail ♂195, ♀220; bill 32; tarsus 74.

Range: Northern Luzon (once); a visitor from Asia.

MONKEY-EATING EAGLE   PLATE 12

Pithecophaga jefferyi Ogilvie-Grant, 1896

1896   *Pithecophaga jefferyi* Ogilvie-Grant, Bull. Brit. Orn. Cl., **6**:17, (Paranas, Samar)

Description: Crown and crest yellowish with dark brown shaft streaks; upperparts dark brown with pale edges to feathers; tail dark brown with blackish bars and a white tip; chin white finely streaked with black; throat, breast, and belly gray-white; thighs buffy with dark shaft streaks. Immature—lacks the dark chin and striped thighs.

Soft Parts: Bill bluish; iris blue-gray; feet yellow.

Measurements: Wing 625; tail 500; bill 85; tarsus 127.

Range: Luzon and Mindanao; formerly on Leyte and Samar. (Endemic.)

PLATE 12

MONKEY-EATING EAGLE
(Pithecophaga jefferyi)—page 47

PLATE 12

PLATE 13

A   CHANGEABLE HAWK EAGLE
    (Spizaetus cirrhatus)—page 52

B   PHILIPPINE FALCONET
    (Microhierax erythrogonys)—page 53

C   PHILIPPINE HAWK EAGLE
    (Spizaetus philippensis)—page 52

D   ORIENTAL HOBBY
    (Falco severus)—page 53

E   KESTREL
    (Falco tinnunculus)—page 53

F   RUFOUS-BELLIED EAGLE
    (Hieraaetus kieneri)—page 52

G   PEREGRINE FALCON
    (Falco peregrinus)—page 54

PLATE 13

RUFOUS-BELLIED EAGLE   PLATE 13

Hieraaetus kieneri formosus Stresemann, 1924

1924 *Hieraaetus kieneri formosus* Stresemann, Orn. Monatsb., **32**:108, (northern Celebes)

Description: Head, crest, back, and wings dark blue-black; tail dark brown with lighter bars; chin white; throat white with fine black streaks; breast dark rufous with wide black stripes; belly and under tail-coverts rufous. Immature—upperparts brown with white tips to feathers; underparts white.

Soft Parts: Bill bluish; cere yellow; iris dark brown; feet yellow.

Measurements: Wing ♂ 340; tail 196; bill 35; tarsus 66.

Range: Luzon, Marinduque, Mindanao, Negros, Panay, Samar, Sibuyan, and Tablas.

CHANGEABLE HAWK EAGLE   PLATE 13

Spizaetus cirrhatus limnaeetus (Horsfield, 1821)

1821 *Falco Limnaeetus* Horsfield, Trans. Linn. Soc. London, **13**:138, (Java)

Description: Found in two phases: dark phase—all dark brownish black with a dark gray patch in the center of the tail; light phase—upperparts dark brown mottled with white, tail heavily barred, and underparts buffy.

Soft Parts: Bill black; cere greenish brown; iris yellow; feet yellow.

Measurements: Wing ♂ 404; tail 276; bill 40; tarsus 98.

Range: Lubang, Mindanao, Mindoro, and Palawan.

PHILIPPINE HAWK EAGLE   PLATE 13

Spizaetus philippensis Gould, 1863

1863 *Spizaetus Philippensis* Gould, Bds. Asia, **1**, pt. 15, (Luzon, Philippines)

Description: Feathers of head and neck buffy with dark brown centers, giving a streaked appearance; crest long and black; back and wings dark brown; tail brown with dark brown bars, underneath light gray with a subterminal black band; chin, throat, and breast pale rufous with heavy dark brown streaks; belly buffy; under tail-coverts brown; thighs and tarsus brown with fine white bars.

Soft Parts: Bill black; cere dark gray; iris yellow; feet light yellow.

Measurements: Wing 367; tail 270; bill 34; tarsus 94; crest 63.

Range: Basilan, Leyte, Lubang, Luzon, Masbate, Mindoro, Negros, Palawan, Samar, and Siquijor. (Endemic.)

Family FALCONIDAE   FALCONS

PHILIPPINE FALCONET   PLATE 13

Microhierax erythrogonys erythrogonys (Vigors, 1831)

1831   *Hierax erythrogonys* Vigors, Proc. Comm. Zool. Soc. London, p. 96, (Luzon)

Description: Top of head and rest of upperparts black with a bluish gloss; throat, breast, and belly white; flanks, thighs, and under tail-coverts black. Immature—ear-coverts reddish.

Soft Parts: Bill black; cere black; iris brown; feet blue-black.

Measurements: Wing ♂105, ♀114; tail 69; bill 14; tarsus 24.

Range: Luzon and Mindoro. (Endemic.)

Microhierax erythrogonys meridionalis Ogilvie-Grant, 1897

1897   *Microhierax meridionalis* Ogilvie-Grant, Ibis, p. 220, (Zamboanga, Mindanao)

Description: Differs from *M. e. erythrogonys* by being larger (wing ♂115, ♀120).

Range: Islands south of Luzon and Mindoro to Mindanao. (Endemic.)

KESTREL   PLATE 13

Falco tinnunculus interstinctus Horsfield, 1840

1840   *Falco interstinctus* Horsfield, (1839), Proc. Zool. Soc. London, p. 154, (Assam)

Description: Forehead rufous; head and neck blue-gray; back and wing-coverts chestnut with black spots; primaries dark red-brown; tail blue-gray with a white tip and a black subterminal band; ear-coverts light gray; throat buff bordered with a black moustache stripe; breast, belly, and flanks dark buff with black spots, much heavier on flanks.

Soft Parts: Bill gray-blue; cere yellow; iris dark brown; feet yellow.

Measurements: Wing 245; tail 162; bill 18; tarsus 40.

Range: Found throughout the Philippines.

ORIENTAL HOBBY   PLATE 13

Falco severus severus Horsfield, 1821

1821   *Falco severus* Horsfield, Trans. Linn. Soc. London, 13:135, (Java)

1843   *Falco guttatus* G. R. Gray, Ann. Mag. Nat. His., 11:371, (Philippines)

Description: Head, neck, and upper back black; lower back, rump, and wing-coverts dark gray; primaries dark slate; tail slate with inconspicuous darker streaks; chin and throat buffy; rest of underparts dark chestnut with black spots and streaks.

Soft Parts: Bill blue-gray; cere yellow; iris dark brown; feet yellow-orange.

Measurements: Wing ♂218, ♀235; tail ♂98, ♀115; bill 18; tarsus 32.

Range: Found throughout the Philippines.

PEREGRINE FALCON   PLATE 13

Falco peregrinus ernesti Sharpe, 1894

1894   *Falco ernesti* Sharpe, Ibis, p. 545, (Mt. Dulit, North Borneo)

Description: Top of head, face, and hind neck black; back, rump, and tail dark blue-gray mottled with black; primaries black; chin white; throat and upper breast buffy white finely streaked with black; rest of underparts dark blue-gray spotted and streaked with black.

Soft Parts: Bill bluish with black tip; cere yellow; iris brown; feet orange-yellow.

Measurements: Wing ♂282; tail ♂144; bill 25; tarsus 47.

Range: Found throughout the Philippines.

Falco peregrinus calidus Latham, 1790

1790   *Falco calidus* Latham, Ind. Orn., 1:41, (India)

Description: Differs from *ernesti* by being paler and larger (wing ♂320).

Range: Palawan (once); a winter straggler from Siberia.

Family MEGAPODIIDAE   MEGAPODES

MEGAPODE   PLATE 14

Megapodius freycinet pusillus Tweeddale, 1877

1877   *Megapodius pusillus* Tweeddale, Proc. Zool. Soc. London, p. 765, (Cebu)

1877   *Megapodius dillwyni* Tweeddale, Proc. Zool. Soc. London, p. 766, (Manila)

1924   *Megapodius cumingi balukensis* Oberholser, Journ. Wash. Acad. Sci., 14:294, (Baluk Island)

1931   *Megapodius freycinet tabon* Hachisuka, Bds. Phil. Ids., p. 153, (Piso, Mindanao)

Description: Head olive-gray; all upperparts olive-brown; underparts olive-gray.

Soft Parts: Bill dirty yellow; iris brown; feet dark brown.

Measurements: Wing 239; tail 95; bill 24; tarsus 62.

Range: Found throughout the Philippines, except Palawan. (Endemic.)

Megapodius freycinet cumingi Dillwyn, 1853

1853 *Megapodius Cumingii* Dillwyn, Proc. Zool. Soc. London, p. 119, (Labuan Island)

1875 *Megapodius lowii* Sharpe, Proc. Zool. Soc. London, p. 111, (Labuan Island)

Description: Differs from *pusillus* by being much darker and having slate-blue underparts.

Range: Balabac and Palawan. (Endemic.)

Family PHASIANIDAE   PHEASANTS

CHINESE   FRANCOLIN   PLATE 14

Francolinus pintadeanus pintadeanus (Scopoli, 1786)

1786 *Tetrao Pintadeanus* Scopoli, Del. Flor. et Faun. Insubr., p. 93, (China)

Description: Male—top of head chestnut striped with brownish black; mantle black with white spots; lower back, rump, and upper tail-coverts black finely barred with white; tail black with white bars; scapulars bright chestnut; wing-coverts spotted; lores and stripe through eye black; stripe from bill under eye to ear-coverts white, followed by a black stripe beneath; chin and throat white; breast and belly spotted with black and white; thighs and under tail-coverts chestnut. Female—brown above; buff barred with black below.

Soft Parts: Bill black; iris dark brown; feet dark yellow.

Measurements: Wing 146; tail 79; bill 26; tarsus 46.

Range: Introduced around Manila from China.

BEARDED   PARTRIDGE   PLATE 14

Perdix barbata barbata Verreaux and Des Murs, 1863

1863 *Perdix barbata* Verreaux and Des Murs, Proc. Zool. Soc. London, p. 62, (Transbaikalia)

Description: Male—top of head buffy streaked with black, shafts of feathers almost white; hind neck, back, rump, and central rectrices gray coarsely barred with chestnut and finely barred with black; wing-coverts gray-brown, barred with chestnut and with white shaft streaks; primaries dark brown with buffy spots; outer rectrices chestnut; chin, center of throat, and breast orange-buff; sides of throat and breast gray; chin feathers elongated; belly dirty white with a large black patch in the middle; flanks dirty white, heavily barred with chestnut. Female—similar to male but lacks the black patch on the belly.

Soft Parts: Bill horn; iris brown; feet flesh.
Measurements: Wing 146; tail 73; bill 21; tarsus 35.
Range: Introduced around Manila from China.

PAINTED QUAIL   PLATE 14

Coturnix chinensis lineata (Scopoli, 1786)

1786   *Oriolus lineatus* Scopoli, Del. Flor. et Faun. Insubr., p. 87, (Luzon)

Description: Male—forehead and around eyes blue-gray; lores white; upperparts mottled brown and black, some feathers having white shafts that give a streaked appearance; throat black with white border, which in turn is bordered by black; breast and flanks blue-gray; belly chestnut. Female—like male above except no blue-gray on face; light brown stripes over eyes; throat white; breast dark brown mottled with black; belly buffy white with brown bars.
Soft Parts: Bill bluish; iris dark red; feet dark yellow.
Measurements: Wing 69; tail 30; bill 9; tarsus 16.
Range: Found throughout the Philippines.

ASIATIC MIGRATORY QUAIL   PLATE 14

Coturnix coturnix japonica Temminck and Schlegel, 1849

1849   *Coturnix vulgaris japonica* Temminck and Schlegel, in Siebold's Faun. Jap., Aves, p. 103, (Japan)

Description: Upperparts brown with some dark brown mottling; shafts of neck and back are light buff, giving a streaked appearance; underparts light buffy brown; breast and flanks spotted and streaked with dark brown and chestnut.
Soft Parts: Bill tan; iris yellow-brown; feet flesh.
Measurements: Wing 95; tail 33; bill 14; tarsus 25.
Range: Luzon; a straggler from Asia.

JUNGLE FOWL   PLATE 14

Gallus gallus gallus (Linné, 1758)

1758   *Phasianus gallus* Linné, Syst. Nat., 1:158, (Pulau Condor, off mouth of Mekong River)

1939   *Gallus gallus philippensis* Hachisuka, Tori, **10**:601, (Sigaboy, Mindanao)

Description: Male—head mostly bare red skin; neck has elongated, glossy, reddish orange feathers; back and wing-coverts glossy maroon; rump has elongated, glossy, deep red-orange feathers; wings brown and glossy green; tail black with green gloss; all under-

56

parts dull black. Female—mostly dull brown with fine black streaks; neck feathers black with golden yellow margins. ·

Soft Parts: Bill, upper mandible dark brown, lower mandible light brown; iris orange-red; feet yellowish gray.

Measurements: Wing 240; tail ♂500; bill 21; tarsus 78.

Range: Found throughout the Philippines.

PALAWAN PEACOCK PHEASANT   PLATE 15

Polyplectron emphanum Temminck, 1831

1831 *Polyplectron emphanum* Temminck, Pl. Col., livr. 88, pl. 540, (Puerto Princesa, Palawan)

1831 *Polyplectron napoleonis* Lesson, Traité d' Orn., **8**:650, (Luzon = Palawan)

1891 *Polyplectron nehrkornae* Blasius, Mitth. Orn. Ver. Wien., p. 1, (Palawan)

Description: Male—top of head and crest metallic blue-green; mantle and wing-coverts metallic blue-green with basal half of feathers dull black; back, rump, and tail black with fine buffy specks; upper tail-coverts and rectrices with large metallic blue-green ocelli with black and gray borders; eyebrow stripe and ear-coverts white; underparts dull black. Female—all light brown with fine black specks; face whitish; tail brown with dull blue-green ocelli.

Soft Parts: Bill black; iris dark brown; feet brown.

Measurements: Wing 201; tail ♂273; bill 21; tarsus 70.

Range: Palawan. (Endemic.)

Family TURNICIDAE   BUTTON-QUAIL

STRIPED BUTTON-QUAIL   PLATE 16

Turnix sylvatica whiteheadi Ogilvie-Grant, 1897

1897 *Turnix whiteheadi* Ogilvie-Grant, Handb. Game Bds., 2:276, (Quinta Market, Manila, Luzon; supposedly captured at Parañaque, Luzon)

Description: Male—forehead and sides of face buffy white with fine black spots; top of head blackish with a buffy stripe on center of crown; back, rump, and tail mottled gray-black with some chestnut; wing-coverts pale chestnut with dark brown spots; scapulars mottled with chestnut margins; chin and throat white; breast pale chestnut with fine black spots on the sides; belly white. Female—differs from the male by having a mottled rufous collar and the chestnut breast darker.

Soft Parts: Bill bluish; iris pale yellow; feet pale bluish.
Measurements: Wing ♂63, ♀66; tail ♂24, ♀21; bill 11; tarsus 19.
Range: Central Luzon. (Endemic.)

Turnix sylvatica celestinoi McGregor, 1907

1907 *Turnix celestinoi* McGregor, Phil. Journ. Sci., **2**:317, (Guindulman, Bohol)

Description: Differs from *whiteheadi* by having the upperparts black barred with dark chestnut; chin and throat feathers tipped with buff; feathers on sides of breast have a wide black bar.
Range: Bohol. (Endemic.)

Turnix sylvatica masaaki Hachisuka, 1931

1931 *Turnix sylvatica masaaki* Hachisuka, Ois. et Rev. Fran. d'Orn., **1**:472, (Go-gong, Cotobato Province, Mindanao)

Description: Differs from *celestinoi* by having the barring on the upperparts gray with only the occasional dull rufous bar; chin and center of throat pure white; feathers on sides of breast mottled with chestnut and black; inner secondary coverts have chestnut and black centers with buffy margins.
Range: Mindanao. (Endemic.)

Turnix sylvatica suluensis Mearns, 1905

1905 *Turnix suluensis* Mearns, Proc. Biol. Soc. Wash., **18**:83, (Jolo)

Description: Female differs from *masaaki* by having the spots on the sides of the breast dark chestnut; breast paler; wing-coverts more rufous; lower back, tail-coverts, and tail blacker.
Range: Jolo. (Endemic.)

WORCESTER'S BUTTON-QUAIL   PLATE 16

Turnix worcesteri McGregor, 1904

1904 *Turnix worcesteri* McGregor, Bull. Phil. Mus., 4:8, (Quinta Market, Manila, Luzon)

Description: Top of head dark brown with three buffy streaks, one over each eye and one down the center; back, rump, and tail dark brown with buffy edges; wing-coverts light buff mottled with dark brown; primaries gray-brown; sides of head light buff with some dark brown bars; throat white; breast rufous with dark brown and black mottling on sides; belly white, becoming rufous on thighs and under tail-coverts. Female—similar to male but upperparts are much darker; sides of head black with white specks; throat and belly light rufous.

Soft Parts: Bill bluish; iris pale yellow; feet pinkish.

Measurements: Wing ♂70, ♀74; tail 35; bill 10; tarsus 18.

Range: North and central Luzon. (Endemic.)

BARRED BUTTON-QUAIL
PLATE 16

Turnix suscitator fasciata (Temminck, 1815)

1815 *Hemipodius fasciatus* Temminck, Pig. et Gall., 3:757, (Manila, Luzon)

1888 *Turnix haynaldi* Blasius, Ornis, 4:317, (Puerto Princesa, Palawan)

Description: Male—top of head dark brown with gray stripe; a slight chestnut collar on hind neck; back, rump, and tail mottled with black, gray, and chestnut; wing-coverts buffy with black spots and some chestnut; chin and throat white; breast buff with black bars; belly whitish; under tail-coverts light chestnut. Female—throat black; chestnut collar on hind neck.

Soft Parts: Bill yellow-brown; iris pale buff; feet yellow-brown.

Measurements: Wing 78; tail 30; bill 11; tarsus 22.

Range: Calamianes, Luzon, Masbate, Mindoro, Palawan, Panay, and Sibuyan. (Endemic.)

Turnix suscitator nigrescens Tweeddale, 1877

1877 *Turnix nigrescens* Tweeddale, (1878), Proc. Zool. Soc. London, p. 765, (Cebu)

Description: Differs from *fasciata* by having the chestnut collar on hind neck wider and all upperparts much darker.

Range: Cebu and Negros. (Endemic.)

SPOTTED BUTTON-QUAIL
PLATE 16

Turnix ocellata ocellata (Scopoli, 1786)

1786 *Oriolus ocellatus* Scopoli, Del. Flor. et Faun. Insubr., p. 88, (Manila, Luzon)

Description: Male—top of head blackish chestnut with three white stripes, one over each eye and one down the center of the crown; a slight rufous collar on hind neck; back, rump, and tail dark brown mottled with gray and black; wing-coverts buffy with large black spots; rest of wing gray-brown with buffy edges to primaries; throat and sides of head white; breast rufous; belly buff-brown. Female—differs from male by having a wide chestnut collar on hind neck and throat and by having sides of head black.

Soft Parts: Bill greenish yellow; iris yellow; feet yellow.

Measurements: Wing ♂97, ♀108; tail 43; bill ♂21, ♀19; tarsus 28.

Range: Central Luzon around Manila. (Endemic.)

59

PLATE 14

A   MEGAPODE
      (Megapodius freycinet)—page 54

B   PAINTED QUAIL
      (Coturnix chinensis), male—page 56

C   PAINTED QUAIL
      (Coturnix chinensis), female—page 56

D   BEARDED PARTRIDGE
      (Perdix barbata), male—page 55

E   BEARDED PARTRIDGE
      (Perdix barbata), female—page 55

F   ASIATIC MIGRATORY QUAIL
      (Coturnix coturnix), male—page 56

G   ASIATIC MIGRATORY QUAIL
      (Coturnix coturnix), female—page 56

H   CHINESE FRANCOLIN
      (Francolinus pintadeanus), male—page 55

I   JUNGLE FOWL
      (Gallus gallus), female—page 56

J   JUNGLE FOWL
      (Gallus gallus), male—page 56

PLATE 14

PLATE 15

PALAWAN PEACOCK PHEASANT
(Polyplectron emphanum)—page 57

PLATE 15

PLATE 16

A   STRIPED BUTTON-QUAIL
       (Turnix sylvatica), female—page 57

B   STRIPED BUTTON-QUAIL
       (Turnix sylvatica), male—page 57

C   WORCESTER'S BUTTON-QUAIL
       (Turnix worcesteri), female—page 58

D   WORCESTER'S BUTTON-QUAIL
       (Turnix worcesteri), male—page 58

E   BARRED BUTTON-QUAIL
       (Turnix suscitator), male—page 59

F   BARRED BUTTON-QUAIL
       (Turnix suscitator), female—page 59

G   SPOTTED BUTTON-QUAIL
       (Turnix ocellata), male—page 59

H   SPOTTED BUTTON-QUAIL
       (Turnix ocellata), female—page 59

PLATE 16

Turnix ocellata benguetensis Parkes, 1968

1968   *Turnix ocellata benguetensis* Parkes, Bull. Brit. Orn. Cl., **88**:24, (Mt. Data, Luzon)

Description: Differs from *T. o. ocellata* by having smaller wings (♂ 88, ♀ 97) and bill (♂ 16, ♀ 17); the rufous on the lower breast tends to be more extensive.

Range: Northern Luzon (Mountain Province). (Endemic.)

Family GRUIDAE   CRANES

EASTERN SARUS CRANE   PLATE 6

Grus antigone sharpii Blanford, 1895

1895   *Grus (Antigone) sharpii* Blanford, Bull. Brit. Orn. Cl., **5**:7, (Burma)

Description: Head and neck naked but bright red; upperparts pearl-gray; underneath somewhat darker gray.

Soft Parts: Bill greenish; iris yellow; legs and feet pink.

Measurements: Wing 560; tail 216; bill 120; tarsus 274.

Range: Northern and central Luzon.

Family RALLIDAE   RAILS

SLATY-BREASTED RAIL   PLATE 17

Rallus striatus striatus Linné, 1766

1766   *Rallus striatus* Linné, Syst. Nat., **1**:262, (Manila, Luzon)

1924   *Hypotaenidia striata paraterma* Oberholser, Journ. Wash. Acad. Sci., **14**:295, (Samar)

Description: Top of head and neck dark chestnut with a few inconspicuous dark streaks; back, rump, wings, and tail dark olive-brown with white specks; chin and upper throat white; lower throat and breast slate-blue; belly and flanks dark olive-brown with white bars.

Soft Parts: Bill, basal half reddish pink, terminal half horn; iris red; feet olive-brown.

Measurements: Wing 116; tail 51; bill 34; tarsus 34.

Range: Found throughout the Philippines.

BROWN-BANDED RAIL   PLATE 17

Rallus mirificus Parkes and Amadon, 1959

1959 *Rallus mirificus* Parkes and Amadon, Will. Bull., **71**:303, (Dalton Pass, Nueva Vizcaya, Luzon)

Description: Top of head and neck dark chestnut; back, rump, and tail olive-brown; wings and tail olive-brown with fine buff bars; chin and upper throat whitish; lower throat and breast brownish gray; belly and under tail-coverts dark olive-brown with white bars. Immature—without chestnut on head.

Soft Parts: Bill, upper mandible brownish, lower mandible pale horn at tip becoming redder at base; iris and feet unrecorded.

Measurements: Wing 108; tail 40; bill 25; tarsus 29.

Range: Central Luzon. (Endemic.)

BANDED RAIL   PLATE 17

Rallus philippensis philippensis Linné, 1766

1766 *Rallus philippensis* Linné, Syst. Nat., **1**:263, (Philippines = Luzon)

Description: Top of head and neck brown with black streaks; lores, streak through eye, ear-coverts, and narrow collar on hind neck rufous; back, rump, wings, and tail feathers brownish black with yellow-brown margins having scattered white spots; chin and upper throat whitish; lower throat olive-gray; breast and belly gray-white with black bars.

Soft Parts: Bill, basal half dark red, end tan; iris red; feet olive-brown.

Measurements: Wing 132; tail 61; bill 27; tarsus 44.

Range: Batan, Luzon, Mindoro, and Samar. (Endemic.)

BARRED RAIL   PLATE 17

Rallus torquatus torquatus Linné, 1766

1766 *Rallus torquatus* Linné, Syst. Nat., **1**:262, (Philippines)

1949 *Rallus torquatus quisumbingi* Gilliard, Auk, **66**:275, (Camarines, southern Luzon)

1949 *Rallus torquatus sanfordi* Gilliard, Auk, **66**:276, (Zamboanga, Mindanao)

Description: Forehead olive-gray; crown, back, rump, wings, and tail olive-brown; lores and eye stripe gray-black with a white stripe underneath; chin white; throat black; upper breast black with fine white bars; lower breast has a rufous band with fine black bars; belly black with white bars; thighs gray-brown with faint white bars.

Soft Parts: Bill brownish; iris red; feet olive-brown.

Measurements: Wing 146; tail 58; bill 36; tarsus 43.

Range: Found throughout the Philippines. (Endemic.)

MALAY BANDED CRAKE   PLATE 17

Rallina fasciata (Raffles, 1822)

1822   *Rallus fasciata* Raffles, Trans. Linn. Soc. London, **13**:328, (Benkulen, Sumatra)

Description: Head and neck chestnut fading into dull chestnut on back, wing-coverts, tail, and rump—the latter with a few black and buff bars; chin and throat very pale chestnut; breast chestnut; belly and under tail-coverts with black and white bars of equal width.

Soft Parts: Bill black; iris red; feet bright red.

Measurements: Wings 130; tail 58; bill 23; tarsus 43.

Range: Balabac, Mindoro, and Palawan.

PHILIPPINE BANDED CRAKE   PLATE 17

Rallina eurizonoides eurizonoides (Lafresnaye, 1845)

1845   *Gallinula eurizonoides* Lafresnaye, Rev. et Mag. Zool., p. 368, (no locality = Philippines)

Description: Head and neck chestnut; back, rump, wings, and tail olive-brown; chin and upper throat very pale chestnut; breast chestnut; belly and under tail-coverts black with white bars.

Soft Parts: Bill dark gray above, blue-gray below, apple-green for basal third; iris orange-red; skin around eye orange-yellow; legs slate-gray.

Measurements: Wing 124; tail 67; bill 23; tarsus 40.

Range: Basilan, Bohol, Cagayancillo, Cebu, Leyte, Luzon, Mindanao, Mindoro, Negros, Panay, and Sulu. (Endemic.)

DWARF RAIL   PLATE 18

Porzana pusilla pusilla (Pallas, 1776)

1776   *Rallus pusillus* Pallas, Reise Versch. Prov. Russ. Reichs, **3**:700, (Dauria)

Description: Center of forehead, crown, and whole hind neck chestnut with black streaks; lores and stripe over eye gray; ear-coverts chestnut; back dark chestnut with black and white streaks; rump and tail dark chestnut with black streaks; wing-coverts chestnut, primaries gray-brown; chin and throat light gray; breast blue-gray; belly and under tail-coverts black with white bars.

Soft Parts: Bill dark green; iris red; feet olive-green.

Measurements: Wing 85; tail 42; bill 18; tarsus 28.

Range: Winters on Luzon, Marinduque, and Negros; a visitor from Asia.

RUDDY CRAKE   PLATE 18

Porzana fusca fusca (Linné, 1766)

1766   *Rallus fuscus* Linné, Syst. Nat., 1:262, (Philippines)

Description: All upperparts dark olive-brown; chin and upper throat pale rufous; lower throat and breast dark olive-rufous; belly dark olive-brown with small white bars; under tail-coverts black with white bars.

Soft Parts: Bill dark brown; iris dark red; feet reddish.

Measurements: Wing 98; tail 46; bill 19; tarsus 33.

Range: Cagayancillo, Leyte, Luzon, Mindanao, Mindoro, Negros, and Samar.

CHINESE BANDED CRAKE   PLATE 18

Porzana paykullii (Ljungh, 1813)

1813   *Rallus Paykullii* Ljungh, Kungl. Svenska Vet.—Akad. nya Handl., 34:258, (Borneo
        and Java)

Description: Upperparts dark olive-brown; chin very pale rufous; throat and breast dusty rose; belly white with flanks and under tail-coverts black and white barred.

Soft Parts: Bill dark gray; iris dark red; feet pink-red.

Measurements: Wing 121; tail 54; bill 27; tarsus 39.

Range: Basilan (once) from China.

SOOTY RAIL   PLATE 18

Porzana tabuensis tabuensis Gmelin, 1789

1789   *Porzana tabuensis* Gmelin, Syst. Nat., 1:717, (Tonga Tabu, Tahiti)

1932   *Porzana plumbea filipina* Hachisuka, Bds. Phil. Ids., p. 234, (Luzon)

Description: Head dark slate-black; wings, back, and rump dark reddish brown; throat light slate; breast and belly slate-black; under tail-coverts black with white spots.

Soft Parts: Bill black; iris dark red; feet pinkish.

Measurements: Wing 72; tail 42; bill 18; tarsus 25.

Range: Luzon.

PLATE 17

A   PLAIN SWAMPHEN
      (*Amaurornis olivaceus*)—page 74

B   WHITE-BREASTED SWAMPHEN
      (*Amaurornis phoenicurus*)—page 74

C   MALAY BANDED CRAKE
      (*Rallina fasciata*)—page 68

D   PHILIPPINE BANDED CRAKE
      (*Rallina eurizonoides*)—page 68

E   BANDED RAIL
      (*Rallus philippensis*)—page 67

F   SLATY-BREASTED RAIL
      (*Rallus striatus*)—page 66

G   WHITE-BROWED RAIL
      (*Poliolimnas cinereus*)—page 74

H   BARRED RAIL
      (*Rallus torquatus*)—page 67

I   BROWN-BANDED RAIL
      (*Rallus mirificus*)—page 67

PLATE 17

PLATE 18

A   WATERCOCK
        (Gallicrex cinerea)—page 75

B   PURPLE SWAMPHEN
        (Porphyrio porphyrio)—page 75

C   RUDDY CRAKE
        (Porzana fusca)—page 69

D   CHINESE BANDED CRAKE
        (Porzana paykullii)—page 69

E   SOOTY RAIL
        (Porzana tabuensis)—page 69

F   DWARF RAIL
        (Porzana pusilla)—page 68

G   BLACK COOT
        (Fulica atra)—page 76

H   GALLINULE
        (Gallinula chloropus)—page 75

PLATE 18

WHITE-BROWED RAIL

PLATE 17

Poliolimnas cinereus ocularis Sharpe, 1894

1894   *Poliolimnas cinereus ocularis* Sharpe, Cat. Bds. Brit. Mus., **23**:130, (Philippines)

1926   *Poliolimnas cinereus collingwoodi* Mathews, Bull. Brit. Orn. Cl., **46**:60, (Philippines)

Description: Forehead, crown, and lores dark olive-gray; hind neck, back, rump, wings, and tail dark olive-brown; small stripe above lores and stripe beneath eye, chin, and throat white; ear-coverts and upper breast gray; lower breast and belly white; flanks olive-brown; under tail-coverts pale rufous.

Soft Parts: Bill yellow-brown; iris red; feet greenish yellow.

Measurements: Wing 98; tail 43; bill 24; tarsus 35.

Range: Found throughout the Philippines.

PLAIN SWAMPHEN

PLATE 17

Amaurornis olivaceus olivaceus (Meyen, 1834)

1834   *Gallinula olivacea* Meyen, Nova Acta Acad. Caes. Leop. Carol., **16**, suppl. 109, (Manila, Luzon)

Description: All upperparts dark olive-brown; chin light gray; throat, breast, and belly dark slate with an olive cast; under tail-coverts dark rufous brown.

Soft Parts: Bill greenish; iris red; feet dark yellow.

Measurements: Wing 151; tail 62; bill 34; tarsus 57.

Range: Found throughout the Philippines, except for Palawan and the Sulus. (Endemic.)

WHITE-BREASTED SWAMPHEN

PLATE 17

Amaurornis phoenicurus javanicus (Horsfield, 1821)

1821   *Gallinula Javanica* Horsfield, Trans. Linn. Soc. London, **13**:196, (Java)

Description: Crown and rest of upperparts olive-slate; forehead, sides of head, throat, breast, and belly white; sides of breast and belly dark slate; thighs and under tail-coverts rufous.

Soft Parts: Bill, basal part red, rest dark green; iris dark brown; feet greenish yellow.

Measurements: Wing 158; tail 79; bill 39; tarsus 55.

Range: Found throughout the Philippines.

74

GALLINULE   PLATE 18

Gallinula chloropus lozanoi Lletget, 1918

1918 *Gallinula chloropus lozanoi* Lletget, Bol. R. Soc. Esp. His. Nat., **18**:76, (Luzon)

Description: Head and neck black; back, wings, and tail dark olive-brown; breast and belly slate-gray, some individuals having various amounts of white on the belly; a white stripe on flanks; under tail-coverts white.

Soft Parts: Bill, base red, tip yellow; shield red; iris red; feet olive-green.

Measurements: Wing 155; tail 75; bill 28; tarsus 50.

Range: Found throughout the Philippines. This race is an intermediate population between *indica* to the north and *orientalis* to the south. Some individuals from the northern Philippines are extremely close to *indica* and may prove to be migrants from Asia.

WATERCOCK   PLATE 18

Gallicrex cinerea (Gmelin, 1789)

1789 *Fulica cinerea* Gmelin, Syst. Nat., **1**:702, (China)

Description: Male—head and neck blackish brown; back, wings, and tail dark brown, some feathers having light brown margins; throat and breast black; breast gray-black with light brown edges to feathers; under tail-coverts white with brown bars. Female—brown with light brown streaks above and blackish bars below. Male in eclipse plumage much the same as the female.

Soft Parts: Bill, base red, tip yellow; shield red; iris dull red; feet greenish brown.

Measurements: Wing ♂226, ♀175; tail ♂81, ♀64; bill ♂36, ♀30; tarsus ♂75, ♀58.

Range: Found throughout the Philippines.

PURPLE SWAMPHEN   PLATE 18

Porphyrio porphyrio pulverulentus Temminck, 1826

1826 *Porphyrio pulverulentus* Temminck, Pl. Col., livr. 68, pl. 405, ("South Africa"; error = Philippines)

Description: Head, neck, and upper back gray-blue, the latter a little darker; back, rump, and some wing-coverts bronze-green, rest of wing blue; tail greenish blue; throat, breast, and flanks blue; belly blue-gray, some individuals with varying amounts of white; thigh slate-blue; under tail-coverts white.

Soft Parts: Bill dark red; shield red; iris dull red; feet red-brown.

Measurements: Wing 236; tail 95; bill 39; tarsus 85.

Range: Basilan, Bohol, Luzon, Mindanao, Mindoro, and Panay.

BLACK COOT   PLATE 18

Fulica atra atra Linné, 1758

1758 *Fulica atra* Linné, Syst. Nat., 1:152, (Sweden)

Description: Head and neck black; back, rump, wings, and tail dark slate-gray; edge of primaries white; underneath all slate-gray.

Soft Parts: Bill and shield white; iris brown; feet greenish black.

Measurements: Wing 215; tail 54; bill 32; tarsus 61.

Range: Luzon.

Family JACANIDAE   JACANAS

COMB-CRESTED JACANA   PLATE 19

Irediparra gallinacea gallinacea (Temminck, 1828)

1828 *Parra gallinacea* Temminck, Pl. Col., livr. 78, pl. 464, (Menado, Celebes)

1932 *Irediparra gallinacea nakamurai* Hachisuka, Bds. Phil. Ids., p. 261, (Leguasan Swamp, Mindanao)

Description: Top of head and hind neck black; back, wings, and tail glossy bronze; forehead, sides of throat, and upper breast golden yellow; chin and throat white; center of breast and flanks black; belly and thighs white.

Soft Parts: Bill, lower mandible base yellow, central section black, and tip gray, upper mandible base and comb dark red, central section black, and tip gray; iris yellow; legs green with a red patch on the front of the tibia.

Measurements: Wing 138; tail 41; bill 29; tarsus 58.

Range: Mindanao.

PHEASANT-TAILED JACANA   PLATE 19

Hydrophasianus chirurgus (Scopoli, 1786)

1786 *Tringa Chirurgus* Scopoli, Del. Flor. et Faun. Insubr., p. 92, (Luzon)

Description: Forehead, top of head, face, chin, and throat white; nape and a stripe down the side of the neck black; hind neck golden yellow; back dark brown with a reddish purple gloss; rump and tail black; wings white with black tips to primaries; breast and belly dark brown.

Soft Parts: Bill blue; iris brown; feet bluish.

Measurements: Wing 118; tail 230; bill 26; tarsus 50.

Range: Calayan, Luzon, Mindanao, and Mindoro.

Family ROSTRATULIDAE   PAINTED-SNIPE

PAINTED-SNIPE   **PLATE 19**

Rostratula benghalensis benghalensis (Linné, 1758)

1758 *Rallus benghalensis* Linné, Syst. Nat., **1**:153, (Asia)

Description: Male—top of head greenish brown with a buffy stripe down the center; eye-ring white; back gray finely barred with black; scapulars greenish brown with a metallic wash, feathers with buffy eyes; wings and tail gray barred with black and with large buffy spots; chin white; throat and upper breast gray-brown; rest of underparts white. Female —similar to male in pattern but much more colorful; underparts strongly washed with metallic green; throat and hind neck dark chestnut; band on upper breast dark brown.

Soft Parts: Bill dark brown; iris blue-black; feet dark dull green.

Measurements: Wing 143; tail 42; bill 54; tarsus 45.

Range: Found throughout the Philippines.

Family CHARADRIIDAE   PLOVERS

GRAY-HEADED LAPWING   **PLATE 19**

Vanellus cinereus (Blyth, 1842)

1842 *Pluvianus cinereus* Blyth, Journ. As. Soc. Bengal, **11**:587, (Calcutta)

Description: Top of head, back, and scapulars light olive-brown; wing white except for primaries, which are black; rump and basal two thirds of tail white, subterminal band black, tip buffy; chin, throat, and breast pale gray-brown; brown band separates the breast and the belly; belly and under tail-coverts white.

Soft Parts: Bill, terminal quarter black, rest yellow; iris dark yellow-brown; feet yellow-green.

Measurements: Wing 242; tail 115; bill 44; tarsus 78.

Range: Luzon (once); a straggler from China.

BLACK-BELLIED PLOVER   **PLATE 19**

Pluvialis squatarola (Linné, 1758)

1758 *Tringa squatarola* Linné, Syst. Nat., **1**:149, (Sweden)

Description: Top of head, back, and wing-coverts black with white margins; rump white; tail barred black and white; wings black with a white stripe; axillars black; lores and a faint eyebrow stripe whitish; chin and throat white; breast white mottled with brown; belly and under tail-coverts white.

Soft Parts: Bill black; iris dark brown; feet black.

Measurements: Wing 182; tail 74; bill 28; tarsus 39.

Range: Bantayan, Bohol, Cebu, Cuyo, Luzon, Mindanao, Negros, Palawan, Polillo, and Siquijor.

PACIFIC GOLDEN PLOVER   PLATE 19

Pluvialis dominica fulva (Gmelin, 1789)

1789 *Charadrius fulvus* Gmelin, Syst. Nat., **1**:687, (Tahiti)

Description: Top of head, back, rump, tail, and scapulars black with buffy gold margins; primaries black; sides of head and faint eye stripe golden with fine brown streaks; chin white; throat, breast, and flanks gray with brown margins; belly and under tail-coverts white.

Soft Parts: Bill blackish brown; iris dark brown; feet black.

Measurements: Wing 163; tail 66; bill 26; tarsus 45.

Range: Winters throughout the Philippines from Asia.

RING-NECKED PLOVER   PLATE 20

Charadrius dubius dubius Scopoli, 1786

1786 *Charadrius dubius* Scopoli, Del. Flor. et Faun. Insubr., p. 93, (Luzon)

Description: Forehead and stripe behind eye white; forecrown black; back of head gray-brown; white collar on hind neck; rest of upperparts gray-brown, becoming darker on end of tail; lores, stripe under eye, and ear-coverts black; chin and throat white; breast band black; rest of underparts white.

Soft Parts: Bill black, base of lower mandible orange-yellow; orbital ring yellow; iris brown; feet pinkish black.

Measurements: Wing 110; tail 69; bill 17; tarsus 26.

Range: Breeds throughout the Philippines.

Charadrius dubius curonicus Gmelin, 1789

1789 *Charadrius curonicus* Gmelin, Syst. Nat., **1**:692, (Kurland)

Description: Differs from *C. d. dubius* by having the black markings duller and less extensive; bill slightly shorter and lacks the orange-yellow base of the lower mandible.

Range: Winters in the Philippines from Asia.

KENTISH PLOVER   **PLATE 20**

Charadrius alexandrinus dealbatus (Swinhoe, 1870)

1870   *Aegialites dealbatus* Swinhoe, Proc. Zool. Soc. London, p. 138, (southern China, Formosa, Hainan)

Description: Forehead and stripe over eye white; lores and stripe behind eye blackish; forecrown blackish; crown and hind neck rufous-brown; collar white; back, rump, and tail brown; wing brown with a white stripe; primaries dark brown; underparts white except for incomplete dark brown band on breast.

Soft Parts: Bill black; iris brown; feet black.

Measurements: Wing 107; tail 54; bill 18; tarsus 27.

Range: Winters throughout the Philippines from China and Japan.

MALAY PLOVER   **PLATE 20**

Charadrius peronii Schlegel, 1865

1865   *Charadrius peronii* Schlegel, Mus. Pays-Bas, 4:33, (Samau)

Description: Forehead white followed by some rufous; crown, hind neck, and back pale gray-brown; rump and upper tail-coverts dull black; tail dull black; outer rectrices white; lores dark brown; ear-coverts rufous; eye stripe, chin, and throat white; partial band on breast rufous; rest of underparts white.

Soft Parts: Bill black with some orange on the base of the lower mandible; orbital ring orange; iris brown; feet dark gray.

Measurements: Wing 96; tail 37; bill 17; tarsus 27.

Range: Found throughout the Philippines.

MONGOLIAN PLOVER   **PLATE 20**

Charadrius mongolus mongolus Pallas, 1776

1776   *Charadrius mongolus* Pallas, Reise Versch. Prov. Russ. Reichs, 3:700, (Siberia)

Description: Upperparts pale brown; primaries black; eye stripe whitish; sides of head olive-gray; chin and throat white; breast band olive-gray; belly and under tail-coverts white.

Soft Parts: Bill black; iris dark brown; feet black.

Measurements: Wing 135; tail 54; bill 18; tarsus 30.

Range: Winters throughout the Philippines from Siberia.

79

PLATE 19

A   PAINTED-SNIPE
       (*Rostratula benghalensis*), female—page 77

B   PAINTED-SNIPE
       (*Rostratula benghalensis*), male—page 77

C   PACIFIC GOLDEN PLOVER
       (*Pluvialis dominica*), winter plumage—page 78

D   BLACK-BELLIED PLOVER
       (*Pluvialis squatarola*), winter plumage—page 77

E   COMB-CRESTED JACANA
       (*Irediparra gallinacea*)—page 76

F   GRAY-HEADED LAPWING
       (*Vanellus cinereus*)—page 77

G   PHEASANT-TAILED JACANA
       (*Hydrophasianus chirurgus*)—page 76

80

PLATE 19

PLATE 20

A   ORIENTAL DOTTEREL
    (Charadrius veredus)—page 84

B   RING-NECKED PLOVER
    (Charadrius dubius)—page 78

C   MALAY PLOVER
    (Charadrius peronii)—page 79

D   MONGOLIAN PLOVER
    (Charadrius mongolus)—page 79

E   KENTISH PLOVER
    (Charadrius alexandrinus)—page 79

F   LARGE SAND PLOVER
    (Charadrius leschenaultii)—page 84

PLATE 20

LARGE SAND PLOVER PLATE 20

Charadrius leschenaultii Lesson, 1826

1826 *Charadrius leschenaultii* Lesson, Dict. Sci. Nat., ed. Levrault, **42**:36, (India)

Description: Upperparts pale brown; tail brown, tipped with white; outer rectrices becoming white; forehead and eyebrow stripe white; lores and ear-coverts light brown; underparts white except for a narrow, pale brown band on the breast.

Soft Parts: Bill black; iris brown; feet dark olive.

Measurements: Wing 145; tail 56; bill 25; tarsus 38.

Range: Winters throughout the Philippines from Asia.

ORIENTAL DOTTEREL PLATE 20

Charadrius veredus Gould, 1848

1848 *Charadrius veredus* Gould, Proc. Zool. Soc. London, p. 38, (northern Australia)

Description: Upperparts have brown feathers with rufous margins; primaries dark brown; tail dark brown with white tips to central rectrices; outer rectrices very pale; forehead and eye stripe pale golden brown; patch behind the eye brown; throat dirty white; breast pale buff; belly and under tail-coverts dirty white.

Soft Parts: Bill olive-brown; iris brown; legs yellow-brown; feet dark brown.

Measurements: Wing 165; tail 59; bill 23; tarsus 49.

Range: Winters on Luzon and Palawan from Asia.

Family SCOLOPACIDAE SANDPIPERS

PYGMY CURLEW PLATE 21

Numenius minutus Gould, 1841

1841 *Numenius minutus* Gould, Proc. Zool. Soc. London, p. 176, (New South Wales)

Description: Upperparts dark brown mottled with buff; tail gray with dark brown bars; primaries dark brown; chin and throat pale buff; breast buff with dark red-brown shaft streaks; belly pale buff; thighs barred with dark brown.

Soft Parts: Bill dark brown, base of lower mandible flesh color; iris dark brown; feet gray.

Measurements: Wing 178; tail 74; bill 42; tarsus 50.

Range: Luzon, Marinduque, and Mindanao.

WHIMBREL   PLATE 21

Numenius phaeopus variegatus (Scopoli, 1786)

1786   *Tantalus variegatus* Scopoli, Del. Flor. et Faun. Insubr., p. 92, (Luzon)

Description: Upperparts dark brown slightly mottled with gray; rump gray with fine brown streaks; tail dark brown with light brown bars; superciliary and stripe down center of the crown gray-buff; sides of face and throat gray finely streaked with brown; breast buff streaked with brown; center of belly white; flanks, thighs, and under tail-coverts dirty white with brown bars.

Soft Parts: Bill black, base of lower mandible dark brown; iris dark brown; feet plumbous.

Measurements: Wing 231; tail 108; bill 80; tarsus 54.

Range: Winters throughout the Philippines from Siberia.

COMMON   CURLEW   PLATE 21

Numenius arquata orientalis C. L. Brehm, 1831

1831   *Numenius orientalis* C. L. Brehm, Handb. Naturg. Vög. Deutsch., 1:610, (East Indies)

Description: Upperparts gray-brown heavily streaked with dark brown; rump and upper tail-coverts white with a few dark brown streaks; chin white; rest of underparts white streaked with brown.

Soft Parts: Bill dark brown, base lighter; iris brown; feet whitish gray.

Measurements: Wing 295; tail 145; bill 195; tarsus 87.

Range: Luzon, Masbate, Negros, Palawan, and Samar.

LONG-BILLED   CURLEW   PLATE 21

Numenius madagascariensis (Linné, 1766)

1766   *Scolopax madagascariensis* Linné, Syst. Nat., 1:242, (Macassar, Celebes)

Description: Upperparts gray-brown heavily streaked with dark brown; chin pale buff; sides of face and rest of underparts buffy streaked with brown.

Soft Parts: Bill black, base of lower mandible flesh color; iris brown; feet dark gray.

Measurements: Wing 315; tail 115; bill 190; tarsus 95.

Range: Winters on Bohol, Cebu, and Negros from Siberia.

PLATE 21

A   PYGMY CURLEW
       (Numenius minutus)—page 84

B   WHIMBREL
       (Numenius phaeopus)—page 85

C   COMMON CURLEW
       (Numenius arquata)—page 85

D   LONG-BILLED CURLEW
       (Numenius madagascariensis)—page 85

E   BLACK-TAILED GODWIT
       (Limosa limosa)—page 88

F   BAR-TAILED GODWIT
       (Limosa lapponica)—page 88

G   REDSHANK
       (Tringa totanus)—page 88

H   MARSH SANDPIPER
       (Tringa stagnatilis)—page 89

PLATE 21

BLACK-TAILED GODWIT   PLATE 21

Limosa limosa melanuroides Gould, 1846

1846 *Limosa Melanuroides* Gould, Proc. Zool. Soc. London, p. 84, (Port Essington, Australia)

Description: Upperparts brown; head somewhat grayer; rump dark brown; upper tail-coverts white; tail dark brown; outer rectrices with white bases; wings dark brown with a white band; chin white; throat and breast pale gray-brown; belly and under tail-coverts white.

Soft Parts: Bill, terminal half dark brown, base pinkish; iris brown; feet greenish.

Measurements: Wing 204; tail 78; bill 87; tarsus 70.

Range: Winters on Luzon, Negros, and Samar from Asia.

BAR-TAILED GODWIT   PLATE 21

Limosa lapponica baueri Naumann, 1836

1836 *Limosa baueri* Naumann, Handb. Naturg. Vög. Deutsch., **8**:429, (Victoria, Australia)

Description: Upperparts gray-brown mottled with dark brown; rump gray-white barred with dark brown; tail dark brown with light gray bars; chin and throat buff with fine brown streaks; rest of underparts pure whitish.

Soft Parts: Bill, terminal half blackish, basal half pinkish; iris brown; feet dark brown.

Measurements: Wing 224; tail 79; bill 99; tarsus 57.

Range: Winters on Bantayan, Bohol, Cuyo, Luzon, Negros, and Samar from Asia.

REDSHANK   PLATE 21

Tringa totanus eurhina (Oberholser, 1900)

1900 *Totanus totanus eurhinus* Oberholser, Proc. U. S. Nat. Mus., **22**:207, (Tso Moriri Lake, Ladak)

Description: Upperparts olive-gray; lower back and rump white; tail finely barred with olive-gray and white; forehead, superciliary, and chin white; rest of underparts white finely streaked with rufous-brown.

Soft Parts: Bill black, base of lower mandible orange-red; iris dark brown; feet reddish.

Measurements: Wing 154; tail 63; bill 47; tarsus 48.

Range: Winters on Bantayan, Basilan, Bohol, Cebu, Cuyo, Luzon, Mindanao, Mindoro, Negros, Palawan, and Siquijor.

MARSH SANDPIPER   PLATE 21

Tringa stagnatilis (Bechstein, 1803)

1803   *Totanus stagnatilis* Bechstein, Orn. Taschenb. Deutschl., p. 293, (Germany)

Description: Upperparts pale olive-gray; lower back and rump pure white; tail white mottled with olive-gray; bend of wing and primaries brownish black; underparts pure white.

Soft Parts: Bill black; iris dark brown; feet brownish black.

Measurements: Wing 143; tail 63; bill 38; tarsus 49.

Range: Winters on Luzon from Asia.

GREENSHANK   PLATE 22

Tringa nebularia (Gunnerus, 1767)

1767   *Scolopax nebularia* Gunnerus, in Leem's Beskr. Finm. Lapper, p. 251, (Norway)

Description: Upperparts olive-gray mottled with dark brown; lower back and rump white; tail white barred with olive-gray; bend of wing and primaries dark brown; underparts white.

Soft Parts: Bill dark gray; iris dark brown; feet gray black.

Measurements: Wing 185; tail 77; bill 55; tarsus 56.

Range: Winters on Bohol, Cebu, Luzon, Mindanao, Mindoro, Negros, and Polillo from Asia.

SPOTTED GREENSHANK   PLATE 22

Tringa guttifera (Nordmann, 1835)

1835   *Totanus guttifer* Nordmann, in Erman's Reise Naturh. Atlas, p. 17, (Okhotsk)

Description: Upperparts pale gray; lower back and rump white; tail somewhat grayer; bend of wing and primaries blackish brown; underparts white.

Soft Parts: Bill black; iris dark brown; feet greenish yellow.

Measurements: Wing 179; tail 69; bill 54; tarsus 43.

Range: Winters on Cebu and Luzon from Siberia.

PLATE 22

A   GREENSHANK
    (*Tringa nebularia*)—page 89

B   SPOTTED GREENSHANK
    (*Tringa guttifera*)—page 89

C   GREEN SANDPIPER
    (*Tringa ochrophus*)—page 92

D   WOOD SANDPIPER
    (*Tringa glareola*)—page 92

E   COMMON SANDPIPER
    (*Tringa hypoleucos*)—page 92

F   GRAY-TAILED TATTLER
    (*Tringa incanas*)—page 93

G   TEREK SANDPIPER
    (*Xenus cinereus*)—page 93

H   TURNSTONE
    (*Arenaria interpes*)—page 93

PLATE 22

GREEN SANDPIPER

PLATE 22

Tringa ochrophus Linné, 1758

1758   *Tringa ochrophus* Linné, Syst. Nat., **1**:149, (Sweden)

Description: Upperparts olive-brown; basal half of tail white, terminal half barred with olive-brown; primaries dark brown; chin white; throat white finely streaked with olive-brown; rest of underparts white.

Soft Parts: Bill brownish black; iris dark brown; feet gray-black.

Measurements: Wing 134; tail 60; bill 39; tarsus 32.

Range: Winters on Bohol, Luzon, Negros, Polillo, and Samar from Asia.

WOOD SANDPIPER

PLATE 22

Tringa glareola Linné, 1758

1758   *Tringa glareola* Linné, Syst. Nat., **1**:149, (Sweden)

Description: Upperparts dark metallic brown with a few white spots on the margins of the feathers; rump white; tail white coarsely barred with metallic brown; primaries blackish brown; chin white; sides of face, throat, and upper breast gray finely streaked with olive-brown; rest of underparts white.

Soft Parts: Bill black; iris brown; feet brown.

Measurements: Wing 124; tail 55; bill 28; tarsus 34.

Range: Winters throughout the Philippines from Asia.

COMMON SANDPIPER

PLATE 22

Tringa hypoleucos Linné, 1758

1758   *Tringa hypoleucos* Linné, Syst. Nat., **1**:149, (Sweden)

Description: Upperparts dark metallic olive-brown sparsely barred with dark brown; chin white; throat white with faint olive-brown shaft streaks in the center, becoming heavier towards the sides; rest of underparts white.

Soft Parts: Bill brownish black; iris brown; feet gray-green.

Measurements: Wing 112; tail 57; bill 29; tarsus 22.

Range: Winters throughout the Philippines from Asia.

GRAY-TAILED TATTLER

PLATE 22

Tringa incanas brevipes (Vieillot, 1816)

1816 *Totanus brevipes* Vieillot, Dict. Hist. Nat., **6**:410, (Timor)

Description: Upperparts olive-gray; superciliary white; lores black; chin white; throat, breast, and flanks olive-gray; belly and under tail-coverts white.

Soft Parts: Bill black, base of lower mandible gray-brown; iris dark brown; feet yellowish.

Measurements: Wing 172; tail 72; bill 40; tarsus 31.

Range: Winters throughout the Philippines from Siberia.

TEREK SANDPIPER

PLATE 22

Xenus cinereus (Guldenstaedt, 1774)

1774 *Scolopax cinerea* Guldenstaedt, Novi Comm. Sci. Petropol., **19**:473, (Caspian Sea)

Description: Upperparts pale olive-gray with dark brown shaft streak on the back; superciliary pale gray; chin white; throat white finely streaked with olive-gray; breast, belly, and under tail-coverts white.

Soft Parts: Bill black, lower mandible base yellowish; iris dark brown; feet olive-gray.

Measurements: Wing 130; tail 55; bill 50; tarsus 26.

Range: Winters on Bohol, Cebu, Masbate, Negros, and Palawan from Asia.

TURNSTONE

PLATE 22

Arenaria interpes interpes (Linné, 1758)

1758 *Tringa interpes* Linné, Syst. Nat., **1**:148, (Gotland, Sweden)

Description: Forehead white; sides of face black and white; crown dark brown mottled with white; back and wing-coverts dull chestnut mottled with black; lower back and rump white; upper tail-coverts dark brown; basal half of tail white, terminal half dark brown tipped with white; primaries blackish brown; chin white; throat and sides of breast black; rest of underparts white.

Soft Parts: Bill black; iris brown; feet orange-red.

Measurements: Wing 149; tail 64; bill 24; tarsus 25.

Range: Winters throughout the Philippines from Asia.

ORIENTAL DOWITCHER
PLATE 23

Limnodromus semipalmatus (Blyth, 1848)

1848 *Macrorhamphus semipalmatus* Blyth, Journ. As. Soc. Bengal, **17**:252, (Calcutta)

Description: Upperparts dark brown, feathers having buffy margins; rump white barred with dark brown; tail dark brown with buff bars; primaries dark brown; sides of face and chin gray with fine dark brown specks; throat and breast pale rufous with fine brown streaks; belly pale buff-gray.

Soft Parts: Bill black; iris dark brown; feet black.

Measurements: Wing 172; tail 60; bill 74; tarsus 49.

Range: Winters on Luzon from Asia.

JACK SNIPE
PLATE 23

Limnocryptes minimus (Brunnich, 1764)

1764 *Scolopax minima* Brunnich, Orn. Boreal., p. 49, (Christianso)

Description: Top of head dark brown; superciliary buffy; lores dark brown; back brown with a blue-green metallic wash; scapulars brown mottled with chestnut; innermost scapular pale buff, forming a line on either side of the back; tail brown, feathers having chestnut margins; wings brown with gray tip; chin white; throat, breast, and flanks mottled brown and white; belly white.

Soft Parts: Bill dark brown; iris dark brown; feet greenish brown.

Measurements: Wing 112; tail 50; bill 42; tarsus 21.

Range: Luzon (once); a straggler from Asia.

MARSH SNIPE
PLATE 23

Gallinago megala Swinhoe, 1861

1861 *Gallinago megala* Swinhoe, Ibis, p. 343, (between Takoo and Peking, China)

Description: Upperparts gray-brown streaked and barred with dark brown and buff; throat whitish; breast buffy; belly white; under tail-coverts buffy mottled with brown; tail, the most important key, having eight broad central feathers, the rest narrower. See Plate 23.

Soft Parts: Bill dark brown; iris blackish brown; feet greenish.

Measurements: Wing 137; tail 54; bill 62; tarsus 35.

Range: Winters throughout the Philippines from Asia.

PINTAIL SNIPE

PLATE 23

Gallinago stenura (Bonaparte, 1830)

1830   *Scolopax stenura* Bonaparte, Ann. Stor. Nat. Bologna, 4:335, (Sunda Islands)

Description: Differs from *G. megala* by having 10 broad central tail feathers and the rest very narrow and pinlike, much narrower than the outer tail feathers of *megala*. See Plate 23.

Range: Winters on Calayan, Luzon, Mindanao, and Palawan from Asia.

COMMON SNIPE

PLATE 23

Gallinago gallinago gallinago (Linné, 1758)

1758   *Scolopax gallinago* Linné, Syst. Nat., 1:147, (Sweden)

Description: Differs from *G. megala* and *G. stenura* by having the entire tail consisting of broad feathers. See Plate 23.

Range: Winters on Bohol, Leyte, Luzon, Mindanao, and Mindoro from Asia.

WOODCOCK

PLATE 23

Scolopax rusticola Linné, 1758

1758   *Scolopax Rusticola* Linné, Syst. Nat., 1:146, (Sweden)

Description: Forehead dark buffy brown; rest of upperparts basically brown but heavily mottled and blocked with black, chestnut, and buff; lores black; chin buffy; rest of underparts golden buff finely barred with black.

Soft Parts: Bill flesh color; iris blackish brown; feet dull gray.

Measurements: Wing 178; tail 68; bill 82; tarsus 40.

Range: Winters on Luzon from Asia.

KNOT

PLATE 23

Calidris canutus canutus (Linné, 1758)

1758   *Tringa canutus* Linné, Syst. Nat., 1:149, (Sweden)

1913   *Canutus canutus rogersi* Mathews, Bds. Austr., 3:270, (Shanghai, China)

Description: Upperparts brownish gray; rump and upper tail-coverts barred dark gray and white; tail gray; primaries dark brown; underparts gray-white finely streaked on the throat, breast, and flanks.

Soft Parts: Bill black; iris dark brown; feet dark greenish brown.

Measurements: Wing 165; tail 66; bill 31; tarsus 31.

Range: Luzon; a visitor from Asia.

PLATE 23

A   ORIENTAL DOWITCHER
      (Limnodromus semipalmatus)—page 94

B   JACK SNIPE
      (Limnocryptes minimus)—page 94

C   WOODCOCK
      (Scolopax rusticola)—page 95

D   KNOT
      (Calidris canutus)—page 95

E   GREAT KNOT
      (Calidris tenuirostris)—page 100

F   MARSH SNIPE
      (Gallinago megala)—page 94

G   PINTAIL SNIPE
      (Gallinago stenura)—page 95

H   MARSH SNIPE
      (Gallinago megala)—page 94

I   COMMON SNIPE
      (Gallinago gallinago)—page 95

PLATE 23

PLATE 24

A   SANDERLING
      (Calidris alba)—page 100

B   LITTLE STINT
      (Calidris ruficollis)—page 100

C   LEAST SANDPIPER
      (Calidris subminuta)—page 100

D   TEMMINCK'S STINT
      (Calidris temminckii)—page 101

E   CURLEW SANDPIPER
      (Calidris ferruginea)—page 101

F   BROAD-BILLED SANDPIPER
      (Limicola falcinellus)—page 102

G   SHARP-TAILED SANDPIPER
      (Calidris acuminata)—page 101

H   RUFF
      (Philomachus pugnax)—page 102

PLATE 24

GREAT KNOT   PLATE 23

Calidris tenuirostris (Horsfield, 1821)

1821   *Totanus tenuirostris* Horsfield, Trans. Linn. Soc. London, **13**:192, (Java)

Description: Upperparts pale gray, feathers having brown centers; tail dark gray-brown; primaries dark brown; underparts white except for sides of throat, breast, and flanks, which are finely spotted with brown.
Soft Parts: Bill black; iris dark brown; feet dark greenish brown.
Measurements: Wing 173; tail 62; bill 43; tarsus 35.
Range: Winters on Luzon, Negros, and Sitanki (near Sibutu) from Asia.

SANDERLING   PLATE 24

Calidris alba (Pallas, 1764)

1764   *Trynga alba* Pallas, in Vroeg's Cat., p. 7, (North Sea)

Description: Forehead buffy; upperparts gray mottled with dark brown; white stripe in wing; primaries dark brown; underparts white.
Soft Parts: Bill black; iris dark brown; feet black.
Measurements: Wing 123; tail 52; bill 25; tarsus 25.
Range: Winters on Luzon and Polillo from Asia.

LITTLE STINT   PLATE 24

Calidris ruficollis (Pallas, 1776)

1776   *Trynga ruficollis* Pallas, Reise Versch. Prov. Russ. Reichs, **3**:700, (Transbaikalia)

Description: Upperparts gray-brown, some feathers having dark shaft streaks; rump, tail, and primaries dark brown; underparts white with a gray band across the chest.
Soft Parts: Bill black; iris brown; feet black.
Measurements: Wing 95; tail 42; bill 18; tarsus 20.
Range: Winters throughout the Philippines from Siberia.

LEAST SANDPIPER   PLATE 24

Calidris subminuta (Middendorff, 1853)

1853   *Tringa subminuta* Middendorff, Reise Nord. und Ost. Siberien, **2**:222, (Stanovoi Mountains and mouth of the Uda)

Description: Upperparts dark brown streaked with buff; chin white; breast and flanks buffy finely streaked with dark brown; belly and under tail-coverts white.

100

Soft Parts: Bill black; iris dark brown; feet black.

Measurements: Wing 89; tail 35; bill 20; tarsus 23.

Range: Winters on Basilan, Luzon, Mindanao, and Palawan from Siberia.

TEMMINCK'S STINT
PLATE 24

Calidris temminckii (Leisler, 1812)

1812 *Tringa Temminckii* Leisler, Nachträge zu Bechstein's Naturg. Deutschl., p. 64, (Germany)

Description: Upperparts brownish gray; a pale gray stripe over light brown lores; throat and upper breast dark gray; rest of underparts white.

Soft Parts: Bill olive-brown; iris dark brown; feet olive.

Measurements: Wing 97; tail 48; bill 19; tarsus 16.

Range: Negros; a visitor from Asia.

SHARP-TAILED SANDPIPER
PLATE 24

Calidris acuminata (Horsfield, 1821)

1821 *Totanus acuminatus* Horsfield, Trans. Linn. Soc. London, **13**:192, (Java)

Description: Upperparts brown streaked with dark brown, pale buffy margins to back feathers; wings and tail dark brown; underparts gray-white; throat and breast finely spotted with brown.

Soft Parts: Bill black, base of lower mandible brown; iris dark brown; feet olive-yellow.

Measurements: Wing 132; tail 52; bill 26; tarsus 29.

Range: Winters on Batan, Luzon, Mindanao, and Panay from Asia.

CURLEW SANDPIPER
PLATE 24

Calidris ferruginea (Pontoppidan, 1763)

1763 *Tringa ferruginea* Pontoppidan, Danske Atlas, **1**:624, (Christianso Island off Bornholm, Denmark)

Description: Upperparts gray-brown with a slight olive wash; upper tail-coverts white; tail and primaries dark brown; chin white; throat gray finely streaked with brown; rest of underparts white.

Soft Parts: Bill black; iris brown; feet black.

Measurements: Wing 127; tail 48; bill 40; tarsus 28.

Range: Cebu, Luzon, and Negros; a visitor from Asia.

BROAD-BILLED SANDPIPER

PLATE 24

Limicola falcinellus sibirica Dresser, 1876

1876 *Limicola sibirica* Dresser, Proc. Zool. Soc. London, p. 674, (Siberia and China)

Description: Upperparts gray-brown; rump, tail, and primaries dark brown; chin white; throat and upper breast gray finely striped with dark brown; rest of underparts white.

Soft Parts: Bill black; iris dark brown; feet black.

Measurements: Wing 102; tail 40; bill 34; tarsus 20.

Range: Winters on Bohol, Cebu, Cuyo, Luzon, Negros, and Palawan from Asia.

RUFF

PLATE 24

Philomachus pugnax (Linné, 1758)

1758 *Tringa Pugnax* Linné, Syst. Nat., **1**:148, (Sweden)

Description: Upperparts brown, feathers with buffy edges; tail brown; primaries dark brown; chin white; throat and upper breast gray-brown; rest of underparts white.

Soft Parts: Bill black; iris black; feet yellow.

Measurements: Wing 175; tail 71; bill 34; tarsus 47.

Range: Luzon (once); a straggler from Asia.

Family RECURVIROSTRIDAE   STILTS

WHITE-HEADED STILT

PLATE 25

Himantopus himantopus leucocephalus Gould, 1837

1837 *Himantopus leucocephalus* Gould, Syn. Bds. Austr., pl. 34, (Australia, Java, Sumatra)

Description: Top of head white; neck black; hind neck white; back and wings black with a greenish gloss; rump and tail white; underparts white.

Soft Parts: Bill black; iris red; legs and feet red.

Measurements: Wing 230; tail 73; bill 60; tarsus 115.

Range: Basilan, Luzon, Malamaui, and Mindanao.

Family PHALAROPODIDAE   PHALAROPES

NORTHERN PHALAROPE

PLATE 25

Phalaropus lobatus (Linné, 1758)

1758 *Tringa tobata* [sic] Linné, Syst. Nat., **1**:148, (Hudson Bay)

Description: Winter plumage—upperparts mottled gray-brown; wings have a prominent white stripe; primaries with white shafts; chin and upper throat white; throat and upper breast white with gray bars; rest of underparts white.

Soft Parts: Bill black; iris dark brown; feet black.

Measurements: Wing 103; tail 47; bill 23; tarsus 21.

Range: Winters on islands in Basilan Straits, Calicoan (off Samar), Luzon, and Mindanao from Asia.

Family BURHINIDAE   THICK-KNEES

REEF   THICK-KNEE   PLATE 25

Esacus magnirostris (Latham, 1801)

1801   *Charadrius magnirostris* Latham, Ind. Orn., suppl., p. lxvi, (New South Wales)

Description: Top of head, back, and tail light brown; wings pale gray with dark brown and white stripes; dark brown patch in front of and behind the eye is bordered with white; underparts pale gray, becoming white on the belly.

Soft Parts: Bill, base yellow, rest black; iris yellow; feet chartreuse.

Measurements: Wing 274; tail 117; bill 80; tarsus 86.

Range: Calayan, Camiguin North, Fuga, Luzon, Mindanao, Mindoro, Palaui, Palawan, Polillo, and Tawi Tawi.

Family GLAREOLIDAE   PRATINCOLES

PRATINCOLE   PLATE 25

Glareola maldivarum Forster, 1795

1795   *Glareola (Pratincola) Maldivarum* Forster, Faunula Indica, p. 11, (Maldive Islands)

Description: Top of head, back, rump, and wing-coverts olive-brown; wing primaries dark brown; upper tail-coverts and basal half of rectrices white, terminal half dark brown; outer rectrices longer than inner; chin and throat buff with a white and black necklace; breast brown; belly and under tail-coverts white.

Soft Parts: Bill black, base red; iris brown; feet blackish brown.

Measurements: Wing 178; tail 81; bill 15; tarsus 33.

Range: Calayan, Luzon, Negros, and Palawan.

Family STERCORARIIDAE   SKUAS

POMARINE   JAEGER   PLATE 25

Stercorarius pomarinus (Temminck, 1815)

1815   *Lestris pomarinus* Temminck, Man. d' Orn., p. 514, (arctic Europe)

103

Description: All upperparts dark brown; upper tail-coverts barred with white; chin, throat, and breast white heavily barred with brown; belly dirty white with a few brown flecks; under tail-coverts white with brown bars. Description and illustration taken from only Philippine specimen that is an immature.

Soft Parts: Bill dark brown; iris brown; feet blackish brown.

Measurements: Wing 275 (worn); tail 160; bill 43; tarsus 49.

Range: Mindanao (once); a straggler from Asia.

Family LARIDAE   GULLS AND TERNS

BLACK-HEADED GULL   PLATE 26

Larus ridibundus Linné, 1766

1766 *Larus ridibundus* Linné, Syst. Nat., 1:225, (coasts of Europe)

Description: Head white with brown spot behind eye; upperparts gray; tail white; outer primaries white, forming wedge-shaped neck; primaries blackish below, contrasting with rest of wing; underparts white.

Soft Parts: Bill dark red; iris light brown; feet dark red.

Measurements: Wing 318; tail 120; bill 45; tarsus 45.

Range: Winter records from Luzon and Mindanao; a straggler from Asia.

HERRING GULL   PLATE 26

Larus argentatus vegae Palmén, 1887

1887 *Larus argentatus* Brünn var. *vegae* Palmén, in Nordenskiold's Vega-Expd. Vetensk. Iakttag., 5:370, (Pidlin, Siberia)

Description: Head white; upperparts gray; tail white; primaries tipped with black and a white spot; underparts gray-white.

Soft Parts: Bill yellow with a subterminal spot of red; iris whitish; feet fleshy or yellow; eye-ring yellow.

Measurements: Wing 430; tail 165; bill 54; tarsus 63.

Range: Winters on Luzon from eastern Asia.

WHITE-WINGED BLACK TERN   PLATE 26

Chlidonias leucoptera (Temminck, 1815)

1815 *Sterna leucoptera* Temminck, Man. d' Orn., p. 483, (Mediterranean coasts)

Description: Forehead white; hind crown and nape black; hind neck white; rest of upperparts gray; rump whitish; underparts white.

Soft Parts: Bill black; iris dark brown; feet black.

Measurements: Wing 218; tail 73; bill 27; tarsus 20.

Range: Recorded from Mindanao and Palawan; a straggler from eastern Asia.

WHISKERED TERN   PLATE 26

Chlidonias hybrida javanica (Horsfield, 1821)

1821   *Sterna Javanica* Horsfield, Trans. Linn. Soc. London, 13:198, (Java)

Description: Forehead white; hind crown and nape black; hind neck white; rest of upperparts gray; underparts white. Differs from *C. leucoptera* by having a shorter bill and lacking the contrasting whitish rump.

Soft Parts: Bill, tip blackish, base dark red; iris brown; feet dark red.

Measurements: Wing 225; tail 82; bill 36; tarsus 22.

Range: Leyte, Luzon, Mindanao, Negros, and Palawan.

Chlidonias hybrida fluviatilis (Gould, 1843)

1843   *Hydrochelidon fluviatilis* Gould, Proc. Zool. Soc. London, p. 140, (New South Wales)

Description: Differs from *javanica* by having the upperparts much paler.

Range: Luzon.

GULL-BILLED TERN   PLATE 26

Gelochelidon nilotica nilotica (Gmelin, 1789)

1789   *Sterna nilotica* Gmelin, Syst. Nat., 1:606, (Egypt)

Description: Forehead white; spot in front of eye and ear-coverts gray-black; hind crown and nape dark gray; hind neck white; rest of upperparts gray, primaries darker; underparts white.

Soft Parts: Bill black; iris dark brown; feet black.

Measurements: Wing 312; tail 136; bill 39; tarsus 30.

Range: Winters on Luzon, Negros, and Palawan from eastern Asia.

CASPIAN TERN   PLATE 26

Hydroprogne caspia (Pallas, 1770)

1770   *Sterna caspia* Pallas, Novi Comm. Sci. Petropol., 14:582, (Caspian Sea)

Description: Top of head dark gray-brown flecked with black, darkest around eye; hind neck white; rest of upperparts gray; tail paler; underparts white.

Soft Parts: Bill bright red; iris red-brown; feet black.

Measurements: Wing 400; tail 135; bill 72; tarsus 42.

Range: Manila Bay, Luzon (once); a straggler from Asia.

PLATE 25

A   REEF THICK-KNEE
   (Esacus magnirostris)—page 103

B   NORTHERN PHALAROPE
   (Phalaropus lobatus), winter plumage—page 102

C   WHITE-HEADED STILT
   (Himantopus himantopus)—page 102

D   POMARINE JAEGER
   (Stercorarius pomarinus), immature—page 103

E   PRATINCOLE
   (Glareola maldivarum)—page 103

PLATE 25

PLATE 26

A   BLACK-HEADED GULL
        (Larus ridibundus)—page 104

B   HERRING GULL
        (Larus argentatus)—page 104

C   GULL-BILLED TERN
        (Gelochelidon nilotica)—page 105

D   LITTLE TERN
        (Sterna albifrons)—page 110

E   CASPIAN TERN
        (Hydroprogne caspia)—page 105

F   BLACK-NAPED TERN
        (Sterna sumatrana)—page 110

G   WHITE-WINGED BLACK TERN
        (Chlidonias leucoptera)—page 104

H   WHISKERED TERN
        (Chlidonias hybrida)—page 105

PLATE 26

LITTLE TERN   PLATE 26

Sterna albifrons sinensis Gmelin, 1789

1789 *Sterna sinensis* Gmelin, Syst. Nat., **1**:608, (China)

Description: Forehead white; crown and eye-stripe black; rest of upperparts gray; tail paler; underparts white.
Soft Parts: Bill dull yellow, tip black; iris dark brown; feet yellow.
Measurements: Wing 180; tail 85; bill 31; tarsus 15.
Range: Luzon, Mindanao, Mindoro, Palawan, and Polillo.

BLACK-NAPED TERN   PLATE 26

Sterna sumatrana Raffles, 1822

1822 *Sterna sumatrana* Raffles, Trans. Linn. Soc. London, **13**:329, (Sumatra)

Description: Top of head white; black line runs through eyes and joins on the nape; upperparts pale gray; outer primary edged with black; underparts white.
Soft Parts: Bill black; iris dark brown; feet black.
Measurements: Wing 220; tail 165; bill 36; tarsus 17.
Range: Luzon, Palawan, and Sibuyan.

BLACK-BILLED COMMON TERN   PLATE 27

Sterna hirundo longipennis Nordmann, 1835

1835 *Sterna longipennis* Nordmann, in Erman's Verz. Thier. Pflanz., p. 17, (mouth of Kutchui River)

Description: Forehead white; crown pale gray streaked with blackish brown; upperparts pale gray; bends of wing dark gray; underparts white.
Soft Parts: Bill, base coral-red, tip blackish; iris dark brown; feet reddish.
Measurements: Wing 278; tail 144; bill 38; tarsus 19.
Range: Bohol and Calayan (north of Luzon).

ROSEATE TERN   PLATE 27

Sterna dougallii bangsi Mathews, 1912

1912 *Sterna dougallii bangsi* Mathews, Bds. Austr., **2**:364, (Foochow, China)
Description: Top of head and nape black; upperparts gray; outer three primaries dark gray-black; underparts white.

110

Soft Parts: Bill, terminal half horn, base yellowish; iris dark brown; feet coral-red.

Measurements: Wing 220; tail 170; bill 37; tarsus 20.

Range: Corregidor, Culion, and Palawan.

SOOTY   TERN   **PLATE 27**

Sterna fuscata nubilosa Sparrman, 1788

1788   *Sterna nubilosa* Sparrman, Mus. Carls., p. 63, (Indian Ocean)

Description: Forehead and stripe above eyes white; upperparts black; underparts white.

Soft Parts: Bill dark reddish black; iris dark brown; feet reddish black.

Measurements: Wing 288; tail 173; bill 42; tarsus 20.

Range: Negros, Palawan, Siquijor, and Sulu Archipelago; a visitor from the Indian and Pacific Oceans.

BROWN-WINGED   TERN   **PLATE 27**

Sterna anaethetus anaethetus Scopoli, 1786

1786   *Sterna Anaethetus* Scopoli, Del. Flor. et Faun. Insubr., p. 92, (Panay)

Description: Forehead and stripe that extends behind the eye white; crown black; upperparts brownish black; underparts white.

Soft Parts: Bill black; iris dark brown; feet black.

Measurements: Wing 258; tail 192; bill 42; tarsus 20.

Range: Didikas Rocks (north of Luzon) and Panay.

CRESTED   TERN   **PLATE 27**

Sterna bergii cristata Stephens, 1826

1826   *Sterna cristata* Stephens, in Shaw's Gen. Zool., **13**:146, (China)

1915   *Thalasseus bergii halodramus* Oberholser, Proc. U. S. Nat. Mus., **49**:522, (Pata Island, Sulu)

Description: Forehead white; crown and crest black; hind neck white; rest of upperparts gray; underparts white.

Soft Parts: Bill greenish yellow; iris black; feet black.

Measurements: Wing 315; tail 162; bill 59; tarsus 30.

Range: Found throughout the Philippines.

111

PLATE 27

A   COMMON NODDY
      (Anous stolidus)—page 114

B   WHITE-CAPPED NODDY
      (Anous tenuirostris)—page 114

C   BLACK-BILLED COMMON TERN
      (Sterna hirundo)—page 110

D   CHINESE CRESTED TERN
      (Sterna zimmermanni)—page 114

E   CRESTED TERN
      (Sterna bergii)—page 111

F   ROSEATE TERN
      (Sterna dougallii)—page 110

G   BROWN-WINGED TERN
      (Sterna anaethetus)—page 111

H   SOOTY TERN
      (Sterna fuscata)—page 111

PLATE 27

CHINESE CRESTED TERN   PLATE 27

Sterna zimmermanni Reichenow, 1903

1903 *Sterna zimmermanni* Reichenow, Orn. Monatsb., **11**:82, (Shantung, China)

Description: Forehead white; crown and crest black; hind neck white; rest of upperparts gray; primaries blackish; underparts white.

Soft Parts: Bill orange-yellow with a black tip; iris dark brown; feet black.

Measurements: Wing 305; tail 155; bill 62; tarsus 24.

Range: Once, from "Philippines"; breeds in China.

COMMON NODDY   PLATE 27

Anous stolidus pileatus (Scopoli, 1786)

1786 *Sterna pileatus* Scopoli, Del. Flor. et Faun. Insubr., p. 92, (Philippines)

Description: Forehead and part of crown whitish; rest of bird brownish gray.

Soft Parts: Bill black; iris brown; feet red-brown.

Measurements: Wing 271; tail 164; bill 43; tarsus 20.

Range: Cagayan Sulu, Luzon, Mindanao, and Palawan.

WHITE-CAPPED NODDY   PLATE 27

Anous tenuirostris worcesteri (McGregor, 1911)

1911 *Micranous worcesteri* McGregor, Phil. Journ. Sci., **6**:183, (Cavilli Island)

Description: Similar to *A. stolidus* but smaller.

Soft Parts: Bill black; iris dark brown; feet red-brown.

Measurements: Wing 222; tail 120; bill 43; tarsus 21.

Range: Cavilli Island, Sulu Sea. (Endemic.)

Family COLUMBIDAE   PIGEONS AND DOVES

WHISTLING GREEN PIGEON   PLATE 28

Treron formosae filipina Hachisuka, 1952

1907 *Sphenocercus australis* McGregor, Phil. Journ. Sci., **2**:344, (Camiguin North)

1952 *Treron formosae filipina* Hachisuka, Bull. Brit. Orn. Cl., **72**:95, new name for *Sphenocercus australis* McGregor, 1907

114

1958   *Treron formosae mcgregorii* Husain, Ibis, **100**:343, new name for *Sphenocercus australis* McGregor, 1907

Description: Male—crown dark apricot; collar grayish olive-green; mantle and wing-coverts maroon; rest of upperparts dark olive-green; sides of face, throat, and breast green; belly yellow; thighs and under tail-coverts dark green with wide, pale yellow margins. Female—differs from male by having upperparts all green.

Soft Parts: Bill light blue, tip whitish; iris pink; feet dark red.

Measurements: Wing 192; tail 139; bill 23; tarsus 27.

Range: Batan, Calayan, and Camiguin North. (Endemic.)

THICK-BILLED GREEN PIGEON   PLATE 28

Treron curvirostra erimacra Oberholser, 1924

1924   *Treron curvirostra erimacra* Oberholser, Journ. Wash. Acad. Sci., **14**:297, (Balabac)

Description: Male—top of head gray; neck greenish gray; back and mantle maroon; tail-coverts and tail brownish green; wings black with yellow; underparts green; thighs green and white; under tail-coverts cinnamon. Female—similar to male but mantle is green.

Soft Parts: Bill, base red, rest of bill yellowish green; iris orange; feet red.

Measurements: Wing 138; tail 88; bill 15; tarsus 20.

Range: Balabac, Mindoro, and Palawan. (Endemic.)

POMPADOUR GREEN PIGEON   PLATE 28

Treron pompadora axillaris (Bonaparte, 1855)

1855   *Osmotreron axillaris* Bonaparte, Consp. Av., **2**:13, (no locality=southern Luzon)

Description: Top of head gray; neck green; mantle maroon; rump and tail green; wings black with yellow; underparts yellow-green; thighs green and yellow; under tail-coverts white. Female—similar to male but mantle is green.

Soft Parts: Bill, base red, rest of bill bluish; iris blue; feet blue-black.

Measurements: Wing 154; tail 101; bill 16; tarsus 23.

Range: Central and southern Luzon, Mindoro, and Polillo. (Endemic.)

Treron pompadora amadoni Parkes, 1965

1965   *Treron pompadora amadoni* Parkes, Bull. Brit. Orn. Cl., **85**:138, (San Mariano, Isabela Prov., northern Luzon)

Description: Male—differs from *canescens* by having the gray crown and maroon upperparts darker, without a gray band at posterior edge. Female—grayer below than either *canescens* or *axillaris*.

Range: Northern Luzon. (Endemic.)

PLATE 28

A   THICK-BILLED GREEN PIGEON
      (Treron curvirostra), male—page 115

B   POMPADOUR GREEN PIGEON
      (Treron pompadora), male—page 115

C   PINK-NECKED GREEN PIGEON
      (Treron vernans), male—page 118

D   WHITE-EARED BROWN FRUIT DOVE
      (Phapitreron leucotis)—page 118

E   WHISTLING GREEN PIGEON
      (Treron formosae), male—page 114

F   AMETHYST BROWN FRUIT DOVE
      (Phapitreron amethystina)—page 119

PLATE 28

Treron pompadora canescens Parkes, 1965

1965 *Treron pompadora canescens* Parkes, Bull. Brit. Orn. Cl., **85**:137, (Santa Catalina, Negros)

Description: Male—differs from *axillaris* by having the maroon darker; distinct gray band between the maroon and the green on the upper back; crown tends to be grayer; underparts less yellowish. Female—grayer above and below.

Range: Basilan, Bohol, Leyte, Mindanao, Negros, Panay, Samar, and Siquijor. (Endemic.)

Treron pompadora everetti (Rothschild, 1894)

1894 *Osmotreron everetti* Rothschild, Nov. Zool., **1**:41, (Bongao)

Description: Differs from *canescens* by having the mantle chestnut-maroon; neck lighter green and underparts paler yellow; tends to be somewhat larger.

Range: Sulu Archipelago. (Endemic.)

PINK-NECKED GREEN PIGEON   PLATE 28

Treron vernans vernans (Linné, 1771)

1771 *Columba vernans* Linné, Mantissa, p. 526, (Philippines)

1924 *Dendrophassa vernans nesophasma* Oberholser, Journ. Wash. Acad. Sci., **14**:297, (Cotabato, Mindanao)

Description: Male—head, chin, and upper throat gray; throat and neck gray-violet; mantle, back, and wing-coverts gray-green; tail-coverts tan; tail gray with black tip; breast dull orange; belly green with yellow near vent; under tail-coverts cinnamon. Female—mostly all green.

Soft Parts: Bill, base black, tip bluish; iris blue; feet red.

Measurements: Wing 150; tail 110; bill 15; tarsus 21.

Range: Found throughout the Philippines. (Endemic.)

WHITE-EARED BROWN FRUIT DOVE   PLATE 28

Phapitreron leucotis leucotis (Temminck, 1823)

1823 *Columba leucotis* Temminck, Pl. Col., livr. 32, pl. 189, (Manila, Luzon)

1930 *Phapitreron leucotis mindorensis* Hachisuka, Orn. Soc. Japan, suppl. 14:146, (Balete, Rio Baco, Mindoro)

1930 *Phapitreron amethystina polillensis* Hachisuka, Orn. Soc. Japan, suppl. 14:145, (Polillo)

Description: Forehead and forecrown gray; hind crown and neck brown; lores and eye stripe black; ear lines white; upper back bronze glossed with green; rest of upperparts and tail dull bronze; chin light rufous; throat and breast fulvous with greenish gloss; belly dull fulvous, becoming grayish near vent; under tail-coverts gray.

Soft Parts: Bill black; iris red; feet red.

Measurements: Wing 131; tail 90; bill 15; tarsus 17.

Range: Alabat, Catanduanes, Luzon, Mindoro, Polillo, and Verde. (Endemic.)

Phapitreron leucotis nigrorum (Sharpe, 1877)

1877 *Phabotreron nigrorum* Sharpe, Trans. Linn. Soc. London, 1:346, (San Bernardino, Negros)

1930 *Phapitreron leucotis limucon* Hachisuka, Orn. Soc. Japan, suppl. 14:146, (Badajig, Tablas)

Description: Differs from *P. l. leucotis* by having sides of head and upper throat paler; ear lines buffy, not white.

Range: Cebu, Guimaras, Masbate, Negros, Panay, Sibuyan, Tablas, and Ticao. (Endemic.)

Phapitreron leucotis brevirostris (Tweeddale, 1877)

1877 *Phabotreron brevirostris* Tweeddale, Proc. Zool. Soc. London, p. 832, (Pasananca, Mindanao)

1907 *Phapitreron albifrons* McGregor, Phil. Journ. Sci., 2:317, (Tagbilaran, Bohol)

1909 *Phapitreron samarensis* Mearns, Proc. U. S. Nat. Mus., 36:436, (Samar)

Description: Differs from *nigrorum* by having the upperparts darker and a stronger gloss on the mantle.

Range: Bohol, Dinagat, Leyte, Mindanao, Samar, and Siquijor. (Endemic.)

Phapitreron leucotis occipitalis (Salvadori, 1893)

1893 *Phabotreron occipitalis* Salvadori, Cat. Bds. Brit. Mus., 21:68, (Basilan)

Description: Differs from *brevirostris* by having the nape red-bronze and the throat slightly darker.

Range: Basilan and Sulu. (Endemic.)

AMETHYST BROWN FRUIT DOVE   PLATE 28

Phapitreron amethystina amethystina Bonaparte, 1855

1855 *Phapitreron amethystina* Bonaparte, Consp. Av., 2:28, (Philippines)

1930 *Phapitreron amethystina polillensis* Hachisuka, Orn. Soc. Japan, 14:145, (Polillo)

1936 *Phapitreron amethystina celestinoi* Manuel, Phil. Journ. Sci., 59:300, (Sevilla, Bohol)

Description: Head brownish gray; nuchal collar reddish violet; rest of upperparts bronze with greenish gloss; tail with gray tip; chin and throat cinnamon with dark edges to feathers; breast and belly brownish gray; under tail-coverts dark cinnamon.

Soft Parts: Bill black; iris brown; feet red.

Measurements: Wing 150; tail 100; bill 23; tarsus 23.

Range: Bohol, Leyte, Luzon, Mindoro, Polillo, and Samar. (Endemic.)

Phapitreron amethystina maculipectus (Bourns and Worcester, 1894)

1894   *Phabotreron maculipectus* Bourns and Worcester, Occ. Papers Minn. Acad. Nat. Sci., 1:10, (Negros)

Description: Differs from *P. a. amethystina* by having underparts much paler; otherwise very much the same.

Range: Negros. (Endemic.)

Phapitreron amethystina frontalis (Bourns and Worcester, 1894)

1894   *Phabotreron frontalis* Bourns and Worcester, Occ. Papers Minn. Acad. Nat. Sci., 1:10, (Cebu)

Description: Differs from *maculipectus* by having under tail-coverts gray tipped with chestnut.

Range: Cebu. (Extinct.)

Phapitreron amethystina mindanaoensis Manuel, 1936

1936   *Phapitreron amethystina mindanaoensis* Manuel, Phil. Journ. Sci., 59:301, (Agusan, Mindanao)

Description: Differs from *P. a. amethystina* by having head darker and grayer and under tail-coverts paler.

Range: Mindanao. (Endemic.)

SOUTHERN BROWN FRUIT DOVE

Phapitreron cinereiceps cinereiceps (Bourns and Worcester, 1894)

1894   *Phabotreron cinereiceps* Bourns and Worcester, Occ. Papers Minn. Acad. Nat. Sci., 1:8, (Tawi Tawi)

Description: Similar to *P. amethystina* (Plate 28) but differs in lacking the white line below the eye.

Range: Tawi Tawi. (Endemic.)

120

Phapitreron cinereiceps brunneiceps (Bourns and Worcester, 1894)

1894 *Phabotreron brunneiceps* Bourns and Worcester, Occ. Papers Minn. Acad. Nat. Sci., 1:10, (Basilan)

Description: Differs from *P. c. cinereiceps* by having the hind neck redder.

Range: Basilan, as well as Mt. McKinley and Mt. Katanglad on Mindanao. (Endemic.)

YELLOW-BREASTED FRUIT DOVE   PLATE 29

Ptilinopus occipitalis G. R. Gray, 1844

1844 *Ptilonopus occipitalis* G. R. Gray, Gen. Bds., **2**:467, (Luzon)

1877 *Ptilopus incognita* Tweeddale, Ann. Mag. Nat. His., **20**:538, (Butuan, Mindanao)

1930 *Leucotreron occipitalis brevipes* Hachisuka, Orn. Soc. Japan, 14:147, (Mt. Apo, Mindanao)

Description: Fore part of head gray; maroon band runs from eye and below, to nape, to other eye; mantle, back, and rump green with dull brownish gloss; wings green with yellow margins to primaries and secondaries; tail green; chin white; throat gray; breast deep yellow-orange; upper belly with deep red band, rest greenish gray; under tail-coverts green and white. Immature—all green but differs from immatures of *P. leclancheri* by having under tail-coverts cream color and lighter tips to the rectrices.

Soft Parts: Bill, base red, tip yellow; iris red; feet red.

Measurements: Wing 156; tail 120; bill 17; tarsus 22.

Range: Found throughout the Philippines, except Palawan. (Endemic.)

MERRILL'S FRUIT DOVE   PLATE 29

Ptilinopus merrilli merrilli (McGregor, 1916)

1916 *Leucotreron merrilli* McGregor, Phil. Journ. Sci., **11**:269, (Paete, Luzon)

Description: Head gray; neck greenish gray; mantle, back, rump, and tail green; wings green; primaries black; secondaries green with a crimson hairlike patch near the tip; throat and breast gray with a slight green tinge; narrow dark green line separates the breast from the all-white belly; flanks and under tail-coverts mottled green and white.

Soft Parts: Bill red; iris dark red; feet red.

Measurements: Wing 170; tail 120; bill 15; tarsus 26.

Range: Eastern and southern Luzon and Polillo. (Endemic.)

121

Ptilinopus merrilli faustinoi (Manuel, 1936)

1936   *Neoleucotreron merrilli faustinoi* Manuel, Phil. Journ. Sci., **59**:307, (Mt. Tabuan, Cagayan, Luzon)

Description: Differs from *P. m. merrilli* by having a red patch on the crown.
Range: Northern Luzon. (Endemic.)

MARCHE'S FRUIT DOVE   PLATE 29

Ptilinopus marchei (Oustalet, 1880)

1880   *Ptilopus (Rhamphiculus) Marchei* Oustalet, Le Naturaliste, **1**:325, (Bayabas, Luzon)

Description: Top of head and nape crimson; blackish patch on sides of head from the eye to the ears; sides of neck gray; back, wings, and tail black with green gloss; primaries have yellow edges; secondaries have crimson hairlike patch; tail has gray tip; chin buffy; throat bright orange; upper breast red; lower breast and belly gray; under tail-coverts buffy.
Soft Parts: Bill reddish yellow; iris red; feet dark red.
Measurements: Wing 179; tail 144; bill 17; tarsus 30.
Range: Luzon and Polillo. (Endemic.)

NEGROS FRUIT DOVE   PLATE 29

Ptilinopus arcanus Ripley and Rabor, 1955

1955   *Ptilinopus arcanus* Ripley and Rabor, Postilla, 21:1, (Mt. Canloan, Negros)

Description: Forehead grayish; rest of upperparts bright green; wings green with a yellow stripe; primaries dark greenish black; tail green above, gray below lighter terminal band; underparts green; under tail-coverts yellow.
Soft Parts: Bill black; orbital skin yellowish; feet dull purplish-red.
Measurements: Wing 100; tail 54; bill 13; tarsus 16.
Range: Known only from the type. (Endemic.)

BLACK-CHINNED FRUIT DOVE   PLATE 29

Ptilinopus leclancheri leclancheri (Bonaparte, 1855)

1855   *Tererolaema leclancheri* Bonaparte, Compt. Rend. Acad. Sci. Paris, **41**:247, (New Guinea = Manila, Luzon)

Description: Head, neck, throat, and breast light gray; nape somewhat greenish; upperparts green; chin black; wide brownish maroon band separates the breast from the all-green belly; under tail-coverts cinnamon. Immature—all green but differs from imma-

122

tures of *P. occipitalis* by having the under tail-coverts pale rufous.

Soft Parts: Bill yellow; iris red; feet dark red.

Measurements: Wing 144; tail 110; bill 15; tarsus 21.

Range: Found throughout the Philippines, except for Palawan and the Babuyan and Batan Islands. (Endemic.)

Ptilinopus leclancheri longialis (Manuel, 1936)

1936 *Leucotreron leclancheri longialis* Manuel, Phil. Journ. Sci., **59**:307, (Batan Island)

Description: Differs from *P. l. leclancheri* by being larger (wing 164; tail 118; bill 18; tarsus 25).

Range: Babuyan and Batan Islands. (Endemic.)

Ptilinopus leclancheri gironieri (J. Verreaux and Des Murs, 1862)

1862 *Leucotreron gironieri* J. Verreaux and Des Murs, Ibis, p. 342, (Palawan)

1932 *Leucotreron leclancheri palawana* Hachisuka, Bds. Phil. Ids., p. 187, (Iwahig, Palawan)

Description: Differs from *P. l. leclancheri* by being darker; back much greener.

Range: Palawan. (Endemic.)

SUPERB FRUIT DOVE   PLATE 29

Ptilinopus superbus temminckii (Des Murs and Prevost, 1849)

1849 *Kurukuru Temminckii* Des Murs and Prevost, Voy. "Venus," Zool., pp. 234, 268, (Celebes)

Description: Male—top of head purple; hind neck reddish orange; green patch on sides of head from the eyes to the ears; back and wings bright green, some feathers with blue centers; tail blue-green; chin and throat gray; upper breast reddish purple; lower breast blue-black; belly buffy; thighs green. Female—all green with some yellow on belly; crown dull purple.

Soft Parts: Bill green with red base; iris blue-green; feet olive.

Measurements: Wing 132; tail 93; bill 17; tarsus 21.

Range: Sulu Archipelago.

BLACK-NAPED FRUIT DOVE   PLATE 29

Ptilinopus melanospila bangueyensis (A. B. Meyer, 1891)

1891 *Ptilopus bangueyensis* A. B. Meyer, Journ. f. Orn., **39**:70, (Banguey Island)

1924 *Haemataena melanocephala enantia* Oberholser, Journ. Wash. Acad. Sci., **14**:296, (Cagayan Sulu)

Description: Male—forehead, forecrown, sides of face, and neck gray; hind crown and hind neck black; back, wings, and tail bright green; chin and central throat yellow; breast and belly bright green; feathers around vent and short under tail-coverts orange; long under tail-coverts red. Female—all green with some yellow on belly.
Soft Parts: Bill yellow-green; iris yellow; feet pink.
Measurements: Wing 118; tail 84; bill 15; tarsus 20.
Range: Basilan, Mindanao, Palawan, and Sulu Archipelago.

GREEN IMPERIAL PIGEON   PLATE 30

Ducula aenea aenea (Linné, 1766)

1766   *Columba aenea* Linné, Syst. Nat., **1**:283, (Manila, Luzon)

1854   *Carpophaga chalybura* Bonaparte, Compt. Rend. Acad. Sci. Paris, **39**:1074, (Philippines)

1936   *Ducula aenea glaucocauda* Manuel, Phil. Journ. Sci., **60**:410, (Mt. Matutum, Cotabato, Mindanao)

Description: Head pinkish gray; nape with dark chestnut patch; back, rump, and wing-coverts green with a strong bronze gloss; primaries and tail dark green; all underparts pinkish gray; under tail-coverts dark chestnut.
Soft Parts: Bill gray; iris red; feet dark red.
Measurements: Wing 245; tail 135; bill 25; tarsus 30.
Range: Central Luzon south to the Sulu Archipelago.

Ducula aenea nuchalis (Cabanis, 1882)

1882   *Carpophaga nuchalis* Cabanis, Journ. f. Orn., **30**:126, (Isabela Prov., Luzon)
Description: Differs from *D. a. aenea* by having a chestnut patch on the nape.
Range: Northern Luzon. (Endemic.)

Ducula aenea fugaensis (Hachisuka, 1930)

1930   *Muscadivores aenea fugaensis* Hachisuka, Orn. Soc. Japan, suppl. 14:150, (Fuga Island)
Description: Differs from *aenea* by being much larger (wing 265; tail 165).
Range: Fuga Island, north of Luzon. (Endemic.)

Ducula aenea palawanensis (Blasius, 1888)

1888   *Carpophaga aenea palawanensis* Blasius, Ornis, 4:316, (Palawan)
Description: Differs from *aenea* by having upperparts slightly bluer.
Range: Balabac, Calamianes, Dumeran, Palawan, and Banguey Island off North Borneo.

124

GRAY IMPERIAL PIGEON

PLATE 30

Ducula pickeringii pickeringii (Cassin, 1854)

1854 *Carpophaga Pickeringii* Cassin, Proc. Acad. Nat. Sci. Phila., **7**:228, (Mangsi Islet, North Borneo)

Description: Head gray; back, rump, and wings green; primaries and tail glossy green; throat white; underparts pinkish gray.

Soft Parts: Bill dark gray; iris red; feet dark red.

Measurements: Wing 240; tail 174; bill 20; tarsus 26.

Range: Sulu Archipelago and islands off northern and eastern Borneo.

Ducula pickeringii langhornei (Mearns, 1905)

1905 *Muscadivora langhornei* Mearns, Proc. Biol. Soc. Wash., **18**:84, (West Bolod Island)

Description: Differs from *D. p. pickeringii* by having upperparts paler and underparts darker; white around bill and eye is more extensive.

Range: East and West Bolod Islands and Loran Island. (Endemic.)

Ducula pickeringii palmasensis (Mearns, 1909)

1909 *Muscadivores palmasensis* Mearns, Proc. U. S. Nat. Mus., **32**:436, (Palmas Island)

Description: Differs from *D. p. pickeringii* by having paler underparts; also somewhat smaller (wing 240; tail 156–160). Differs from *langhornei* by having upperparts darker.

Range: Palmas Island. (Endemic.)

PINK-BELLIED IMPERIAL PIGEON

PLATE 30

Ducula poliocephala poliocephala (G. R. Gray, 1844)

1844 *Carpophaga poliocephala* G. R. Gray, Gen. Bds., **2**:469, (Philippines=southern Luzon)

Description: Head gray; back, rump, and wings dark green with coppery reflections; tail green with a subterminal white band; chin light chestnut; throat and breast dark green; belly pinkish gray; thighs, area around vent, and under tail-coverts dark chestnut.

Soft Parts: Bill black; iris yellow; feet bright red.

Measurements: Wing 216; tail 151; bill 21; tarsus 34.

Range: Cebu, Luzon, Mindoro, and Panay. (Endemic.)

PLATE 29

A   MERRILL'S FRUIT DOVE
(Ptilinopus merrilli)—page 121

Head of *P. m. faustinoi*—page 122

B   BLACK-CHINNED FRUIT DOVE
(Ptilinopus leclancheri)—page 122

C   YELLOW-BREASTED FRUIT DOVE
(Ptilinopus occipitalis)—page 121

D   BLACK-NAPED FRUIT DOVE
(Ptilinopus melanospila)—page 123

E   MARCHE'S FRUIT DOVE
(Ptilinopus marchei)—page 122

F   SUPERB FRUIT DOVE
(Ptilinopus superbus)—page 123

G   NEGROS FRUIT DOVE
(Ptilinopus arcanus)—page 122

PLATE 29

PLATE 30

A   GRAY IMPERIAL PIGEON
(Ducula pickeringii)—page 125

B   SPOTTED IMPERIAL PIGEON
(Ducula carola)—page 130

C   NUTMEG IMPERIAL PIGEON
(Ducula bicolor)—page 130

D   MINDORO IMPERIAL PIGEON
(Ducula mindorensis)—page 130

E   PINK-BELLIED IMPERIAL PIGEON
(Ducula poliocephala)—page 125

F   GREEN IMPERIAL PIGEON
(Ducula aenea)—page 124

128

PLATE 30

Ducula poliocephala nobilis (Hachisuka, 1931)

1931 *Zonophaps poliocephala nobilis* Hachisuka, Ois. et Rev. Fran. d'Orn., **7**:398, (Mt. Canloan, Negros)

Description: Differs from *D. p. poliocephala* by having very strong coppery reflections on back and wing-coverts.

Range: Basilan, Dinagat, Leyte, Masbate, Mindanao, Negros, Samar, Sibuyan, Tawi Tawi. (Endemic.)

NUTMEG IMPERIAL PIGEON   PLATE 30

Ducula bicolor (Scopoli, 1786)

1786 *Columba bicolor* Scopoli, Del. Flor. et Faun. Insubr., p. 94, (New Guinea)

Description: All white except for primaries, secondaries, and terminal third of tail, which are black.

Soft Parts: Bill bluish; iris dark brown; feet black.

Measurements: Wing 225; tail 138; bill 25; tarsus 28.

Range: Found throughout the Philippines on small islands.

MINDORO IMPERIAL PIGEON   PLATE 30

Ducula mindorensis (Whitehead, 1896)

1896 *Carpophaga mindorensis* Whitehead, Ann. Mag. Nat. His., **18**:189, (Mindoro)

Description: Forehead, chin, and throat pinkish gray; top of head and neck gray; a gray-black ring around eye and line extending from behind down the neck; mantle has a purple-black V, becoming reddish purple as it extends down back and on wing-coverts; back and rump bronze-green; basal third of tail green; middle third of tail dark gray; terminal third of tail blue-black; wings glossy green; breast gray; rest of underparts dirty gray.

Soft Parts: Bill black; iris yellow; feet red.

Measurements: Wing 240; tail 173; bill 17; tarsus 31.

Range: Mindoro. (Endemic.)

SPOTTED IMPERIAL PIGEON   PLATE 30

Ducula carola carola (Bonaparte, 1854)

1854 *Ptilocolpa carola* Bonaparte, Compt. Rend. Acad. Sci. Paris, **39**:1075, (Philippines)

1854 *Ptilocolpa griseipectus* Bonaparte, Compt. Rend. Acad. Sci. Paris, **39**:1075, (Philippines)

Description: Male—head, neck, and mantle light gray; wing-coverts, back, and rump gray with black spots and a strong reddish purple gloss; primaries and tail glossy dark green; throat white; upper breast light gray, followed by a white line; lower breast dark gray; belly dark chestnut. Female—differs from male by being somewhat darker, with chestnut belly lighter.

Soft Parts: Bill pink with white tip; iris white with some pink; feet pink.

Measurements: Wing 205; tail 121; bill 18; tarsus 28.

Range: Luzon, Mindoro, and Sibuyan. (Endemic.)

Ducula carola nigrorum (Whitehead, 1897)

1897 *Ptilocolpa nigrorum* Whitehead, Bull. Brit. Orn. Cl., **6**:34, (Negros)

Description: Differs from *D. c. carola* by having upper breast black.

Range: Negros. (Endemic.)

Ducula carola mindanensis (Ogilvie-Grant, 1905)

1905 *Ptilocolpa mindanensis* Ogilvie-Grant, Bull. Brit. Orn. Cl., **16**:16, (Mt. Apo, Mindanao)

Description: Differs from *nigrorum* by having chin and throat white; breast gray-black.

Range: Mindanao. (Endemic.)

METALLIC WOOD PIGEON   PLATE 31

Columba vitiensis griseogularis (Walden and Layard, 1872)

1872 *Ianthoenas griseogularis* Walden and Layard, Ibis, p. 104, (Guimaras)

Description: All upperparts black; head with purple gloss; hind neck with green gloss; mantle, back, and rump with purple gloss; primaries, secondaries, and tail without gloss; chin, upper throat, and sides of face gray; breast dark gray with purple gloss; belly gray, slightly glossed with purple.

Soft Parts: Bill red with yellow tip; iris yellow; feet red.

Measurements: Wing 251; tail 174; bill 24; tarsus 32.

Range: Found throughout the Philippines, except Palawan.

SLENDER-BILLED CUCKOO DOVE   PLATE 31

Macropygia phasianella tenuirostris Bonaparte, 1854

1854 *Macropygia tenuirostris* Bonaparte, Compt. Rend. Acad. Sci. Paris, **39**:1111, (Philippines)

Description: Male—head rufous; upper back rufous with fine black bars and washed with lilac; rump, wings, and tail having dark brown feathers with rufous edges; chin

131

buffy; rest of underparts rufous. Female—no lilac gloss on back; darker in appearance because of fine black bars on breast which are more extensive on back.

Soft Parts: Bill brown; iris reddish; feet bright red.

Measurements: Wing 178; tail 175; bill 17; tarsus 23.

Range: Found throughout the Philippines, except for the islands north of Luzon. (Endemic.)

Macropygia phasianella phaea McGregor, 1904

1904   *Macropygia phaea* McGregor, Bull. Phil. Mus., 4:9, (Calayan Island)

1930   *Macropygia tenuirostris septentrionalis* Hachisuka, Orn. Soc. Japan, suppl. 14: 151, (Botel Tobago)

Description: Differs from *tenuirostris* by being darker and larger (wing 200; tail 207; bill 18; tarsus 23).

Range: Islands of Batan, Botel Tobago, and Calayan. (Endemic.)

PHILIPPINE TURTLE DOVE   PLATE 31

Streptopelia bitorquata dusumieri (Temminck, 1823)

1823   *Columba dusumieri* Temminck, Pl. Col., livr. 32, pl. 188, (Manila, Luzon)

1930   *Streptopelia dusumieri gutierrezi* Hachisuka, Orn. Soc. Japan, suppl. 2:152, (Cotabato, Mindanao)

Description: Forehead light gray; top of head gray; hind neck having black collar with green gloss, followed by a reddish collar; back, rump, wings, and tail brownish gray; chin white; throat and sides of head gray; breast pinkish gray; belly whitish; under tail-coverts white.

Soft Parts: Bill bluish tan; iris red-brown; feet red.

Measurements: Wing 155; tail 126; bill 17; tarsus 26.

Range: Found throughout the Philippines and North Borneo.

DWARF TURTLE DOVE   PLATE 31

Streptopelia tranquebarica humilis (Temminck, 1824)

1824   *Columba humilis* Temminck, Pl. Col., livr. 44, pl. 259, (Bengal and Luzon)

Description: Forehead light gray; crown and neck dark gray, followed by a black collar on hind neck; upper back and wing-coverts vinaceous red; lower back and rump dark gray; wings and tail almost black; outer tail feathers have terminal third white; chin pinkish gray; breast and belly vinaceous red; thighs and vent gray; under tail-coverts white.

132

Soft Parts: Bill black; iris dark brown; feet black.

Measurements: Wing 132; tail 98; bill 14; tarsus 19.

Range: Calayan, Lubang, Luzon, and Mindoro.

SPOTTED DOVE   PLATE 31

Streptopelia chinensis tigrina (Temminck, 1810)

1810   *Columba Tigrina* Temminck, in Knip's Les Pigeons, p. 94, (Timor and Batavia)

1932   *Streptopelia chinensis palawana* Hachisuka, Bds. Phil. Ids., p. 212, (Iwahig, Palawan)

Description: Forehead light gray; top of head and neck pinkish gray; nuchal collar black with white spots; upperparts brown; feathers of wing-coverts have dark shaft streaks; outer tail feathers with white tips; chin light gray; throat and breast vinaceous red; belly and under tail-coverts buffy.

Soft Parts: Bill black; iris gray; feet pink.

Measurements: Wing 145; tail 138; bill 16; tarsus 24.

Range: Balabac, Cebu, Leyte, Mindanao, Negros, and Palawan.

ZEBRA DOVE   PLATE 32

Geopelia striata striata (Linné, 1766)

1766   *Columba striata* Linné, Syst. Nat., **1**:282, (Java)

Description: Forehead gray; head brown; back, rump, and wings brown with black bars; tail brown, outer feathers with white tips; throat pure blue-gray; sides of throat, breast, and belly buffy white with fine black bars; center of breast vinaceous red; belly and under tail-coverts whitish.

Soft Parts: Bill bluish; iris pale blue; feet red.

Measurements: Wing 98; tail 102; bill 12; tarsus 16.

Range: Introduced on Lubang, Luzon, Mindoro, and Verde from Borneo.

GREEN-WINGED GROUND DOVE   PLATE 32

Chalcophaps indica indica (Linné, 1758)

1758   *Columba indica* Linné, Syst. Nat., **1**:164, (East Indies=Amboina Island)

Description: Forehead, lores, and stripe over eye gray; top of head dark gray; mantle dull vinaceous; back, rump, and tail grayish black; wing-coverts bright emerald-green with a bronze gloss; shoulders white; chin pale vinaceous; throat and breast vinaceous; belly dull gray. Immature—dark brown; paler below.

Soft Parts: Bill red with darker base; iris brown; feet bluish.

Measurements: Wing 148; tail 104; bill 19; tarsus 22.

Range: Found throughout the Philippines.

PLATE 31

A   METALLIC WOOD PIGEON
      (Columba vitiensis)—page 131

B   DWARF TURTLE DOVE
      (Streptopelia tranquebarica), male—page 132

C   SLENDER-BILLED CUCKOO DOVE
      (Macropygia phasianella)—page 131

D   PHILIPPINE TURTLE DOVE
      (Streptopelia bitorquata)—page 132

E   SPOTTED DOVE
      (Streptopelia chinensis)—page 133

PLATE 31

PLATE 32

A   GREEN-WINGED GROUND DOVE
    (Chalcophaps indica), male—page 133

B   BLEEDING-HEART PIGEON
    (Gallicolumba luzonica)—page 138

C   ZEBRA DOVE
    (Geopelia striata)—page 133

D   NICOBAR PIGEON
    (Caloenas nicobarica)—page 139

A

B

C

D

JUHN R. PEIRCE

PLATE 32

BLEEDING-HEART PIGEON   PLATE 32

Gallicolumba luzonica luzonica (Scopoli, 1786)

1786 *Columba Luzonica* Scopoli, Del. Flor. et Faun. Insubr., p. 94, (Luzon = Manila, Luzon)

Description: Forehead and crown gray; nape and hind neck purplish; mantle, back, and rump brownish purple with green gloss; wings brown; wing-coverts with light gray tips forming bars; tail blue-gray with a black band; a black line runs from the lores behind eye and down the neck; throat white; sides of breast gray with green gloss; bright red spot in center of breast with lighter pinkish feathers around outside, giving a "bleeding" effect; belly pinkish white; under tail-coverts buffy white.

Soft Parts: Bill black; iris purplish; feet dark red.

Measurements: Wing 158; tail 125; bill 17; tarsus 35.

Range: Central and southern Luzon and Polillo. (Endemic.)

Gallicolumba luzonica griseolateralis Parkes, 1962

1962 *Gallicolumba luzonica griseolateralis* Parkes, Postilla, 67:1, (Mt. Sicapo-o, Ilocos Norte, Luzon)

Description: Differs from *G. l. luzonica* by having the crown and wings darker gray; female has flanks and under tail-coverts darker; lower breast and belly whiter, less "stained" in appearance.

Range: Northern Luzon. (Endemic.)

Gallicolumba luzonica platenae (Salvadori, 1893)

1893 *Phlogoenas platenae* Salvadori, Cat. Bds. Brit. Mus., 21:583, (Mindoro)

Description: Differs from *G. l. luzonica* by having head and neck green without gray cap; back, rump and wing-coverts more chestnut; tail gray; red spot on breast is much reduced in size and is orange.

Range: Mindoro. (Endemic.)

Gallicolumba luzonica keayi (Clarke, 1900)

1900 *Phlegoenas keayi* Clarke, Ibis, p. 359, (Negros)

Description: Differs from *G. l. platenae* by having the red patch elongated, not round; prominent white bar on the wings; tail browner.

Range: Negros. (Endemic.)

Gallicolumba luzonica criniger (Pucheran, 1853)

1853 *Pampusanna criniger* Pucheran, Voy. Pole Sud, Zool., 3:118, (Mindanao)

1918 *Phlegoenas crinigera basilanica* Hartert, Nov. Zool., 25:434, (Basilan)

138

Description: Top of head and neck green; rest of upperparts cinnamon; tail dark gray with black subterminal band; chin and throat white; breast gray-green with central red spot bordered with white; rest of underparts buffy.
Range: Basilan and Mindanao. (Endemic.)

Gallicolumba luzonica leytensis (Hartert, 1918)

1918 *Phlegoenas criniger leytensis* Hartert, Nov. Zool., **25**:434, (Leyte)

Description: Differs from *G. l. criniger* by lacking white borders to red breast spot, which lies in a green and gray breast band; cinnamon of underparts more restricted; belly whiter.
Range: Leyte and Samar. (Endemic.)

Gallicolumba luzonica menagei (Bourns and Worcester, 1894)

1894 *Phlogoenas menagei* Bourns and Worcester, Occ. Papers Minn. Acad. Nat. Sci., 1: 10, (Tawi Tawi)

Description: Differs from *criniger* by having the underparts much paler; breast spot is orange and belly is off-white.
Range: Tawi Tawi. (Endemic.)

NICOBAR PIGEON   **PLATE 32**

Caloenas nicobarica nicobarica (Linné, 1758)

1758 *Columba nicobarica* Linné, Syst. Nat., **1**:164, (Nicobar Islands)

Description: Head and neck black with purplish blue gloss; neck with long blue-green feathers that form a ruff; back, rump, and wing-coverts green with a bronze gloss; wings bluish; tail white; breast blackish; belly dark green.
Soft Parts: Bill black; iris brown; feet purplish.
Measurements: Wing 248; tail 80; bill 22; tarsus 40.
Range: Found throughout the Philippines on small islands.

Family PSITTACIDAE   PARROTS

MINDANAO LORIKEET   **PLATE 33**

Trichoglossus johnstoniae johnstoniae Hartert, 1903

1903 *Trichoglossus johnstoniae* Hartert, Bull. Brit. Orn. Cl., **14**:10, (Mt. Apo, Mindanao)

Description: Forehead, lores, malar patch, and chin rose-red; crown green; dark purple band runs around back of head from eye to eye; rest of upperparts green; some yellow on underside of secondaries; throat, breast, and belly feathers yellowish green with dark tips.

Soft Parts: Bill yellow-red; iris brown; feet blue-black.

Measurements: Wing 105; tail 72; bill 14; tarsus 13.

Range: Mt. Apo and Mt. Katanglad, Mindanao. (Endemic.)

Trichoglossus johnstoniae pistra Rand and Rabor, 1959

1959 *Trichoglossus johnstoniae pistra* Rand and Rabor, Fieldiana: Zoology, **39**:275, (Mt. Malindang, Mindanao)

Description: Differs from *T. j. johnstoniae* by having darker red on head; nuchal band is blue-black, not deep purple; upperparts darker; underparts more vivid yellow.

Range: Mt. Malindang, Mindanao. (Endemic.)

PHILIPPINE COCKATOO   PLATE 33

Kakatoe haematuropygia (P. L. S. Müller, 1776)

1776 *Psittacus haematuropygius* P. L. S. Müller, Natursyst., suppl., 1776:77, (Philippines)

1930 *Kakatoe haematuropygia mcgregori* Hachisuka, Orn. Soc. Japan, suppl. 14:157, (Polillo)

Description: Bird all white except for crest, wings, and tail, which have varying degrees of yellow; under tail-coverts reddish pink.

Soft Parts: Bill dirty white; iris brown; feet bluish.

Measurements: Wing 212; tail 113; bill 26; tarsus 19.

Range: Found throughout the Philippines.

BLUE-HEADED RACKET-TAILED PARROT   PLATE 33

Prioniturus discurus discurus (Vieillot, 1822)

1822 *Psittacus discurus* Vieillot, Gal. Ois., **1**:7, (Mindanao)

1890 *Prioniturus discurus* var. *suluensis* Blasius, Journ. f. Orn., **38**:140, (Jolo)

Description: Top of head and neck blue; back, rump, wings, and tail green; more yellowish on foreback; tail with two central feathers elongated with bare shafts on outer half and terminated with rackets; sides of head and underparts light green.

Soft Parts: Bill bluish tan; iris dark brown; feet dark blue-gray.

Measurements: Wing 142; tail (without rackets) 73; bill 17; tarsus 12.

Range: Jolo and Mindanao. (Birds from Bohol, Leyte, and Samar are intermediate with *whiteheadi*.) (Endemic.)

140

Prioniturus discurus mindorensis Steere, 1890

1890 *Prioniturus Mindorensis* Steere, List Bds. Mamms. Steere Expd., p. 6, (Mindoro)

Description: Differs from *P. d. discurus* by having a green forehead, not blue; also, the blue on the head is tinged with violet.
Range: Mindoro. (Endemic.)

Prioniturus discurus whiteheadi Salomonsen, 1953

1953 *Prioniturus discurus whiteheadi* Salomonsen, Vid. Medd. Dansk nat. Foren., **115**: 224, (Negros)

Description: Differs from *P. d. discurus* by having the blue on the head much reduced to just the crown; green of back darker, lacking yellowish area; also, wing is longer (164).
Range: Cebu, Masbate, and Negros. (Endemic.)

Prioniturus discurus nesophilus Salomonsen, 1953

1953 *Prioniturus discurus nesophilus* Salomonsen, Vid. Medd. Dansk nat. Foren., **115**: 225, (Catanduanes Island)

Description: Differs from *whiteheadi* by having blue reduced to center of the crown, and then only a slight wash; underparts darker green.
Range: Catanduanes, Sibuyan, and Tablas. (Endemic.)

CRIMSON-SPOTTED RACKET-TAILED PARROT   PLATE 33

Prioniturus montanus montanus Ogilvie-Grant, 1895

1895 *Prioniturus montanus* Ogilvie-Grant, Bull. Brit. Orn. Cl., 4:41, (Mt. Data, northern Luzon)

Description: Male—forehead and crown blue with a crimson spot in the center of the crown; back and rump brownish green; wings and tail green; tail with two central feathers elongated with bare shafts on outer half and terminated with rackets; sides of head and underparts dull yellow-green. Female—all-green head.
Soft Parts: Bill bluish; iris dark brown; feet blue-black.
Measurements: Wing 150; tail (without rackets) 79; bill 16; tarsus 14.
Range: Luzon. (Endemic.)

Prioniturus montanus waterstradti Rothschild, 1904

1904 *Prioniturus waterstradti* Rothschild, Bull. Brit. Orn. Cl., **14**:72, (Mt. Apo, Mindanao)

1909 *Prioniturus malindangensis* Mearns, Proc. U. S. Nat. Mus., **36**:437, (Mt. Malindang, Mindanao)

Description: Differs from *P. m. montanus* by lacking the crimson spot on the head, but blue is more extensive and darker.

Range: Mindanao. (Endemic.)

Prioniturus montanus verticalis Sharpe, 1893

1893 *Prioniturus verticalis* Sharpe, Bull. Brit. Orn. Cl., **3**:10, (Tawi Tawi)

Description: Differs from *P. m. montanus* by having bluer cheeks, lighter yellowish back, and blue in the wings.

Range: Bongao, Jolo, Sibutu, and Tawi Tawi. (Endemic.)

GREEN-HEADED RACKET-TAILED PARROT   PLATE 33

Prioniturus luconensis Steere, 1890

1890 *Prioniturus Luconensis* Steere, List Bds. Mamms. Steere Expd., p. 6, (Marinduque and Luzon)

Description: Entire bird yellow-green; head and underparts paler; tail with two central feathers elongated with bare shafts on outer half and terminated with rackets.

Soft Parts: Bill light blue; iris dark brown; feet blue-gray.

Measurements: Wing 155; tail (without rackets) 74; bill 16; tarsus 11.

Range: Luzon and Marinduque. (Endemic.)

PALAWAN RACKET-TAILED PARROT   PLATE 33

Prioniturus platenae Blasius, 1888

1888 *Prioniturus platenae* Blasius, Braunschweig. Anz., **37**:335, (Palawan)

1888 *Prioniturus cyaniceps* Sharpe, Ibis, p. 194, (Puerto Princesa, Palawan)

Description: Head and neck blue; back, wings, and tail green; tail has two central feathers elongated with the outer half of shaft bare except for rackets on the end; underparts green washed with blue.

Soft Parts: Bill bluish white; iris yellowish; feet black.

Measurements: Wing 160; tail (without rackets) 90; bill 20; tarsus 12.

Range: Balabac, Calamianes, and Palawan. (Endemic.)

BLUE-NAPED PARROT   PLATE 34

Tanygnathus lucionensis salvadorii Ogilvie-Grant, 1896

1896 *Tanygnathus salvadorii* Ogilvie-Grant, Ibis, p. 562, (Mantanani Islands)

1927 *Tanygnathus lucionensis horrisonus* Bangs and Peters, Occ. Papers Boston Soc. Nat. His., **5**:263, (Maratua Island)

1930 *Tanygnathus lucionensis koikei* Hachisuka, Orn. Soc. Japan, suppl. 14:160, (Davao, Mindanao)

1930 *Tanygnathus lucionensis paraguenus* Hachisuka, Orn. Soc. Japan, suppl. 14:160, (Puerto Princesa, Palawan)

1934 *Tanygnathus lucionensis moro* Hachisuka, Bds. Phil. Ids., p. 87, (Jolo, Sulu Archipelago)

1953 *Tanygnathus lucionensis nigrorum* Salomonsen, Vid. Medd. Dansk nat. Foren., **115**:218, (Mt. Canloan, Negros)

1953 *Tanygnathus lucionensis siquijorensis* Salomonsen, Vid. Medd. Dansk nat. Foren., **115**:220, (Siquijor)

Description: Head blue-green; neck and back brownish green; rump and tail green; wings green mottled with blues and browns; underparts dull brownish green.

Soft Parts: Bill, upper mandible red with yellow tip, lower mandible yellow; iris light orange; feet black.

Measurements: Wing 175; tail 119; bill 31; tarsus 18.

Range: Found throughout the Philippines, except for Luzon, Mindoro, and Polillo.

Tanygnathus lucionensis lucionensis (Linné, 1766)

1766 *Psittacus lucionensis* Linné, Syst. Nat., **1**:146, (Philippines=Luzon)

Description: Differs from *salvadorii* by having more blue on the head; back is bluish, not green.

Range: Luzon and Mindoro. (Endemic.)

Tanygnathus lucionensis hybridus Salomonsen, 1952

1952 *Tanygnathus lucionensis hybridus* Salomonsen, Vid. Medd. Dansk nat. Foren., **114**:347, (Polillo)

Description: Differs from *T. l. lucionensis* by having less blue on the head, also paler; tends to be somewhat larger.

Range: Polillo. (Endemic.)

LARGE-BILLED PARROT   PLATE 34

Tanygnathus megalorynchos megalorynchos (Boddaert, 1783)

1783 *Psittacus megalorynchos* Boddaert, Table Pl., enlum., p. 45, (New Guinea)

Description: Head bright green; back and rump light blue; tail-coverts light green; tail green; wings blue-green with black and yellow coverts; underparts yellowish green.

Soft Parts: Bill red; iris yellow; feet black.

Measurements: Wing 242; tail 144; bill 43; tarsus 20.

Range: Balut Island, off southern Mindanao.

PLATE 33

A   PHILIPPINE COCKATOO
(Kakatoe haematuropygia)—page 140

B   PALAWAN RACKET-TAILED PARROT
(Prioniturus platenae)—page 142

C   GREEN-HEADED RACKET-TAILED PARROT
(Prioniturus luconensis)—page 142

D   BLUE-HEADED RACKET-TAILED PARROT
(Prioniturus discurus)—page 140

E   MINDANAO LORIKEET
(Trichoglossus johnstoniae)—page 139

F   CRIMSON-SPOTTED RACKET-TAILED PARROT
(Prioniturus montanus), male—page 141

144

PLATE 33

PLATE 34

A   BLUE-BACKED PARROT
      (Tanygnathus sumatranus), female—page 148

B   LARGE-BILLED PARROT
      (Tanygnathus megalorynchos)—page 143

C   BLUE-NAPED PARROT
      (Tanygnathus lucionensis)—page 142

D   GUAIABERO
      (Bolbopsittacus lunulatus), male—page 148

E   PHILIPPINE HANGING PARAKEET
      (Loriculus philippensis)—page 149

PLATE 34

BLUE-BACKED PARROT PLATE 34

Tanygnathus sumatranus everetti Tweeddale, 1877

1877 *Tanygnathus Everetti* Tweeddale, Ann. Mag. Nat. His., **20**:533, (Butuan, Mindanao)

Description: Head green; mantle, wings, and tail dark green; lower back and rump blue; underparts dull green.

Soft Parts: Bill, male red, female whitish; iris red; feet black.

Measurements: Wing 189; tail 132; bill 33; tarsus 19.

Range: Leyte, Mindanao, Negros, Panay, and Samar. (Endemic.)

Tanygnathus sumatranus duponti Parkes, 1971

1971 *Tanygnathus sumatranus duponti* Parkes, Bull. Brit. Orn. Cl., **91**:97, (Bo. Disulap, Isabela Province, Luzon)

Description: Differs from *everetti* by having the blue of the lower back lighter and less purplish blue; under wing-coverts yellowish instead of green.

Range: Luzon. (Endemic.)

Tanygnathus sumatranus freeri McGregor, 1910

1910 *Tanygnathus freeri* McGregor, Phil. Journ. Sci., 5:108, (Polillo)

Description: Differs from *everetti* by having the crown lighter green and a yellow collar on the hind neck; back lighter blue; also, much larger (wing 235; tail 170).

Range: Polillo. (Endemic.)

Tanygnathus sumatranus burbidgii Sharpe, 1879

1879 *Tanygnathus burbidgii* Sharpe, Proc. Zool. Soc. London, p. 313, (Sulu Islands)

Description: Differs from *everetti* by being darker; head slightly lighter; also, larger wing (220).

Range: Sulu Archipelago.

GUAIABERO PLATE 34

Bolbopsittacus lunulatus lunulatus (Scopoli, 1786)

1786 *Psittacus lunulatus* Scopoli, Del. Flor. et Faun. Insubr., p. 86, (Luzon)

Description: Male—top of head green; lores, orbital ring, chin, and narrow collar on hind neck are blue; mantle and wings green; primaries have blue edges; lower back and rump greenish yellow; tail green; underparts light green. Female—less blue on face; yellow collar instead of blue; rump with fine black bars.

148

Soft Parts: Bill gray with black tip; iris dark brown; feet black.

Measurements: Wing 101; tail 35; bill 18; tarsus 11.

Range: Luzon. (Endemic.)

Bolbopsittacus lunulatus intermedius Salvadori, 1891

1891 *Bolbopsittacus intermedius* Salvadori, Cat. Bds. Brit. Mus., **20**:505, (Leyte)

Description: Differs from *B. l. lunulatus* by having face and collar darker blue; underparts more green.

Range: Leyte. (Endemic.)

Bolbopsittacus lunulatus callainipictus Parkes, 1971

1971 *Bolbopsittacus lunulatus callainipictus* Parkes, Bull. Brit. Orn. Cl., **91**:96, (Bonga, Samar)

Description: Male—differs from *intermedius* by having the face and nuchal band paler and more greenish blue; blue area on cheeks less extensive; body color yellower green. Female—nuchal band richer yellow.

Range: Samar. (Endemic.)

Bolbopsittacus lunulatus mindanensis (Steere, 1890)

1890 *Cyclopsitta Mindanensis* Steere, List Bds. Mamms. Steere Expd., p. 6, (Mindanao)

Description: Differs from *intermedius* by having less blue in face and darker blue collar; top of head sometimes brighter green.

Range: Mindanao and Panaon. (Endemic.)

PHILIPPINE HANGING PARAKEET   PLATE 34

Loriculus philippensis philippensis (P. L. S. Müller, 1776)

1776 *Psittacus philippensis* P. L. S. Müller, Natursyst., suppl., 1776:80, (Luzon)

Description: Male—forehead bright red; crown yellow-green; hind neck with small golden collar; back, wings, and tail green; rump and tail-coverts bright red; chin green; throat with a bright red patch; rest of underparts green. Female—differs by having blue on face and throat instead of red.

Soft Parts: Bill, male bright red with black tip, female light yellow; iris dark brown; feet dark orange.

Measurements: Wing 98; tail 47; bill 14; tarsus 11.

Range: Banton, Catanduanes, Luzon, Marinduque, and Polillo. (Endemic.)

Loriculus philippensis mindorensis Steere, 1890

1890 *Loriculus Mindorensis* Steere, List Bds. Mamms. Steere Expd., p. 6, (Mindoro)

149

Description: Differs from *L. p. philippensis* by lacking yellow on the crown, having no collar on the hind neck, and having a turquoise patch each side of the red rump.
Range: Mindoro. (Endemic.)

Loriculus philippensis bournsi McGregor, 1905

1905 *Loriculus bournsi* McGregor, Bur. Govt. Lab., Manila, **25**:16, (Sibuyan)
Description: Differs from *L. p. philippensis* by having a small yellow patch next to the bright red on the crown.
Range: Romblon, Sibuyan, and Tablas. (Endemic.)

Loriculus philippensis panayensis Tweeddale, 1877

1877 *Loriculus panayensis* Tweeddale, Proc. Zool. Soc. London, p. 538, (Ilo Ilo, Panay)
Description: Differs from *bournsi* by having more yellow on the crown and some red feathers on the hind neck.
Range: Masbate, Panay, and Ticao. (Endemic.)

Loriculus philippensis regulus Souance, 1856

1856 *Loriculus regulus* Souance, Rev. et Mag. Zool., **8**:222, (Negros)
Description: Differs from *panayensis* by having whole crown yellow and with more red on hind neck.
Range: Guimaras and Negros. (Endemic.)

Loriculus philippensis chrysonotus Sclater, 1872

1872 *Loriculus chrysonotus* Sclater, Ibis, p. 324, (Cebu)
Description: Differs from more northern forms by having hind crown, neck, and upper back bright golden yellow; throat orange-red.
Range: Cebu. (Extinct.)

Loriculus philippensis worcesteri Steere, 1890

1890 *Loriculus Worcesteri* Steere, List Bds. Mamms. Steere Expd., p. 6, (Samar and Leyte)
Description: Differs from *L. p. philippensis* by having entire crown reddish orange, which extends down on the back; red throat patch smaller.
Range: Bohol, Leyte, and Samar. (Endemic.)

Loriculus philippensis siquijorensis Steere, 1890

1890 *Loriculus Siquijorensis* Steere, List Bds. Mamms. Steere Expd., p. 6, (Siquijor)

150

Description: Differs from *worcesteri* by having crown, neck, and back green; throat, rump, and tail-coverts dark red.

Range: Siquijor. (Endemic.)

Loriculus philippensis apicalis Souance, 1856

1856 *Loriculus apicalis* Souance, Rev. et Mag. Zool., **8**:220, (Mindanao)

1877 *Loriculus hartlaubi* Finsch, Proc. Zool. Soc. London, p. 819, (Mindanao)

1930 *Loriculus salvadorii* Hachisuka, Orn. Soc. Japan, suppl. 14:163, (Zamboanga, Mindanao)

Description: Differs from *L. p. philippensis* by having the entire crown scarlet and the nape orange; rest of upperparts more golden.

Range: Bazol, Dinagat, and Mindanao. (Endemic.)

Loriculus philippensis dohertyi Hartert, 1906

1906 *Loriculus philippensis dohertyi* Hartert, Nov. Zool., **13**:757, (Basilan)

Description: Differs from *apicalis* by having the hind neck bright red and the back reddish yellow.

Range: Basilan. (Endemic.)

Loriculus philippensis bonapartei Souance, 1856

1856 *Loriculus Bonapartei* Souance, Rev. et Mag. Zool., **8**:222, (Sulu Archipelago)

Description: Differs from *apicalis* by having the nape deeper orange, becoming an orange wash on mantle; bill black (red in other races.)

Range: Bongao, Jolo, and Tawi Tawi. (Endemic.)

Family CUCULIDAE   CUCKOOS

RED-WINGED CRESTED-CUCKOO   PLATE 35

Clamator coromandus (Linné, 1766)

1766 *Cuculus coromandus* Linné, Syst. Nat., **1**:171, (Coromandel)

Description: Top of head and crest black, crest having a blue gloss; white collar on hind neck; back and mantle black with green gloss; tail black with purple gloss, small white tips to feathers; wings bright chestnut; throat orange-buff; breast and belly white; thighs gray.

Soft Parts: Bill black; iris pale red-brown; feet dark blue-black.

Measurements: Wing 168; tail 226; bill 25; tarsus 24.

Range: Winters in the Philippines from China.

PLATE 35

A   LARGE HAWK-CUCKOO
       (Cuculus sparverioides)—page 154

B   RED-WINGED CRESTED-CUCKOO
       (Clamator coromandus)—page 151

C   COMMON CUCKOO
       (Cuculus canorus)—page 155

D   ORIENTAL CUCKOO
       (Cuculus saturatus)—page 155

E   VIOLET CUCKOO
       (Chrysococcyx xanthorhynchus), male and female—page 159

F   MALAY BRONZE CUCKOO
       (Chrysococcyx malayanus)—page 158

G   HORSFIELD'S HAWK-CUCKOO
       (Cuculus fugax)—page 154

H   SHORT-WINGED CUCKOO
       (Cuculus micropterus)—page 154

PLATE 35

LARGE HAWK-CUCKOO   PLATE 35

Cuculus sparverioides sparverioides Vigors, 1831

1831 *Cuculus sparverioides* Vigors, Proc. Comm. Zool. Soc. London, p. 173, (Himalayas)

Description: All upperparts with bronze gloss; head and neck gray; mantle, back, and wings brown; tail brown with three dark brown bars, buffy at tip; lores white; chin dark gray; throat and breast streaked with rufous, gray, and white; lower breast and belly white barred with dark brown; under tail-coverts white with one or two brown bars.

Soft Parts: Bill, upper mandible black, lower mandible yellow; iris dark brown; feet bright yellow.

Measurements: Wing 234; tail 184; bill 27; tarsus 23.

Range: Found throughout the Philippines.

HORSFIELD'S HAWK-CUCKOO   PLATE 35

Cuculus fugax pectoralis (Cabanis and Heine, 1863)

1863 *Hiracococcyx pectoralis* Cabanis and Heine, Mus. Hein., p. 27, (Philippines)

Description: Head, neck, back, and wings slate-gray; tail slate with dark bars, rufous at end; chin gray; throat white with gray streaks; rest of underparts rufous with some white; under tail-coverts white. Immature—upperparts dark brown barred with chestnut; underparts whitish heavily streaked with dark brown.

Soft Parts: Bill olive-green with black tip; iris brown; feet yellow.

Measurements: Wing 173; tail 155; bill 19; tarsus 19.

Range: Found throughout the Philippines, except Palawan. (Endemic.)

Cuculus fugax hyperythrus Gould, 1856

1856 *Cuculus hyperythrus* Gould, Proc. Zool. Soc. London, p. 96, (China)

Description: Differs from *pectoralis* by being lighter in color and having longer wing (200).

Range: Winters in the Philippines from China.

SHORT-WINGED CUCKOO   PLATE 35

Cuculus micropterus micropterus Gould, 1837

1837 *Cuculus micropterus* Gould, Proc. Zool. Soc. London, p. 137, (Himalayas)

Description: Upperparts light bluish gray; tail black with white spots; throat and upper breast gray; lower breast and belly white coarsely barred with black; under tail-coverts buffy barred with black.

154

Soft Parts: Bill tan with yellow base; iris brown; feet dull yellow.

Measurements: Wing 214; tail 140; bill 24; tarsus 21.

Range: Recorded from Mindoro and Negros; a straggler from eastern Asia, Borneo, and Java.

COMMON CUCKOO PLATE 35

Cuculus canorus telephonus Heine, 1863

1863 *Cuculus telephonus* Heine, Journ. f. Orn., **11**:352, (Japan)

Description: Head, neck, mantle, back, rump, and wings dark gray; primaries and tail dark olive-gray, the latter with a white tip; throat gray; breast and belly white with fine black bars.

Soft Parts: Bill black; iris yellow; feet yellow.

Measurements: Wing 210; tail 165; bill 22; tarsus 20.

Range: Winters in the Philippines from northeast Asia.

ORIENTAL CUCKOO PLATE 35

Cuculus saturatus horsfieldi Moore, 1857

1857 *Cuculus horsfieldi* Moore, in Moore and Horsfield's Cat. Bds. Mus. Hon. East-India Co., **2**:703, (Java)

Description: Upperparts bluish gray with bronze gloss; tail black with white spots; throat and upper breast light gray; lower breast and belly white with black bars; under tail-coverts slightly rufous with black bars.

Soft Parts: Bill, upper mandible black, lower mandible dark green; iris gray; feet greenish yellow.

Measurements: Wing 185; tail 150; bill 22; tarsus 16.

Range: Winters in the Philippines from China.

BAY-BANDED CUCKOO PLATE 36

Cacomantis sonneratii fasciolatus (P. L. S. Müller, 1843)

1843 *Cuculus fasciolatus* P. L. S. Müller, Verh. nat. gesch. Nederl., p. 177, (Sumatra)

Description: Upperparts dark chestnut, barred with dark brown, and glossed with bronze; underparts grayish white with fine black bars.

Soft Parts: Bill black; iris dark brown; feet dark gray.

Measurements: Wing 106; tail 107; bill 19; tarsus 17.

Range: Calamianes, Palawan, and Tablas; also Borneo, Malay Peninsula, and Sumatra.

PLATE 36

A   KOEL
        (Eudynamys scolopacea), female—page 160

B   KOEL
        (Eudynamys scolopacea), male—page 160

C   SCALE-FEATHERED CUCKOO
        (Phoenicophaeus cumingi)—page 161

D   BRUSH CUCKOO
        (Cacomantis variolosus)—page 158

E   BAY-BANDED CUCKOO
        (Cacomantis sonneratii)—page 155

F   PLAINTIVE CUCKOO
        (Cacomantis merulinus)—page 158

G   DRONGO CUCKOO
        (Surniculus lugubris)—page 159

H   PALAWAN MALCOHA
        (Phoenicophaeus curvirostris)—page 160

I   ROUGH-CRESTED CUCKOO
        (Phoenicophaeus superciliosus)—page 161

PLATE 36

PLAINTIVE CUCKOO   PLATE 36

Cacomantis merulinus merulinus (Scopoli, 1786)

1786 *Cuculus merulinus* Scopoli, Del. Flor. et Faun. Insubr., p. 89, (Panay)

Description: Top of head gray-bronze; back, wings, and tail glossy bronze; throat and upper chest pale gray; rest of underparts pale rufous; tail feathers barred with white. Immature—upperparts light chestnut streaked and barred with brown; underparts, chin, and throat creamy white streaked with brown and washed with light chestnut; rest of underparts creamy white barred with dark brown.

Soft Parts: Bill black; iris yellow; feet dark gray.

Measurements: Wing 112; tail 115; bill 15; tarsus 17.

Range: Found throughout the Philippines. (Endemic.)

BRUSH CUCKOO   PLATE 36

Cacomantis variolosus sepulcralis (S. Müller, 1843)

1843 *Cuculus sepulcralis* S. Müller, Verh. nat. gesch. Nederl., p. 177, (Java and Sumatra)

Description: Upperparts gray with a strong bronze gloss; chin and upper throat gray; rest of underparts dark cinnamon; white tips to tail feathers. Immature—upperparts dark chestnut barred with dark brown; underparts gray barred with dark brown.

Soft Parts: Bill lemon-yellow with black tip; iris brown-gray; feet bright lemon-yellow.

Measurements: Wing 118; tail 128; bill 16; tarsus 16.

Range: Found throughout the Philippines, except for Basilan and Sulu Archipelago.

Cacomantis variolosus everetti Hartert, 1925

1925 *Cacomantis variolosus everetti* Hartert, Nov. Zool., **32**:166, (Tawi Tawi)

Description: Differs from *sepulcralis* by having cinnamon chin and throat, darker underparts, and somewhat less clear gray head; also smaller wing (113.5).

Range: Basilan and Sulu Archipelago. (Endemic.)

MALAY BRONZE CUCKOO   PLATE 35

Chrysococcyx malayanus malayanus (Raffles, 1822)

1822 *Cuculus Malayanus* Raffles, Trans. Linn. Soc. London, **13**:286, (Malay Peninsula)

Description: Head, neck, back, wings, and tail dark bronze with green gloss; underparts barred with bronze and white; throat and breast washed with rufous.

Soft Parts: Bill dark black-red at base; iris red; feet dark green.

Measurements: Wing 95; tail 66; bill 16; tarsus 17.

Range: Basilan, Bongao, Mindanao, Negros, and Tawi Tawi.

158

VIOLET   CUCKOO

PLATE 35

Chrysococcyx xanthorhynchus amethystinus (Vigors, 1831)

1831   *Lampromorpha amethystina* Vigors, Proc. Comm. Zool. Soc. London, p. 98, (Manila, Luzon)

Description: Male—entire bird bright blue-violet except for lower breast and belly, which are barred with dark green and white; tail feathers with white tips. Female—upperparts bright bronze tinged with green; throat and upper breast barred with bronze and white washed with rufous; lower breast and belly barred with bronze and white; tail feathers with white tips.

Soft Parts: Bill yellow, base red; iris red; feet dark olive.

Measurements: Wing 100; tail 70; bill 19; tarsus 17.

Range: Basilan, Cebu, Leyte, Luzon, Mindoro, and Samar. (Endemic.)

Chrysococcyx xanthorhynchus xanthorhynchus (Horsfield, 1821)

1821   *Chalcites xanthorhynchus* Horsfield, Trans. Linn. Soc. London, **13**:179, (Java)

Description: Differs from *amethystinus* by being lighter, more reddish purple, not dark blue-violet; also, more white in tail.

Range: Palawan.

DRONGO   CUCKOO

PLATE 36

Surniculus lugubris velutinus Sharpe, 1877

1877   *Surniculus velutinus* Sharpe, Trans. Linn. Soc. London, **1**:320, (Malamaui)

1953   *Surniculus lugubris suluensis* Salomonsen, Vid. Medd. Dansk nat. Foren., **115**: 237, (Tawi Tawi)

Description: Entire bird dull velvety black; thigh feathers mostly white; under tail with small white spots; primaries with a white spot.

Soft Parts: Bill black; iris dark brown; feet black.

Measurements: Wing 117; tail 110; bill 22; tarsus 15.

Range: Basilan, Bohol, Leyte, Mindanao, Samar, and Sulu Archipelago. (Endemic.)

Surniculus lugubris chalybaeus Salomonsen, 1953

1953   *Surniculus lugubris chalybaeus* Salomonsen, Vid. Medd. Dansk nat. Foren., **115**: 237, (Lamao, Bataan Peninsula, Luzon)

1958   *Surniculus lugubris mindorensis* Ripley and Rabor, Bull. Peabody Mus. Nat. Hist., **13**:38, (Alcate, Victoria, Mindoro)

Description: Differs from *velutinus* by having head, neck, and underparts glossy black.

Range: Luzon, Mindoro, and Negros. (Endemic.)

Surniculus lugubris minimus Baker, 1919

1919   *Surniculus lugubris minimus* Baker, Nov. Zool., **26**:292, (Iwahig, Palawan)

Description: Differs from *velutinus* by being greener and lighter on upperparts; under tail-coverts with more white.

Range: Balabac and Palawan. (Endemic.)

KOEL   **PLATE 36**

Eudynamys scolopacea mindanensis (Linné, 1766)

1766   *Cuculus mindanensis* Linné, Syst. Nat., **1**:169, (Philippines)

1934   *Eudynamys scolopacea onikakko* Hachisuka, Bds. Phil. Ids., p. 214, (Calapan, Mindoro)

1934   *Eudynamys scolopacea paraguena* Hachisuka, Bds. Phil. Ids., p. 213, (Taguso, Palawan)

Description: Male—entire bird glossy blue-black. Female—upperparts dark brown barred with light rufous; underparts buffy with wide dark brown bars on breast, becoming narrower on belly.

Soft Parts: Bill dark green; iris red; feet steel-blue.

Measurements: Wing 188; tail 186; bill 28; tarsus 32.

Range: Found throughout the Philippines, except for Calayan and Fuga.

Eudynamys scolopacea frater McGregor, 1904

1904   *Eudynamis* [sic] *frater* McGregor, Bull. Phil. Mus., 4:21, (Calayan North)

Description: Differs from *mindanensis* by being larger (wing 240; tail 227; bill 31; tarsus 33).

Range: Calayan and Fuga Islands. (Endemic.)

PALAWAN   MALCOHA   **PLATE 36**

Phoenicophaeus curvirostris harringtoni (Sharpe, 1877)

1877   *Dryococcyx Harringtoni* Sharpe, Trans. Linn. Soc. London, **1**:321, (Balabac)

Description: Head and neck dark gray; naked red patch extends from bill to behind the eye; mantle, wings, back, and basal half of tail glossy green with some deep blue on ends of feathers; terminal half of tail chestnut; throat light rufous; rest of underparts dark chestnut.

Soft Parts: Bill green; iris red; feet dark gray.

Measurements: Wing 175; tail 280; bill 38; tarsus 38.

Range: Balabac, Calamianes, and Palawan. (Endemic.)

160

ROUGH-CRESTED CUCKOO   PLATE 36

Phoenicophaeus superciliosus superciliosus Dumont, 1823

1823   *Phaenicophaus superciliosus* Dumont, Dict. Sci. Nat., ed. Levrault, **28**:451, (Philippines)

Description: Upperparts black with strong greenish gloss; a large, bare orange patch around eye; long superciliary feathers bright red; underparts dull black with slight greenish gloss; tail feathers with a white tip.

Soft Parts: Bill pale green; iris yellow; feet greenish.

Measurements: Wing 155; tail 235; bill 37; tarsus 37.

Range: Catanduanes, central and southern Luzon, Marinduque, and Polillo. (Endemic.)

Phoenicophaeus superciliosus cagayanensis Rand and Rabor, 1967

1967   *Phoenicophaeus superciliosus cagayanensis* Rand and Rabor, Fieldiana: Zoology, **51**:85, (Mt. Cague, Sierra Madre, Luzon)

Description: Differs from *P. s. superciliosus* by having shorter superciliary feathers and less white at the base of these feathers; tail feathers with smaller white tips; breast with a more yellowish green wash.

Range: Cagayan Province, northeast Luzon.

SCALE-FEATHERED CUCKOO   PLATE 36

Phoenicophaeus cumingi Fraser, 1839

1839   *Phoenicophaus Cumingi* Fraser, Proc. Zool. Soc. London, p. 112, (Luzon)

Description: Head and throat gray, the latter being lighter and both with elongated feathers terminated with a black spangle; upper back dark chestnut; wings, lower back, and tail glossy dark green; tail feathers with a white tip; breast chestnut; belly dull black.

Soft Parts: Bill tan; iris red; feet gray.

Measurements: Wing 155; tail 233; bill 37; tarsus 41.

Range: Luzon and Marinduque. (Endemic.)

COMMON COUCAL   PLATE 37

Centropus sinensis bubutus Horsfield, 1821

1821   *Centropus Bubutus* Horsfield, Trans. Linn. Soc. London, **13**:180, (Java)

Description: Head, neck, and throat black glossed with blue; upper back and wings chestnut; lower back and tail black glossed with green; underparts dull black.

161

Soft Parts: Bill black; iris red; feet black.
Measurements: Wing 210; tail 298; bill 40; tarsus 58.
Range: Balabac, Cagayan Sulu, Luzon, and Palawan.

Centropus sinensis anonymous Stresemann, 1913

1913 *Centropus sinensis anonymous* Stresemann, Nov. Zool., **20**:323, (Tawi Tawi)
Description: Differs from *bubutus* by having wings darker chestnut; also smaller (wing 163; tail 230; bill 47; tarsus 41).
Range: Basilan, Jolo, and Tawi Tawi. (Endemic.)

STEERE'S COUCAL   PLATE 37

Centropus steerii Bourns and Worcester, 1894

1894 *Centropus steerii* Bourns and Worcester, Occ. Papers Minn. Acad. Nat. Sci., 1:14, (Mindoro)
Description: Head and throat black glossed with green; neck, back, and wings blackish brown; tail glossy green; breast and belly dark brown.
Soft Parts: Bill black; iris brown; feet black.
Measurements: Wing 150; tail 220; bill 41; tarsus 42.
Range: Mindoro. (Endemic.)

PHILIPPINE   COUCAL   PLATE 37

Centropus viridis viridis (Scopoli, 1786)

1786 *Cuculus viridis* Scopoli, Del. Flor. et Faun. Insubr., p. 89, (Antigua, Panay)
1790 *Cuculus aegyptius* Gmelin, Syst. Nat., **1**:420, (Philippines)
1812 *Centropus rufipennis* Illiger, Abhandl. Berl. Acad., p. 224, (Philippines)
1817 *Cuculus philippensis* Cuvier, Regne An., **1**:436, (Philippines)
1823 *Corydonix pyrrhopterus* Vieillot, Enc. Meth., **3**:1353, (Philippines)
1850 *Centropus molkenboeri* Bonaparte, Consp. Av., **1**:108, (Philippines)
Description: Entire bird dull black glossed with green, except for wings, which are bright chestnut; tips of primaries darker. Immature—top of head, back, chin, throat, and breast dark brownish black barred with white; shaft streaks buffy; wings chestnut barred with dark brown.
Soft Parts: Bill black; iris red; feet black.
Measurements: Wing 157; tail 255; bill 26; tarsus 42.
Range: Found throughout the Philippines, except for Batan and Mindoro. (Endemic.)

Centropus viridis mindorensis (Steere, 1890)

1890 *Centrococcyx Mindorensis* Steere, List Bds. Mamms. Steere Expd., p. 12, (Calapan, Mindoro)

Description: Differs from *C. v. viridis* by having wings much blacker, similar to rest of body. Wing 160; tail 250; tarsus 41.

Range: Mindoro and Semirara. (Endemic.)

Centropus viridis carpenteri Mearns, 1907

1907 *Centropus carpenteri* Mearns, Phil. Journ. Sci., **2**:356, (Batan Island)

Description: Similar in color to *mindorensis* but differs by being larger (wing 166; tail 278; tarsus 42).

Range: Batan Island. (Endemic.)

BLACK-FACED COUCAL   PLATE 37

Centropus melanops Lesson, 1830

1830 *Centropus melanops* Lesson, Traité, d'Orn., **2**:137, (Mindanao)

1848 *Centropus nigrifrons* Peale, U. S. Expl. Exped., **8**:137, (Philippines)

1934 *Centropus melanops banken* Hachisuka, Bds. Phil. Ids., p. 221, (Paranas, Samar)

Description: Forehead, lores, cheek, and behind the eye black; crown pale buff; neck buffy chestnut; wings dark chestnut; back and tail black with a greenish gloss; throat pale buff; breast and belly black.

Soft Parts: Bill black; iris red; feet black.

Measurements: Wing 168; tail 244; bill 36; tarsus 41.

Range: Basilan, Bohol, Leyte, Mindanao, and Samar. (Endemic.)

RUFOUS COUCAL   PLATE 37

Centropus unirufus (Cabanis and Heine, 1863)

1863 *Pyrrhocentor unirufus* Cabanis and Heine, Mus. Hein., p. 118, (Luzon)

1930 *Centropus unirufus polillensis* Hachisuka, Orn. Soc. Japan, suppl. 14:177, (Polillo)

Description: Entire bird rufous; black shaft streaks make crown look darker; underparts slightly lighter.

Soft Parts: Bill green with yellow tip; iris rufous; feet black.

Measurements: Wing 165; tail 242; bill 37; tarsus 43.

Range: Luzon and Polillo. (Endemic.)

PLATE 37

A   PHILIPPINE COUCAL
      (Centropus viridis)—page 162

B   RUFOUS COUCAL
      (Centropus unirufus)—page 163

C   LESSER COUCAL
      (Centropus bengalensis), breeding plumage—page 166

D   STEERE'S COUCAL
      (Centropus steerii)—page 162

E   COMMON COUCAL
      (Centropus sinensis)—page 161

F   BLACK-FACED COUCAL
      (Centropus melanops)—page 163

PLATE 37

LESSER COUCAL · PLATE 37

Centropus bengalensis philippinensis Mees, 1971

1971 *Centropus bengalensis philippinensis* Mees, Zool. Med., **45**:190, (Calapan, Mindoro)

Description: Head, neck, and throat black glossed with green; shaft streaks quite shiny; back and tail black, slightly glossed with green; tips of tail feathers buffy; wings mottled brown and chestnut; wing-covert shafts are whitish, giving a streaked appearance; underparts dull black. Eclipse plumage—head, neck, and back dark brownish black with light shaft streaks, giving a streaked appearance; wings and tail light chestnut heavily barred with blackish brown; underparts pale buff with light shaft streaks; sides of throat, breast, and flanks lightly barred with dark brown.

Soft Parts: Bill black; iris brown; feet black.

Measurements: Wing 160; tail 218; bill 25; tarsus 40.

Range: Found throughout the Philippines.

Family TYTONIDAE · BARN OWLS

GRASS OWL · PLATE 39

Tyto capensis amauronota (Cabanis, 1872)

1872 *Strix amauronota* Cabanis, Journ. f. Orn., **20**:316, (Luzon)

Description: Crown dark orange-brown; face white; black spot in front of eyes; ruff-feathers white, outer ones having black ends; hind neck buffy; mantle and wings dark orange-brown with small white spots; tail white with four dark brown bars; throat and belly white; breast washed with buff.

Soft Parts: Bill white; iris dark brown; feet dark brown.

Measurements: Wing 360; tail 135; bill 45; tarsus 89.

Range: Basilan, Batan, Calamianes, Cebu, Luzon, Mindanao, Negros, Panay, and Siquijor. (Endemic.)

BAY OWL · PLATE 38

Phodilus badius badius (Horsfield, 1821)

1821 *Strix badia* Horsfield, Trans. Linn. Soc. London, **13**:139, (Java)

1927 *Phodilus riverae* McGregor, Phil. Journ. Sci., **32**:518, (Wright, Samar)

Description: Crown dark chestnut; face pinkish white; ruff-feathers white with chestnut edges; mantle, back, and wings chestnut with some black and white spots; underparts pinkish with small black spots having white edges.

166

Soft Parts: Bill yellowish; iris black; feet yellowish brown.

Measurements: Wing 220; tail 115; bill 35; tarsus 54.

Range: Samar (once, in 1924). Outside the Philippines: Burma and Malay Peninsula to Borneo.

Family STRIGIDAE   OWLS

SCOPS OWL   PLATE 38

Otus scops longicornis (Ogilvie-Grant, 1894)

1894   *Scops longicornis* Ogilvie-Grant, Bull. Brit. Orn. Cl., 3:51, (northern Luzon)

Description: Forehead white; crown bright rufous; a white line over each eye; face light buff; hind neck whitish, a part of a white collar that is wider and whiter on the breast; mantle, back, and rump rufous with black spots; wings and tail similar but darker; throat white with black spots; breast rufous with large black spots; belly white with rufous and black.

Soft Parts: Bill dull green, tip dark brown; iris yellow; feet flesh color.

Measurements: Wing 148; tail 72; bill 17; tarsus 33; ear-tufts 31.

Range: Luzon. (Endemic.)

Otus scops calayensis McGregor, 1904

1904   *Otus calayensis* McGregor, Bull. Phil. Mus., 4:18, (Calayan Island)

1952   *Otus bakkamoena batanensis* Manuel and Gilliard, Am. Mus. Novit., 1545:4, (Basco, Batan Island)

Description: Differs from *longicornis* by being larger (wing 169; tail 85).

Range: Batan and Calayan. (Endemic.)

Otus scops mindorensis (Whitehead, 1899)

1899   *Scops mindorensis* Whitehead, Ibis, p. 98, (Mindoro)

Description: Differs from *longicornis* by being smaller (wing 135; tail 63).

Range: Mindoro. (Endemic.)

Otus scops romblonis McGregor, 1905

1905   *Otus romblonis* McGregor, Bur. Govt. Lab., Manila, 25:12, (Romblon)

Description: Differs from *longicornis* by having very distinct black streaks on the head; also, somewhat larger (wing 158).

Range: Banton and Romblon. (Endemic.)

167

Otus scops cuyensis McGregor, 1904

1904   *Otus cuyensis* McGregor, Bull. Phil. Mus., 4:17, (Cuyo)

Description: Differs from *romblonis* by being larger (wing 175).

Range: Cuyo. (Endemic.)

Otus scops mirus Ripley and Rabor, 1968

1968   *Otus scops mirus* Ripley and Rabor, Proc. Biol. Soc. Wash., **81**:31, (Agusan Province, Mindanao)

Description: Differs from *longicornis* by having the upperparts more heavily streaked and the underparts lighter, especially the belly; also smaller (wing 131; tail 58).

Range: Mindanao. (Endemic.)

Otus scops sibutuensis (Sharpe, 1893)

1893   *Scops sibutuensis* Sharpe, Bull. Brit. Orn. Cl., **3**:9, (Sibutu)

1909   *Otus steerei* Mearns, Proc. U. S. Nat. Mus., **36**:437, (Tumindao Island)

Description: Differs from *mirus* by having the wing-coverts paler and the underparts darker; also, somewhat larger (wing 136).

Range: Sibutu. (Endemic.)

RUFOUS SCOPS OWL   PLATE 38

Otus rufescens burbidgei Hachisuka, 1934

1934   *Otus rufescens burbidgei* Hachisuka, Bds. Phil. Ids., p. 51, (Sulu)

Description: Forehead fulvous; head and ear-coverts dark tawny-rufous; face rufous, darker around eyes; black line runs from ear-coverts down sides of neck; upperparts red-brown with buff spots; tail rufous, darker than back; underparts rufous with some black streaks on breast.

Soft Parts: Bill cream; iris gold; feet yellowish.

Measurements: Wing 132; tail 66; bill 19; tarsus 27; ear-tufts 25.

Range: Sulu. (Endemic.)

ORIENTAL SCREECH OWL   PLATE 38

Otus bakkamoena megalotis (Walden, 1875)

1875   *Lempijius megalotis* Walden, Trans. Zool. Soc. London, **9**:145, (Manila)

1895   *Scops whiteheadi* Ogilvie-Grant, Bull. Brit. Orn. Cl., **4**:40, (Lepanto, northern Luzon)

Description: Gray phase crown blackish; eye stripe white; upperparts gray brown with white; scapulars form a white line; underparts light gray with dark streaks; red phase similar but rufous.

Soft Parts: Bill brownish with a light tip; iris yellow-brown; feet dirty white.

Measurements: Wing 190; tail 108; bill 28; tarsus 44; ear-tufts 40.

Range: Luzon. (Endemic.)

Otus bakkamoena everetti (Tweeddale, 1878)

1878 *Scops everetti* Tweeddale, Proc. Zool. Soc. London, p. 942, (Zamboanga, Mindanao)

1907 *Otus boholensis* McGregor, Phil. Journ. Sci., 2:323, (Sevilla, Bohol)

Description: Differs from *megalotis* by being smaller (wing 162; tail 71) and not having the feathering of the tarsus reaching the foot.

Range: Basilan, Bohol, Leyte, Mindanao, and Samar. (Endemic.)

Otus bakkamoena nigrorum Rand, 1950

1950 *Otus bakkamoena nigrorum* Rand, Nat. His. Misc., 72:3, (Negros)

Description: Differs from *everetti* by having head and neck bright rufous; also, wing smaller (147).

Range: Negros. (Endemic.)

Otus bakkamoena fuliginosus (Sharpe, 1888)

1888 *Scops fuliginosus* Sharpe, Ibis, p. 197, (Puerto Princesa, Palawan)

Description: Differs from *everetti* by having a reduced collar on the hind neck and more rufous above; face and chin rufous-brown, not white; underparts darker brown with heavy dark brown streaks; also smaller (wing 139).

Range: Palawan. (Endemic.)

GIANT SCOPS OWL   **PLATE 38**

Mimizuku gurneyi (Tweeddale, 1879)

1879 *Pseudoptynx gurneyi* Tweeddale, (1878), Proc. Zool. Soc. London, p. 940, (Zamboanga, Mindanao)

Description: Crown dark rufous with dark brown stripes; back, rump, and upper tail-coverts rufous with black spots that form three long stripes; wings rufous with brown; tail brown; throat plain rufous; breast and flanks rufous with black streaks; belly lighter rufous with fewer streaks.

Soft Parts: Bill gray; iris brown; feet light gray.

Measurements: Wing 240; tail 119; bill 31; tarsus 45; ear-tufts 42.

Range: Mindanao. (Endemic).

PLATE 38

A   PHILIPPINE HAWK OWL
      (Ninox scutulata)—page 176

B   BAY OWL
      (Phodilus badius)—page 166

C   GIANT SCOPS OWL
      (Mimizuku gurneyi)—page 169

D   RUFOUS SCOPS OWL
      (Otus rufescens)—page 168

E   ORIENTAL SCREECH OWL
      (Otus bakkamoena)—page 168

F   PHILIPPINE BOOBOOK OWL
      (Ninox philippensis)—page 174

G   SCOPS OWL
      (Otus scops)—page 167

PLATE 38

PLATE 39

A   SELOPUTO OWL
       (Strix seloputo)—page 176

B   GRASS OWL
       (Tyto capensis)—page 166

C   SHORT-EARED OWL
       (Asio flammeus)—page 177

D   PHILIPPINE HORNED OWL
       (Bubo philippensis)—page 174

172

PLATE 39

PHILIPPINE HORNED OWL   PLATE 39

Bubo philippensis philippensis (Kaup, 1851)

1844 *Scops Philippensis* G. R. Gray, List Spec. Bds. Brit. Mus., Accipitres, p. 45,
      (nomen nudum)

1848 *Syrnium philippense* G. R. Gray, List Spec. Bds. Brit. Mus., Accipitres, p. 105,
      (nomen nudum)

1851 *Pseudoptynx philippensis* Kaup, Arch. f. Natürg., **17**:110, (Luzon)

Description: Feathers of all upperparts rufous with a black streak in center; tail dull
rufous barred with dark brown; chin light rufous; throat whitish; rest of underparts very
pale rufous with dark brown streaks.

Soft Parts: Bill tan with light tip; iris yellow-brown; feet light gray.

Measurements: Wing 341; tail 170; bill 47; tarsus 70; ear-tufts 34.

Range: Luzon. (Endemic.)

Bubo philippensis mindanensis (Ogilvie-Grant, 1906)

1906 *Pseudoptynx philippensis* Ogilvie-Grant, Bull. Brit. Orn. Cl., **16**:99, (Davao,
      Mindanao)

Description: Differs from *B. p. philippensis* by having upperparts darker; underparts
with darker and more numerous streaks. Also may be larger, but this proves doubtful.

Range: Cebu, Leyte, Mindanao, and Samar. (Endemic.)

PHILIPPINE   BOOBOOK   OWL   PLATE 38

Ninox philippensis philippensis Bonaparte, 1855

1855 *Ninox philippensis* Bonaparte, Compt. Rend. Acad. Sci. Paris, **41**:655, (Luzon)

Description: Head, mantle, back, rump, and wings dark brown; scapulars with large
white spots; tail brown with dark brown bars; chin white; rest of underparts white with
broad rufous-brown stripes.

Soft Parts: Bill greenish with yellow tip; iris yellow; feet yellow.

Measurements: Wing 162; tail 88; bill 20; tarsus 29.

Range: Leyte, Luzon, Marinduque, Polillo, and Samar. (Endemic.)

Ninox philippensis proxima Mayr, 1945

1945 *Ninox philippensis proxima* Mayr, Zoologica, **30**:108, (Masbate)

Description: Differs from *N. p. philippensis* by having the upperparts darker brown,
white spots on wings smaller, and striping of underparts darker; also, longer wing (175)
and shorter tail (80).

Range: Masbate and Ticao. (Endemic.)

174

Ninox philippensis centralis Mayr, 1945

1945 *Ninox philippensis centralis* Mayr, Zoologica, **30**:108, (Siquijor)

Description: Differs from *proxima* by having the upperparts duller brown; also larger (wing 186; tail 91).

Range: Bohol, Guimaras, Negros, Panay, and Siquijor. (Endemic.)

Ninox philippensis spilocephala Tweeddale, 1878

1878 *Ninox spilocephala* Tweeddale, Proc. Zool. Soc. London, p. 939, (Zamboanga, Mindanao)

Description: Differs from *N. p. philippensis* by having more rufous spots on head and neck; white spots on wings slightly larger.

Range: Basilan and Mindanao. (Endemic.)

Ninox philippensis reyi Oustalet, 1880

1880 *Ninox Reyi* Oustalet, Bull. Assoc. Sci. France, **1**:206, (Sulu Archipelago)

1897 *Ninox everetti* Sharpe, Bull. Brit. Orn. Cl., **6**:47, (Siasi Island)

Description: Differs from *spilocephala* by having more prominent rufous barring on the head and back; striping underneath is lacking on the belly; also larger (wing 194).

Range: Bongao, Siasi, Sulu, and Tawi Tawi. (Endemic.)

Ninox philippensis mindorensis Ogilvie-Grant, 1896

1896 *Ninox mindorensis* Ogilvie-Grant, Ibis, p. 463, (Mindoro)

1899 *Ninox Plateni* "Blasius" Hartlaub, Abh. Naturwiss. Ver. Bremen, **16**:271, (Mindoro)

Description: Differs from *N. p. philippensis* by having the upperparts duller brown and barred; underparts barred; also larger (wing 170).

Range: Mindoro. (Endemic.)

Ninox philippensis spilonota Bourns and Worcester, 1894

1894 *Ninox spilonotus* Bourns and Worcester, Occ. Papers Minn. Acad. Nat. Sci., 1:8, (Cebu)

Description: Differs from *mindorensis* by having the underparts heavily barred; also larger (wing 191; tail 98).

Range: Cebu, Sibuyan, and Tablas. (Endemic.)

PHILIPPINE HAWK OWL PLATE 38

Ninox scutulata randi Deignan, 1951

1951 *Ninox scutulata randi* Deignan, Proc. Biol. Soc. Wash., **64**:41, (Mt. Malindang, Mindanao)

Description: Forehead white; top of head dark brown; rest of upperparts very dark red-brown; tail red-brown with dark brown bars; primaries dark brown with lighter red-brown edges; underparts white heavily streaked with red-brown. Bill and feet much larger than in other races.
Soft Parts: Bill black; iris yellow; feet yellow.
Measurements: Wing 240; tail 135; bill 28; tarsus 33.
Range: Basilan, Cebu, Luzon, Marinduque, Mindanao, Mindoro, and Siquijor. (Endemic.)

Ninox scutulata palawanensis Ripley and Rabor, 1962

1962 *Ninox scutulata palawanensis* Ripley and Rabor, Postilla, 73:4, (Puerto Princesa, Palawan)

Description: Differs from *randi* by being smaller (wing 195; tail 108).
Range: Palawan. (Endemic.)

Ninox scutulata japonica (Temminck and Schlegel, 1850)

1850 *Strix hirsuta japonica* Temminck and Schlegel, in Siebold's Faun. Jap., Aves, p. 28, (Japan)

Description: Differs from *randi* by having the upperparts browner and the red-brown in the wings and tail much reduced; underparts not as heavily streaked.
Range: Winters in the Philippines from Japan.

Ninox scutulata florensis (Wallace, 1864)

1864 *Athene florensis* Wallace, Proc. Zool. Soc. London, p. 488, (Flores)
Description: Differs from *japonica* by having the upperparts much paler and the underparts not so heavily streaked.
Range: Luzon; a straggler from China.

SELOPUTO OWL PLATE 39

Strix seloputo wiepkeni (Blasius, 1888)

1888 *Syrnium Wiepkeni* Blasius, (March) Braunschweig. Anz., **52**:467, (Puerto Princesa, Palawan)

1888 *Syrnium whiteheadi* Sharpe, (April) Ibis, p. 196, (Puerto Princesa, Palawan)

Description: Upperparts dark brown with white spots; wings slightly lighter; tail brown with light brown bars; face and chin buffy; white patch in middle of the throat; breast has brown feathers with white bars; lower breast and belly have white feathers with brown bars.

Soft Parts: Bill black; iris brown; feet feathered, with black nails.

Measurements: Wing 330; tail 190; bill 34; tarsus 58.

Range: Palawan. (Endemic.)

SHORT-EARED OWL   PLATE 39

Asio flammeus flammeus (Pontoppidan, 1763)

1763   *Strix Flammea* Pontoppidan, Danske Atlas, 1:617, (Sweden)

Description: Upperparts golden brown with dark brown streaks; tail light brown with dark brown bars; underparts golden brown, not so heavily streaked with dark brown.

Soft Parts: Bill blackish brown; iris yellow; toes black.

Measurements: Wing 310; tail 168; bill 27; tarsus 41; ear-tufts 30.

Range: Luzon; a straggler from eastern Asia.

Family PODARGIDAE   FROGMOUTHS

PHILIPPINE FROGMOUTH   PLATE 40

Batrachostomus septimus microrhynchus Ogilvie-Grant, 1895

1895   *Batrachostomus microrhynchus* Ogilvie-Grant, Bull. Brit. Orn. Cl., 4:41, (Mt. Data, Luzon)

Description: Head red-brown with a few lighter bars; white collar on hind neck; scapulars buffy; back, rump, and tail red-brown; wings brown with a few white spots; underparts pale brown with two white stripes, one on lower throat and the other on lower breast.

Soft Parts: Bill light brown; iris light yellow; feet buff.

Measurements: Wing 132; tail 104; bill 21; tarsus 17.

Range: Northern Luzon. (Endemic.)

Batrachostomus septimus menagei Bourns and Worcester, 1894

1894   *Batrachostomus menagei* Bourns and Worcester, Occ. Papers Minn. Acad. Nat. Sci., 1:11, (no locality = Philippines)

177

Description: Differs from *microrhynchus* by having browns darker and light areas lighter. Also larger (wing 140; tail 106).

Range: Negros and Panay. (Endemic.)

Batrachostomus septimus septimus Tweeddale, 1877

1877 *Batrachostomus septimus* Tweeddale, Proc. Zool. Soc. London, p. 542, (Pasananca, Mindanao)

Description: Differs from *menagei* by being larger (wing 160; tail 121).

Range: Basilan, Bohol, Leyte, Mindanao, and Samar. (Endemic.)

JAVA FROGMOUTH   PLATE 40

Batrachostomus javensis chaseni Stresemann, 1937

1937 *Batrachostomus javensis chaseni* Stresemann, Mitt. Zool. Mus. Berlin, **22**:326, (Taguso, Palawan)

Description: Upperparts rufous with a white collar on hind neck; tail barred with dark rufous; throat with large white spots; rest of underparts rufous.

Soft Parts: Bill horn color; iris yellow; feet brownish.

Measurements: Wing 129; tail 98; bill 24; tarsus 12.

Range: Banguey Island and Palawan. (Endemic.)

Family CAPRIMULGIDAE   NIGHTJARS

PHILIPPINE EARED NIGHTJAR   PLATE 40

Eurostopodus macrotis macrotis (Vigors, 1831)

1831 *Caprimulgus macrotis* Vigors, Proc. Comm. Zool. Soc. London, p. 97, (Manila, Luzon)

1878 *Lyncornis mindanensis* Tweeddale, Proc. Zool. Soc. London, p. 945, (Mindanao)

Description: Crown rufous with black spots; sides of head and ear-coverts darker; hind neck with light brown band, becoming white on throat; mantle, back, rump, and wings mottled with browns; scapulars with black spots; tail black with buff bars; chin, breast, and belly dark brown with black bars.

Soft Parts: Bill brown; iris brown; feet brown.

Measurements: Wing 280; tail 178; bill 10; tarsus 18.

Range: Basilan, Bohol, Leyte, Luzon, Mindanao, Mindoro, and Samar. (Endemic.)

178

JAPANESE NIGHTJAR

PLATE 40

Caprimulgus indicus jotaka Temminck and Schlegel, 1847

1847 *Caprimulgus jotaka* Temminck and Schlegel, in Siebold's Faun. Jap., Aves, p. 37, (Japan)

Description: Upperparts dark gray mottled with black and a little chestnut; tail dark gray with black bars; wings dark brown with a white stripe near tip; chin and lower throat dark gray with fine black bars; upper throat white; breast and belly gray and dark rufous with fine black bars.

Soft Parts: Bill brown; iris brown; feet brown.

Measurements: Wing 210; tail 143; bill 12; tarsus 16.

Range: Winters in the northern Philippines; a visitor from Japan.

LONG-TAILED NIGHTJAR

PLATE 40

Caprimulgus macrurus johnsoni Deignan, 1955

1955 *Caprimulgus macrurus johnsoni* Deignan, Sarawak Mus. Journ., **6**:315, (Puerto Princesa, Palawan)

Description: Crown and nape gray-brown with buff streaks; back and rump gray and black; tail brown with black marks; outer tail feathers with white tips; wings brown and black with three white bars and a white patch near end of wing; chin dark brown and black; throat with a white stripe; underparts gray with fine brown and black bars.

Soft Parts: Bill black; iris dark brown; feet brown.

Measurements: Wing 195; tail 139; bill 13; tarsus 14.

Range: Calamianes and Palawan. (Endemic.)

Caprimulgus macrurus manillensis Walden, 1875

1875 *Caprimulgus manillensis* Walden, Trans. Zool. Soc. London, **9**:159, (Manila, Luzon)

Description: Differs from *johnsoni* by having the white patch in the wing primaries and in the outer rectrices reduced.

Range: Most of Philippine Islands, except for Basilan, Mindanao, and Palawan. (Endemic.)

Caprimulgus macrurus delacouri Hachisuka, 1931

1931 *Caprimulgus macrurus delacouri* Hachisuka, Ois. et Rev. Fran. d'Orn., **1**:471, (Sigaboy, Mindanao)

Description: Differs from *manillensis* by having upperparts darker; white spots on wings much sharper.

Range: Basilan and Mindanao. (Endemic.)

PLATE 40

A   PHILIPPINE EARED NIGHTJAR
     (Eurostopodus macrotis)—page 178

B   JAVA FROGMOUTH
     (Batrachostomus javensis)—page 178

C   SAVANNA NIGHTJAR
     (Caprimulgus affinis)—page 182

D   PHILIPPINE FROGMOUTH
     (Batrachostomus septimus)—page 177

E   JAPANESE NIGHTJAR
     (Caprimulgus indicus)—page 179

F   LONG-TAILED NIGHTJAR
     (Caprimulgus macrurus)—page 179

A

B

C

D

E

F

PLATE 40

SAVANNA NIGHTJAR   PLATE 40

Caprimulgus affinis griseatus Walden, 1875

1875   *Caprimulgus griseatus* Walden, Trans. Zool. Soc. London, **9**:160, (Philippines=
        Manila, Luzon)

Description: Male—upperparts pale sandy brown vermiculated with black; underparts much the same but more rufous; white patch on sides of throat, in wing, and on sides of tail. Female—without white areas.

Soft Parts: Bill dark brown; iris brown; feet brown.

Measurements: Wing 168; tail 102; bill 9; tarsus 18.

Range: Catanduanes, Cebu, Luzon, Mindoro, Negros, and Sibuyan. (Endemic.)

Caprimulgus affinis mindanensis Mearns, 1905

1905   *Caprimulgus affinis mindanensis* Mearns, Proc. Biol. Soc. Wash., **18**:85,
        (Malabang, Mindanao)

Description: Differs from *C. a. griseatus* by being darker and having less white in the tail.

Range: Mindanao. (Endemic.)

Family APODIDAE   SWIFTS

HIMALAYAN SWIFTLET   PLATE 41

Collocalia brevirostris whiteheadi Ogilvie-Grant, 1895

1895   *Collocalia whiteheadi* Ogilvie-Grant, Ibis, p. 459, (Mt. Data, Luzon)

Description: Head and upperparts sooty black with a slight greenish gloss; tail has a more purplish gloss and is slightly forked; underparts brownish gray; tarsus without feathers.

Soft Parts: Bill black; iris brown; feet red-brown.

Measurements: Wing 137; tail 55; bill 6; tarsus 12.

Range: Bantayan, Batan, Bohol, Cagayancillo, Catanduanes, Cebu, Luzon, Mindoro, Sibuyan, and Verde.

Collocalia brevirostris origenis Oberholser, 1906

1906   *Collocalia origenis* Oberholser, Proc. Acad. Nat. Sci. Phila., **58**:191, (Mt. Apo,
        Mindanao)

1930   *Collocalia apoensis* Hachisuka, Orn. Soc. Japan, suppl. 14:172, (Apo Lake, Mindanao)

Description: Differs from *C. b. whiteheadi* by being darker above and below.

Range: Mindanao. (Endemic.)

Collocalia brevirostris palawanensis Stresemann, 1914

1914 *Collocalia lowi palawanensis* Stresemann, Ver. Orn. Ges. Bayern, **12**:10, (Puerto Princesa, Palawan)

1934 *Collocalia whiteheadi tsubame* Hachisuka, Bds. Phil. Ids., p. 176, (Puerto Princesa, Palawan)

Description: Head and upperparts dirty black with a green gloss; underparts brownish gray; tarsus feathered.

Soft Parts: Bill black; iris dark brown; feet dark brown.

Measurements: Wing 127; tail 53; bill 5; tarsus 10.

Range: Palawan. (Endemic.)

EDIBLE-NEST SWIFTLET   PLATE 41

Collocalia fuciphaga germani Oustalet, 1878

1878 *Collocalia germani* Oustalet, Bull. Soc. Philom., **2**:1, (Cochinchina)

Description: Head and upperparts sooty black with green; rump pale gray with dark shaft streaks; tail dull greenish purple; underparts grayish brown.

Soft Parts: Bill black; iris dark brown; feet light brown.

Measurements: Wing 115; tail 50; bill 5; tarsus 9.

Range: Palawan and Sulu Islands to Indonesia.

GRAY   SWIFTLET   PLATE 41

Collocalia vanikorensis amelis Oberholser, 1906

1906 *Collocalia unicolor amelis* Oberholser, Proc. Acad. Nat. Sci. Phila., **58**:193, (Irisan, Benguet, Luzon)

1912 *Collocalia vestita mearnsi* Oberholser, Proc. U. S. Nat. Mus., **42**:17, (Paoay, Benguet, Luzon)

Description: Head and upperparts blackish with dark green; back and rump paler; throat gray-brown; breast and belly gray-brown.

Soft Parts: Bill black; iris dark brown; feet black.

Measurements: Wing 115; tail 56; bill 4; tarsus 10.

Range: Bohol, Cebu, Luzon, Marinduque, Mindanao, Mindoro, Negros, Palawan, and Panay. (Endemic.)

PLATE 41

A   GRAY SWIFTLET
    (Collocalia vanikorensis)—page 183

B   EDIBLE-NEST SWIFTLET
    (Collocalia fuciphaga)—page 183

C   GLOSSY SWIFTLET
    (Collocalia esculenta)—page 186

D   HIMALAYAN SWIFTLET
    (Collocalia brevirostris)—page 182

E   PYGMY SWIFTLET
    (Collocalia troglodytes)—page 186

184

A

B

C

D

E

John R. Peirce

PLATE 41

PYGMY SWIFTLET   PLATE 41

Collocalia troglodytes G. R. Gray, 1845

1845   *Collocalia troglodytes* G. R. Gray, Gen. Bds., **1**:55, (Philippines)

Description: Head, back, wings, and tail black with a blue-green gloss; rump mostly white; throat and breast light brown; belly buff. Tail with slight fork.

Soft Parts: Bill black; iris dark brown; feet black.

Measurements: Wing 90; tail 40; bill 3.5; tarsus 9.

Range: Luzon, south to Mindanao and Palawan. (Endemic.)

GLOSSY SWIFTLET   PLATE 41

Collocalia esculenta isonota Oberholser, 1906

1906   *Collocalia linchi isonota* Oberholser, Proc. Acad. Nat. Sci. Phila., **58**:208, (Irisan, Benguet, Luzon)

1945   *Collocalia esculenta septentrionalis* Mayr, Zoologica, **30**:110, (Calayan)

Description: Crown, tail-coverts, and tail dark green with bluish cast; rest of upperparts greenish; wings blue-green; sides of head, throat, and breast brown with narrow white margins to feathers; belly and flanks grayer with wider white margins to·feathers.

Soft Parts: Bill black; iris dark brown; feet brownish.

Measurements: Wing 101; tail 42; bill 4; tarsus 8.

Range: Babuyan, Calayan, Camiguin North, and northern Luzon. (Endemic.)

Collocalia esculenta marginata Salvadori, 1882

1882   *Collocalia marginata* Salvadori, (March) Atti. R. Accad. Sci. Torino, **17**:448, (Cebu)

1882   *Collocalia cebuensis* Kutter, (April) Journ. f. Orn., **30**:171, (Cebu)

Description: Differs from *isonota* by being slightly smaller; feathers of rump have white margins. Wing 97; tail 42.

Range: Central Luzon, south to Bohol and Palawan. (Endemic.)

Collocalia esculenta bagobo Hachisuka, 1930

1930   *Collocalia esculenta bagobo* Hachisuka, Orn. Soc. Japan, suppl. 14:173, (Apo Lake, Mindanao)

Description: Differs from *isonota* by having somewhat darker throat and less white on abdomen.

Range: Mindanao and Sulu Archipelago. (Endemic.)

NORTHERN SPINE-TAILED SWIFT   PLATE 42

Chaetura caudacuta caudacuta (Latham, 1801)

1801   *Hirundo caudacuta* Latham, Ind. Orn., suppl., p. lvii, (New South Wales)

Description: Top of head and upperparts light brown; tail and wings black with a green gloss; chin and throat white; breast and belly brown; under tail-coverts white tipped with brown.

Soft Parts: Bill black; iris black; feet black.

Measurements: Wing 215; tail 60; bill 10; tarsus 16.

Range: During migration it may be found most anywhere in the Philippines because it breeds in Siberia and winters south to Australia; however, as yet it is unrecorded from the Philippines.

MALAYSIAN SPINE-TAILED SWIFT   PLATE 42

Chaetura gigantea gigantea (Temminck, 1825)

1825   *Cypselus giganteus* Temminck, Pl. Col., livr. 61, pl. 364, (Bantam, Java)

Description: Head and upperparts black with a blue gloss; sides of forehead, flanks, and under tail-coverts white; rest of underparts gray-brown.

Soft Parts: Bill black; iris brown; feet reddish brown.

Measurements: Wing 200; tail 68; bill 9; tarsus 16.

Range: Calamianes, Culion, and Palawan.

Chaetura gigantea dubia McGregor, 1905

1905   *Chaetura dubius* McGregor, Bur. Govt. Lab., Manila, 34:15, (Mindoro)

Description: Differs from *C. g. gigantea* by having gloss more violet, less blue; wing 222.

Range: Luzon and Mindoro. (Endemic.)

Chaetura gigantea manobo Salomonsen, 1953

1953   *Chaetura gigantea manobo* Salomonsen, Vid. Medd. Dansk nat. Foren., **115**:239,
        (Malaybalay, Mindanao)

Description: Differs from *dubia* by having a shorter wing (215).

Range: Basilan, Mindanao, and Negros. (Endemic.)

PHILIPPINE SPINE-TAILED SWIFT   PLATE 42

Chaetura picina Tweeddale, 1878

1878   *Chaetura picina* Tweeddale, Proc. Zool. Soc. London, p. 944, (Zamboanga, Min-
        danao)

Description: Entire bird black with a blue gloss, except for throat and under wing-coverts, which are white.
Soft Parts: Bill black; iris dark brown; feet dark gray.
Measurements: Wing 161; tail 32; bill 6; tarsus 9.
Range: Cebu, Leyte, Mindanao, and Negros. (Endemic.)

WHITE-RUMPED SWIFT   PLATE 42

Apus pacificus pacificus (Latham, 1801)

1801   *Hirundo pacificus* Latham, Ind. Orn., suppl., p. lviii, (New South Wales)
Description: Head, wings, back, and tail dark brown; rump white; throat white; breast and belly brown.
Soft Parts: Bill black; iris brown; feet dark brown.
Measurements: Wing 178–182; tail 77; bill 7–8; tarsus 14.
Range: Found throughout the Philippines on migration from eastern Siberia to Australia.

HOUSE SWIFT   PLATE 42

Apus affinis subfurcatus (Blyth, 1849)

1849   *Cypselus subfurcatus* Blyth, Journ. As. Soc. Bengal, **18**:807, (Penang)
Description: Upperparts black; rump white; chin and throat light gray; breast and belly white.
Soft Parts: Bill black; iris dark brown; feet black.
Measurements: Wing 143; tail 51; bill 7; tarsus 10.
Range: Camiguin North, Luzon, and Mindoro.

PALM SWIFT   PLATE 42

Cypsiurus parvus pallidior (McGregor, 1905)

1905   *Tachornis pallidior* McGregor, Bur. Govt. Lab., Manila, 25:27, (Anao, Luzon)
Description: Head and back almost black; wings and tail dark brown; rump and tail-coverts light brown; throat gray; breast and belly lighter gray, some feathers showing white margins.
Soft Parts: Bill black; iris brown; feet blackish.
Measurements: Wing 119; tail 62; bill 5; tarsus 7.
Range: Bohol, Cebu, Leyte, Luzon, Mindanao, Negros, Polillo, and Ticao. (Endemic.)

Family HEMIPROCNIDAE

TREE SWIFTS

LESSER TREE SWIFT

PLATE 42

Hemiprocne comata major (Hartert, 1895)

1895 *Macropteryx comata major* Hartert, Nov. Zool., **2**:473, (Luzon)

1930 *Hemiprocne comata nakamurai* Hachisuka, Orn. Soc. Japan, suppl. 14:172, (Samal Island, off Mindanao)

1939 *Hemiprocne comata barbarae* Peters, Bull. Mus. Comp. Zool., **86**:95, (Bayog, Mindoro)

Description: Head deep blue; a white stripe above and below eye; ear-coverts chestnut on male only; back and rump bronze; wings and tail deep blue with a green gloss; outer half of tertials white; chin white followed by a deep blue band on throat; rest of underparts bronze, except for latter half of belly, which is white.

Soft Parts: Bill black; iris dark brown; feet black.

Measurements: Wing 132; tail 80; bill 5; tarsus 6.

Range: Luzon, south through the Sulu Archipelago; not found on Palawan. (Endemic.)

Family TROGONIDAE

TROGONS

PHILIPPINE TROGON

PLATE 43

Harpactes ardens ardens (Temminck, 1826)

1826 *Trogon ardens* Temminck, Pl. Col., livr. 68, pl. 404, (Mindanao)

1848 *Harpactes rodiosternus* Peale, U. S. Expl. Exped., **8**:166, (Zamboanga, Mindanao)

Description: Male—crown black, suffused with maroon; neck and mantle orange-brown, becoming lighter on rump; central tail feathers rufous with black tips, outer feathers mostly white, rest black; wing-coverts black with fine white bars; primaries all black; throat black; breast pink; belly scarlet. Female—upperparts like those of male but duller; wing with tan stripes, not white; breast and belly orange-brown.

Soft Parts: Bill green, tip yellow; iris dark brown; feet olive.

Measurements: Wing 145; tail 181; bill 25; tarsus 16.

Range: Basilan and Mindanao. (Endemic.)

Harpactes ardens linae Rand and Rabor, 1959

1959 *Harpactes ardens linae* Rand and Rabor, Fieldiana: Zoology, **39**:276, (Sandayong, Bohol)

189

Description: Differs from *H. a. ardens* by having somewhat more black on the head; upperparts also slightly duller and black throat is wider.

Range: Bohol, Leyte, and Samar. (Endemic.)

Harpactes ardens luzoniensis Rand and Rabor, 1952

1952 *Harpactes ardens luzoniensis* Rand and Rabor, Nat. His. Misc., 100:2, (Dinampan, Luzon)

Description: Differs from *H. a. ardens* by having a smaller bill (22); upperparts darker and duller brown. Males have anterior half of crown black, without maroon wash.

Range: Central and southern Luzon and Marinduque. (Endemic.)

Harpactes ardens minor Manuel, 1957

1957 *Harpactes ardens minor* Manuel, Phil. Journ. Sci., 86:3, (Anibawan, Polillo)

Description: Differs from *luzoniensis* by having the reds much darker; also smaller (wing 133).

Range: Polillo. (Endemic.)

Harpactes ardens herberti Parkes, 1970

1970 *Harpactes ardens herberti* Parkes, Nat. Hist. Bull. Siam Soc., 23:351, (Mt. Palanan, Isabela Province, Luzon)

Description: Male—differs from *luzoniensis* by having the entire crown washed with maroon; underparts duller and less rufescent. Female—differs by having head browner.

Range: Northeast Luzon. (Endemic.)

Family ALCEDINIDAE   KINGFISHERS

RIVER KINGFISHER   **PLATE 44**

Alcedo atthis bengalensis Gmelin, 1788

1788 *Alcedo bengalensis* Gmelin, Syst. Nat., 1:450, (Bengal)

Description: Head blue-green, feathers tipped with light blue; lores and a stripe to ear-coverts ferruginous; greenish blue band with light blue spots runs from lower mandible to a white patch on the side of the neck; back, rump, and tail-coverts light blue; wings and tail blue-green; throat white; rest of underparts rufous.

Soft Parts: Bill, upper mandible black, lower mandible pinkish; iris dark brown; feet red.

Measurements: Wing 73; tail 33; bill 39; tarsus 9.

Range: Found throughout the Philippines; probably a migrant.

190

MALAYSIAN KINGFISHER
PLATE 44

Alcedo meninting amadoni duPont, 1971

1971   *Alcedo meninting amadoni* duPont, Nemouria, 3:2, (Iwahig, Palawan)

Description: Head mostly black with azure-blue on sides and bars on crown; lores rufous; white patch on the sides of the neck; hind neck azure-blue; back, rump, and tail-coverts very bright blue; wings blue; tail black; throat white; rest of underparts rufous.
Soft Parts: Bill blackish; iris brown; feet red.
Measurements: Wing 65; tail 30; bill 42; tarsus 9.
Range: Palawan. (Endemic.)

Alcedo meninting verreauxii De La Berge, 1851

1851   *Alcedo Verreauxii* De La Berge, Rev. et Mag. Zool., 3:305, (Borneo)

Description: Differs from *amadoni* by having the blue of the upperparts darker and less azure-blue.
Range: Borneo and Sulu Archipelago.

DWARF RIVER KINGFISHER
PLATE 44

Ceyx cyanopectus cyanopectus Lafresnaye, 1840

1840   *Ceyx cyano-pectus* Lafresnaye, Rev. et Mag. Zool., 4:33, (Luzon)
1892   *Ceyx steerii* Sharpe, Cat. Bds. Brit. Mus., 17:187, (Mindoro)

Description: Male—head has mostly deep blue feathers with light blue tips; lores rufous; a rufous spot on sides of neck; back, rump, and tail-coverts bright blue; tail black; wings dark bluish green with light blue spot on the scapulars; chin white; underparts chestnut with two rich blue bands on chest. Female—similar to male but chestnut underparts are darker and only one blue band on chest.
Soft Parts: Bill, upper mandible black, lower mandible red; iris dark brown; feet red.
Measurements: Wing 61; tail 23; bill 36; tarsus 10.
Range: Luzon, Marinduque, Masbate, Mindoro, Polillo, Sibuyan, and Ticao. (Endemic.)

Ceyx cyanopectus nigrirostris Bourns and Worcester, 1894

1894   *Ceyx nigrirostris* Bourns and Worcester, Occ. Papers Minn. Acad. Sci., 1:13, (Panay, Cebu, and Negros)

Description: Differs from *C. c. cyanopectus* by having upperparts lighter blue; breast has only one blue band, which is darker (navy blue) in the male and incomplete in the female; bill is all black.
Range: Cebu, Negros, and Panay. (Endemic.)

PLATE 42

A   HOUSE SWIFT
    (Apus affinis)—page 188

B   NORTHERN SPINE-TAILED SWIFT
    (Chaetura caudacuta)—page 187

C   WHITE-RUMPED SWIFT
    (Apus pacificus)—page 188

D   LESSER TREE SWIFT
    (Hemiprocne comata)—page 189

E   MALAYSIAN SPINE-TAILED SWIFT
    (Chaetura gigantea)—page 187

F   PHILIPPINE SPINE-TAILED SWIFT
    (Chaetura picina)—page 187

G   PALM SWIFT
    (Cypsiurus parvus)—page 188

A

B

C

D

E

F

G

PLATE 42

PLATE 43

PHILIPPINE TROGON
(Harpactes ardens)—page 189

PLATE 43

PLATE 44

A   MALAY FOREST KINGFISHER
    (Ceyx erithacus rufidorsum)—page 198

B   SILVERY KINGFISHER
    (Ceyx argentatus)—page 198

C   PHILIPPINE FOREST KINGFISHER
    (Ceyx melanurus)—page 199

D   DWARF RIVER KINGFISHER
    (Ceyx cyanopectus)—page 191

E   VARIABLE FOREST KINGFISHER
    (Ceyx lepidus)—page 198

F   MINDORO FOREST KINGFISHER
    (Ceyx erithacus motleyi)—page 199

G   MALAYSIAN KINGFISHER
    (Alcedo meninting)—page 191

H   RIVER KINGFISHER
    (Alcedo atthis)—page 190

PLATE 44

SILVERY KINGFISHER
PLATE 44

Ceyx argentatus argentatus Tweeddale, 1877

1877 *Ceyx argentatus* Tweeddale, Ann. Mag. Nat. His., **20**:533, (Dinagat)

Description: Head black with small white spots on sides of crown from eyes to nape; a white patch on the sides of the neck; back, rump, and tail-coverts white; tail black; wings black; secondary coverts have white tips; throat and belly white; breast, flanks, and under tail-coverts black with bluish cast.

Soft Parts: Bill black; iris black; feet red.

Measurements: Wing 61; tail 25; bill 39; tarsus 10.

Range: Basilan, Cebu, Dinagat, Mindanao, Negros, and Panay. (Endemic.)

Ceyx argentatus flumenicola Steere, 1890

1890 *Ceyx flumenicola* Steere, List Bds. Mamms. Steere Expd., p. 10, (Samar and Leyte)

Description: Differs from *C. a. argentatus* by having underparts darker and with a purplish cast.

Range: Bohol, Leyte, and Samar. (Endemic.)

VARIABLE FOREST KINGFISHER
PLATE 44

Ceyx lepidus margarethae Blasius, 1890

1890 *Ceyx margarethae* Blasius, Braunschweig. Anz., **87**:877, (Mindanao)

1890 *Ceyx suluensis* Blasius, Journ. f. Orn., **38**:141, (Jolo)

1890 *Ceyx Bournsii* Steere, List Bds. Mamms. Steere Expd., p. 10, (Basilan)

1890 *Ceyx Malamaui* Steere, List Bds. Mamms. Steere Expd., p. 11, (Basilan)

1905 *Ceyx goodfellowi* Ogilvie-Grant, Bull. Brit. Orn. Cl., **16**:17, (Piso, Mindanao)

1941 *Ceyx goodfellowi virgicapitus* Manuel, Phil. Journ. Sci., **74**:367, (Batobato, Tawi Tawi)

Description: Head, neck, back, rump, wings, and tail deep to light blue (the variation is quite extreme); lores rufous; a white patch on side of neck; chin, throat, and middle of belly white; rest of underparts rufous.

Soft Parts: Bill red; iris dark brown; feet red.

Measurements: Wing 64; tail 24; bill 38; tarsus 8.

Range: Banton, Basilan, Bongao, Cebu, Jolo, Mindanao, Negros, Romblon, Sibuyan, Siquijor, Tablas, and Tawi Tawi. (Endemic.)

MALAY FOREST KINGFISHER
PLATE 44

Ceyx erithacus rufidorsum Strickland, 1847

1847 *Ceyx rufidorsa* Strickland, Proc. Zool. Soc. London, p. 99, (Malacca)

1892   *Ceyx euerythra* Sharpe, Cat. Bds. Brit. Mus., **17**:179, (Malacca, Sumatra, Labuan, northwest Borneo, Palawan, Mindoro)

Description: Upperparts red washed with lilac; head and rump slightly darker; wing primaries and secondaries black; tail reddish; lores deep yellow; chin and throat white washed with yellow; rest of underparts deep yellow.

Soft Parts: Bill red; iris dark brown; feet red.

Measurements: Wing 59; tail 25; bill 39; tarsus 9.

Range: Balabac, Bongao, Calamianes, Palawan, Panay, and Tawi Tawi; a hybrid with *motleyi*.

Ceyx erithacus motleyi Chasen and Kloss, 1929—PLATE 44

1929   *Ceyx erithacus motleyi* Chasen and Kloss, Journ. f. Orn., **77**:106, (Bettotan, North Borneo)

1939   *Ceyx erithacus vargasi* Manuel, Phil. Journ. Sci., **69**:383, (Puerto Galera, Mindoro)

Description: Head red with two black spots near bill; bluish patch near ear-coverts; back, rump, and tail reddish purple; wings black with a bluish gloss; chin white; rest of underparts yellow.

Soft Parts: Bill red; iris brown; feet red.

Measurements: Wing 55; tail 22; bill 34; tarsus 8.

Range: Mindoro; a hybrid with *rufidorsum*.

PHILIPPINE   FOREST   KINGFISHER   PLATE 44

Ceyx melanurus melanurus (Kaup, 1848)

1848   *Alcedo melanura* Kaup, Verh. naturhist. Ver. Grossherz. Hessen, p. 74, (Luzon)

Description: Head lilac-rufous with brighter rufous spots; lores deep yellow; band of white on sides of neck with a blue spot above; back, rump, and tail lilac-rufous; black band on each side of the mantle; wings black with faint blue spots; throat and belly white; rest of underparts lilac-rufous.

Soft Parts: Bill red; iris dark brown; feet red.

Measurements: Wing 53; tail 18; bill 30; tarsus 8.

Range: Luzon and Polillo. (Endemic.)

Ceyx melanurus samarensis Steere, 1890

1890   *Ceyx Samarensis* Steere, List Bds. Mamms. Steere Expd., p. 10, (Samar and Leyte)

Description: Differs from *C. m. melanurus* by being darker, especially on the back; less white on belly; also much larger (wing 66; tail 30; bill 30; tarsus 11).

Range: Leyte and Samar. (Endemic.)

Ceyx melanurus platenae Blasius, 1890

1890   *Ceyx Platenae* Blasius, Braunschweig. Anz., **87**:877, (Davao, Mindanao)

1890   *Ceyx Mindanensis* Steere, List Bds. Mamms. Steere Expd., p. 10, (Ayala, Mindanao)

1890   *Ceyx Basilanica* Steere, List Bds. Mamms. Steere Expd., p. 10, (Basilan)

Description: Differs from *C. m. melanurus* by being much larger and from *samarensis* by being not so dark and having more rufous on back and wings. Also lacks the blue spot on the neck found in the other two forms. Wing 58; tail 21; bill 36; tarsus 9.

Range: Basilan and Mindanao. (Endemic.)

STORK-BILLED   KINGFISHER   PLATE 45

Pelargopsis capensis gouldi Sharpe, 1870

1870   *Pelargopsis gouldi* Sharpe, Proc. Zool. Soc. London, p. 62, (Manila, Luzon)

Description: Head, neck, and underparts rich ochraceous; back and rump light blue; wings and tail bluish green.

Soft Parts: Bill red; iris dark brown; feet red.

Measurements: Wing 152; tail 89; bill 81; tarsus 13.

Range: Balabac, Calamianes, Lubang, Luzon (north and central), Mindoro, Palawan, and Polillo. (Endemic.)

Pelargopsis capensis smithi (Mearns, 1909)

1909   *Ramphalcyon capensis smithi* Mearns, Proc. U. S. Nat. Mus., **36**:466, (Dumurug Point, Masbate)

Description: Differs from *gouldi* by having head and underparts more buffy.

Range: Basilan, Bohol, Leyte, southeast Luzon, Masbate, Mindanao, Negros, Panay, and Samar. (Endemic.)

Pelargopsis capensis gigantea Walden, 1874

1874   *Pelargopsis gigantea* Walden, Ann. Mag. Nat. His., **13**:123, (Salok, Sulu Islands)

Description: Differs from *smithi* by having head and underparts very pale buff.

Range: Sulu Archipelago. (Endemic.)

WHITE-COLLARED   KINGFISHER   PLATE 45

Halcyon chloris collaris (Scopoli, 1786)

1786   *Alcedo collaris* Scopoli, Del. Flor. et Faun. Insubr., p. 67, (Manila, Luzon)

Description: Crown greenish blue with a black circle around the bottom extending from one corner of the mouth around to the other; spot of white behind each nostril; back and wings greenish blue; rump light blue; tail dark blue; throat, collar, and underparts white.

Soft Parts: Bill black; iris dark brown; feet black.

Measurements: Wing 105; tail 70; bill 50; tarsus 13.

Range: Found throughout the Philippines.

RUDDY KINGFISHER   PLATE 45

Halcyon coromanda major (Temminck and Schlegel, 1848)

1848   *Alcedo (Halcyon) coromanda minor* Temminck and Schlegel, in Siebold's Faun. Jap., Aves, p. 75, (Japan)

1915   *Entomothera coromanda ochrothorectis* Oberholser, Proc. U. S. Nat. Mus., **48**: 652, (Palanoc, Masbate)

Description: Upperparts rufous lightly washed with violet; stripe on lower back and rump bright blue-violet; tail heavily washed with violet; chin white; rest of underparts buffy, darker on breast.

Soft Parts: Bill red; iris brown; feet red.

Measurements: Wing 118; tail 73; bill 60; tarsus 16.

Range: Luzon, south to Mindanao; a visitor from Japan.

Halcyon coromanda bangsi (Oberholser, 1915)

1915   *Entomothera coromanda bangsi* Oberholser, Proc. U. S. Nat. Mus., **48**:652, (Yaeyama, Ishigaki Island, Riu Kiu Islands)

Description: Differs from *major* by having the upperparts heavily washed with violet, the rump light whitish lilac, and the underparts darker.

Range: Luzon, south to Mindanao; a visitor from the Riu Kiu Islands.

Halcyon coromanda minor (Temminck and Schlegel, 1848)

1848   *Alcedo (Halcyon) coromanda minor* Temminck and Schlegel, in Siebold's Faun. Jap., Aves, p. 76, (Borneo and Sumatra)

Description: Differs from *major* by being much darker.

Range: Palawan and Tawi Tawi.

WHITE-THROATED KINGFISHER   PLATE 45

Halcyon smyrnensis gularis (Kuhl, 1820)

1820   *Alcedo gularis* Kuhl, in T. von Swinderen's Buffoni et Daubentoni Fig. Av. Col. Nom. Syst., p. 4, (Philippines)

Description: Head and neck dark chestnut; back, wings, and tail blue; upper wing-coverts black; rump light blue; throat white; underparts dark chestnut; underside of tail black.

Soft Parts: Bill red; iris dark brown; feet red.

Measurements: Wing 124; tail 80; bill 62; tarsus 15.

Range: Found throughout the Philippines.

BLACK-CAPPED KINGFISHER   PLATE 45

Halcyon pileata (Boddaert, 1783)

1783 *Alcedo pileata* Boddaert, Table Pl., enlum., p. 41, (China)

1934 *Halcyon pileata palawanensis* Hachisuka, Bds. Phil. Ids., p. 142, (Palawan)

Description: Crown black; cheek white; neck with a white collar; wings, back, and tail purplish blue; rump lighter blue; throat and breast white; flanks and belly dark rufous.

Soft Parts: Bill dark red; iris dark brown; feet dark red.

Measurements: Wing 132; tail 78; bill 56; tarsus 14.

Range: Balabac, Basilan, Palawan, and Sulu Islands; a migrant from China and Korea.

WINCHELL'S KINGFISHER   PLATE 45

Halcyon winchelli winchelli Sharpe, 1877

1877 *Halcyon Winchelli* Sharpe, Trans. Linn. Soc. London, 1:318, (Isabella, Basilan)

Description: Male—crown dark blue with a light blue margin; lores and collar rufous; black patch on the sides of the head; back, wings, and tail dark blue; lower back and rump light blue; underparts white. Female—underparts light rufous. Immature—crown and back dull black.

Soft Parts: Bill black; iris dark brown; feet dirty green.

Measurements: Wing 104; tail 74; bill 44; tarsus 14.

Range: Basilan. (Endemic.)

Halcyon winchelli mindanensis Parkes, 1966

1966 *Halcyon winchelli mindanensis* Parkes, Bull. Brit. Orn. Cl., **86**:83, (Matam, Mindanao)

Description: Differs from *H. w. winchelli* by having upperparts brighter blue, sides of head not so black, and wing and tail shorter. Immature—crown and back black with blue wash. Wing 98; tail 72; bill 42.

Range: Mindanao. (Endemic.)

Halcyon winchelli alfredi Oustalet, 1890

1890   *Halcyon alfredi* Oustalet, Le Naturaliste, p. 62, (Bongao)

Description: Differs from *mindanensis* as females are paler buff underneath; tail a bit longer (79). Immature—only crown has blue wash.

Range: Sulu Archipelago. (Endemic.)

Halcyon winchelli nigrorum Hachisuka, 1934

1934   *Halcyon winchelli nigrorum* Hachisuka, Bds. Phil. Ids., p. 142, (Canloan Volcano, Negros)

Description: Differs from *H. w. winchelli* by having more black and less blue on head, especially on crown; also, a black patch at the bend of the wing of males; bill shorter (38).

Range: Bohol, Cebu, Leyte, Negros, Samar, and Siquijor. (Endemic.)

Halcyon winchelli nesydrionetes Parkes, 1966

1966   *Halcyon winchelli nesydrionetes* Parkes, Bull. Brit. Orn. Cl., **86**:84, (Badajoz, Tablas)

Description: Differs from *alfredi* as the females have much paler underparts but a bright orange-buff breast band. Upperparts of both sexes slightly darker.

Range: Romblon, Sibuyan, and Tablas. (Endemic.)

SPOTTED   WOOD   KINGFISHER   PLATE 45

Halcyon lindsayi lindsayi (Vigors, 1831)

1831   *Dacelo Lindsayi* Vigors, Proc. Comm. Zool. Soc. London, p. 97, (Manila, Luzon)

Description: Male—crown green with a yellowish rufous streak extending back from the bill in the center and to each eye; band of blue extends from above the eye below the crown around to the other eye. This is followed by a black band that runs from the lores around under the blue band, then followed by a chestnut band that extends down the throat, except for the malar patch, which is blue; wings and mantle olive-brown with buff spots; tail olive-brown; breast and belly have white feathers with green margins. Female—similar to male but chestnut on head and throat is replaced by green.

Soft Parts: Bill black, lower mandible yellow underneath; iris dark brown; feet light green.

Measurements: Wing 108; tail 83; bill 47; tarsus 16.

Range: Luzon. (Endemic.)

PLATE 45

A   RUDDY KINGFISHER
    (*Halcyon coromanda*)—page 201

B   STORK-BILLED KINGFISHER
    (*Pelargopsis capensis*)—page 200

C   WHITE-COLLARED KINGFISHER
    (*Halcyon chloris*)—page 200

D   SPOTTED WOOD KINGFISHER
    (*Halcyon lindsayi*)—page 203

E   WHITE-THROATED KINGFISHER
    (*Halcyon smyrnensis*)—page 201

F   BLACK-CAPPED KINGFISHER
    (*Halcyon pileata*)—page 202

G   HOMBRON'S KINGFISHER
    (*Halcyon hombroni*)—page 206

H   WINCHELL'S KINGFISHER
    (*Halcyon winchelli*)—page 202

A

B

C

F

D

E

G

H

PLATE 45

Halcyon lindsayi moseleyi (Steere, 1890)

1890 *Actenoides Moseleyi* Steere, List Bds. Mamms. Steere Expd., p. 11, (Negros)

Description: Differs from *lindsayi* by having the head darker; breast and flank feathers outlined with black, not green.

Range: Negros. (Endemic.)

HOMBRON'S KINGFISHER   PLATE 45

Halcyon hombroni (Bonaparte, 1850)

1850 *Actenoides hombroni* Bonaparte, Consp. Av., 1:157, (Mindanao)

Description: Male—head and nape blue; lores black; ear-coverts chestnut; malar stripe blue; hind neck and upper back chestnut, feathers with black edges; wings blue-green with rufous spots; lower back and rump light blue; tail dark blue; throat white; underparts pale rufous, feathers with slight black tips. Female—similar to male but crown malar stripe and tail green.

Soft Parts: Bill red, upper mandible black on top; iris dark brown; feet dirty green.

Measurements: Wing 126; tail 105; bill 51; tarsus 19.

Range: Mindanao. (Endemic.)

Family MEROPIDAE   BEE-EATERS

BLUE-TAILED BEE-EATER   PLATE 46

Merops philippinus philippinus Linné, 1766

1766 *Merops philippinus* Linné, Syst. Nat., 1:183; see errata page [1364], (Philippines)

Description: Head, neck, mantle, and back green with brownish wash; rump and tail-coverts light blue; tail green washed with blue; wings brownish green above, rich chestnut below, with dark ends to feathers; lores and ear patch black with narrow blue stripe above and below; upper throat yellowish white; lower throat chestnut; rest of underparts greenish.

Soft Parts: Bill black; iris red; feet black.

Measurements: Wing 127; tail 91 (without central feathers); bill 33; tarsus 11.

Range: Found throughout the Philippines.

CHESTNUT-HEADED BEE-EATER   PLATE 46

Merops viridis americanus P. L. S. Müller, 1776

1776 *Merops americanus* P. L. S. Müller, Natursyst., suppl., 1776:95, (Philippines)

Description: Head, neck, and upper back bright chestnut; lores and ear patch black; lower back, rump, and tail-coverts light blue; wings green with some brown; tail blue; underparts light green.

Soft Parts: Bill black; iris red; feet black.

Measurements: Wing 115; tail 89 (without central feathers); bill 35; tarsus 11.

Range: Found throughout the Philippines. (Endemic.)

Family CORACIIDAE   ROLLERS

DOLLAR BIRD   PLATE 46

Eurystomus orientalis cyanocollis Vieillot, 1819

1819   *Eurystomus cyanocollis* Vieillot, Nouv. Dict. d'Hist. Nat., ed. 2, **29**:425, ("Les Indes" = near Chandernagor [near Calcutta]).

Description: Head and mantle dark brown; back and rump brownish green; wing-coverts light green; secondaries black; primaries black with a light blue patch toward the end of wing; tail black; throat black with blue streaks; breast dull green; belly light green.

Soft Parts: Bill red; iris brown; feet red.

Measurements: Wing 185; tail 98; bill 33; tarsus 17.

Range: Found throughout the Philippines.

Family UPUPIDAE   HOOPOES

HOOPOE   PLATE 46

Upupa epops (?) longirostris Jerdon, 1862

1862   *Upupa longirostris* Jerdon, Bds. India, **1**:393, (Burma)

Description: Head, crest, and neck pinkish brown; crest with black tips; mantle light brown; back and rump black and white barred; tail black with a white band in the middle; wings black with white bars; throat and breast pinkish brown; belly white with dark streaks.

Soft Parts: Bill dark brown; iris brown; feet dark brown.

Measurements: Wing 148; tail 100; bill 52; tarsus 19.

Range: One was seen on Palawan by Harrison in 1961. Normally found outside the Philippines from Burma and Indochina to Sumatra. Here attributed to this race as it is the closest race to Palawan.

PLATE 46

A   DOLLAR BIRD
    (Eurystomus orientalis)—page 207

B   CRIMSON-BREASTED BARBET
    (Megalaima haemacephala)—page 213

C   BLUE-TAILED BEE-EATER
    (Merops philippinus)—page 206

D   CHESTNUT-HEADED BEE-EATER
    (Merops viridis)—page 206

E   HOOPOE
    (Upupa epops)—page 207

208

PLATE 46

Family BUCEROTIDAE   HORNBILLS

TARICTIC HORNBILL   PLATE 47

Penelopides panini manilloe (Boddaert, 1783)

1783   *Buceros Manilloe* Boddaert, Table Pl., enlum., p. 54, (Manila, Luzon)

1903   *Penelopides talisi* Finsch, Notes Leyden Mus., **23**:190, (Cagayan Prov., Luzon)

Description: Male—head and neck dirty white; back, wings, and tail-coverts brown glossed with dull green; outer margins of primaries and secondaries buff; throat and ear-coverts black; lower neck, breast, belly, and under tail-coverts buffy white; tail, basal half brown followed by a white band, then black with green gloss. Female—head, neck, and underparts dark brown, blackest on throat; rest similar to male.

Soft Parts: Bill basically brown with four or five ochre ridges, surmounted by a low casque; young birds lack casque and ridges; iris crimson; feet black.

Measurements: Wing 225; tail 188; bill 96; tarsus 42.

Range: Luzon and Marinduque. (Endemic.)

Penelopides panini subnigra McGregor, 1910

1910   *Penelopides subnigra* McGregor, Phil. Journ. Sci., **5**:110, (Polillo)

Description: Differs from *manilloe* by having upperparts and tail black glossed with green, not brown; also larger.

Range: Polillo. (Endemic.)

Penelopides panini mindorensis Steere, 1890

1890   *Penelopides mindorensis* Steere, List Bds. Mamms. Steere Expd., p. 13, (no locality=Mindoro)

1891   *Penelopides schmackeri* Hartert, Kat. Vogelsamml. Mus. Senckenb., p. 139, (Mt. Halcon, Mindoro)

Description: Differs from *manilloe* by having back glossed with green, not brown, and much more white on tail. The head of the female is white as in males, not brown as in other subspecies. Females and some males have blackish foreheads.

Range: Mindoro. (Endemic.)

Penelopides panini panini (Boddaert, 1783)

1783   *Buceros Panini* Boddaert, Table Pl., enlum., p. 48, (Panay)

Description: Differs from *manilloe* by having upperparts with a stronger green gloss, less brown. Underparts are more rufous, not so pale buff. Much more white on tail.

Range: Guimaras, Masbate, Negros, and Panay. (Endemic.)

210

Penelopides panini ticaensis Hachisuka, 1930

1930   *Penelopides panini ticaensis* Hachisuka, Orn. Soc. Japan, suppl. 14:169, (Ticao)

Description: Differs from *P. p. panini* by being larger (wing 286; tail 270).
Range: Ticao. (Endemic.)

Penelopides panini affinis Tweeddale, 1877

1877   *Penelopides affinis* Tweeddale, Ann. Mag. Nat. His., **20**:534, (Butuan, Mindanao)

Description: Differs from *mindorensis* by having the green gloss on upperparts much darker and also having in the tail a basal black band, which is lacking in *mindorensis*. Female—similar to that of *manilloe*.
Range: Dinagat and Mindanao. (Endemic.)

Penelopides panini samarensis Steere, 1890

1890   *Penelopides Samarensis* Steere, List Bds. Mamms. Steere Expd., p. 13, (Samar and Leyte)

1930   *Penelopides panini boholensis* Hachisuka, Orn. Soc. Japan, suppl. 14:168, (Guindulman, Bohol)

1930   *Penelopides panini leytensis* Hachisuka, Orn. Soc. Japan, suppl. 14:169, (Leyte)

Description: Male—differs from *affinis* by having upper tail-coverts much paler. Female —inseparable from *affinis*.
Range: Bohol, Leyte, and Samar. (Endemic.)

Penelopides panini basilanica Steere, 1890

1890   *Penelopides Basilanica* Steere, List Bds. Mamms. Steere Expd., p. 13, (Basilan)

Description: Differs from *affinis* by having the basal half of the tail rufous; base of mandibles flesh color, not black.
Range: Basilan. (Endemic.)

WRITHED-BILLED HORNBILL   PLATE 47

Aceros leucocephalus waldeni (Sharpe, 1877)

1877   *Craniorrhinus* [sic] *waldeni* Sharpe, Journ. Linn. Soc. London, Zool., **13**:156, (mountains west of Ilo Ilo, Panay)

Description: Male—head, neck, and upper chest chestnut; some specimens darker than others. Upperparts black glossed with green. Belly black. Tail is white with a terminal black band; basal third is black; rest is white with black tips on feathers, often stained with rufous. Female—similar to male but with a black head and neck.
Soft Parts: Bill red with dark grooves; iris red; feet black.
Measurements: Wing 330; tail 240; bill 122; tarsus 50.
Range: Guimaras, Negros, and Panay. (Endemic.)

Aceros leucocephalus leucocephalus (Vieillot, 1816)

1816 *Buceros leucocephalus* Vieillot, Nouv. Dict. d'Hist. Nat., 4:592, (Mindanao)

Description: Differs from *waldeni* by having head and neck buff, not chestnut; however, crest is chestnut; tail all white with terminal black band.

Range: Camiguin South and Mindanao. (Endemic.)

SULU   HORNBILL   PLATE 47

Anthracoceros montani (Oustalet, 1880)

1880 *Buceros Montani* Oustalet, Bull. Assoc. Sci. France, **2**:205, (Sulu Archipelago)

Description: All black; upperparts glossed with dark green; tail white.

Soft Parts: Bill black; iris white; feet black.

Measurements: Wing 293; tail 243; bill 130; tarsus 52.

Range: Jolo, Sulu, and Tawi Tawi. (Endemic.)

PALAWAN   HORNBILL   PLATE 47

Anthracoceros marchei Oustalet, 1885

1885 *Anthracoceros marchei* Oustalet, Le Naturaliste, p. 108, (Palawan, Busuanga, Balabac)

1885 *Anthracoceros lemprieri* Sharpe, Proc. Zool. Soc. London, p. 446, (Palawan)

Description: All black; upperparts glossed with green, except for the tail, which is white with cream-colored shafts.

Soft Parts: Bill white; iris brown; feet black; naked skin of face white with black spot on base of bill.

Measurements: Wing 290; tail 240; bill 126; tarsus 52.

Range: Balabac, Busuanga, Calamianes, and Palawan. (Endemic.)

RUFOUS   HORNBILL   PLATE 47

Buceros hydrocorax hydrocorax Linné, 1766

1766 *Buceros Hydrocorax* Linné, Syst. Nat., **1**:153, ("Molucces," error = Luzon)

Description: Head and neck chestnut; black trim around bill; back and wings brown; tail white but often stained with buffy brown; breast black; belly chestnut.

Soft Parts: Bill red; iris red; feet red-brown.

Measurements: Wing 410; tail 350; bill 175; tarsus 60.

Range: Luzon and Marinduque. (Endemic.)

Buceros hydrocorax semigaleatus Tweeddale, 1878

1878 *Buceros semigaleatus* Tweeddale, Proc. Zool. Soc. London, p. 279, (Amparo, Leyte)

Description: Differs by having casque reduced in front so that it forms a continuous line with the upper mandible; the tip of upper mandible is whitish.

Range: Bohol, Leyte, Panaon, and Samar. (Endemic.)

Buceros hydrocorax mindanensis Tweeddale, 1877

1877 *Buceros mindanensis* Tweeddale, Proc. Zool. Soc. London, p. 543, (Pasananca, Mindanao)

1934 *Hydrocorax hydrocorax basilanica* Hachisuka, Bds. Phil. Ids., p. 154, (Basilan)

Description: Differs from *hydrocorax* by having casque much narrower; terminal half is white.

Range: Basilan and Mindanao. (Endemic.)

Family CAPITONIDAE   BARBETS

CRIMSON-BREASTED BARBET   PLATE 46

Megalaima haemacephala haemacephala (P. L. S. Müller, 1776)

1776 *Bucco haemacephalus* P. L. S. Müller, Natursyst., suppl., 1776:88, (Philippines = Lamao, Bataan, Luzon)

1788 *Bucco philippinensis* Gmelin, Syst. Nat., **1**:407, (Philippine Islands)

Description: Crown and forehead bright red; latter half of crown black; hind neck blue-green; a yellow patch above and below eye; upperparts and tail olive-green; throat light yellow followed by a red band and a deeper gold band on upper chest; rest of underparts buffy with greenish stripes.

Soft Parts: Bill black; iris brown; feet red.

Measurements: Wing 85; tail 41; bill 21; tarsus 9.

Range: Luzon and Mindoro. (Endemic.)

Megalaima haemacephala celestinoi Gilliard, 1949

1949 *Megalaema haemacephala celestinoi* Gilliard, Auk, **66**:277, (Bonga, Samar)

Description: Differs from *M. h. haemacephala* by having primaries, secondaries, and lesser wing-coverts edged with blue; throat brighter yellow; dorsum darker, bluer green; blue area of nape darker and extends farther posteriorly; lower flanks and under tail-coverts more yellow.

Range: Leyte and Samar. (Endemic.)

PLATE 47

A RUFOUS HORNBILL
   (Buceros hydrocorax)—page 212

B WRITHED-BILLED HORNBILL
   (Aceros leucocephalus)—page 211

C TARICTIC HORNBILL
   (Penelopides panini), male—page 210

D SULU HORNBILL
   (Anthracoceros montani)—page 212

E PALAWAN HORNBILL
   (Anthracoceros marchei)—page 212

PLATE 47

Megalaima haemacephala mindanensis Rand, 1948

1948 *Megalaema haemacephala mindanensis* Rand, Fieldiana: Zoology, **31**:202, (Mt. Apo, Mindanao)

Description: Differs from *M. h. haemacephala* by having throat deeper yellow.
Range: Mindanao. (Endemic.)

Megalaima haemacephala intermedia (Shelley, 1891)

1891 *Xantholaema intermedia* Shelley, Cat. Bds. Brit. Mus., **19**:97, (Negros and Cebu)

Description: Differs from *M. h. haemacephala* by having throat, eyebrow, and ear-coverts red.
Range: Cebu, Guimaras, Masbate, Negros, Romblon, and Tablas. (Endemic.)

Family PICIDAE   WOODPECKERS

THREE-TOED WOODPECKER   PLATE 48

Dinopium javanense everetti (Tweeddale, 1878)

1878 *Tiga everetti* Tweeddale, Proc. Zool. Soc. London, p. 612, (Puerto Princesa, Palawan)

Description: Male—forehead, crown, crest, lower back, and rump bright red; back golden with red flecks; tail dark brown; wing-coverts and secondaries deep yellow; primaries dark brown with white spots; a black line extends down the neck from the eye and another from the corner of the bill down the neck; lores, between black stripes, and throat buffy; upper chest reddish buff; rest of underparts buffy with dark brown spots and bars. Female—similar to male except having black instead of red on head.
Soft Parts: Bill black; iris brown; feet greenish brown.
Measurements: Wing 142; tail 84; bill 29; tarsus 22.
Range: Balabac, Busuanga, Calamianes, Culion, and Palawan. (Endemic.)

GREAT SLATY WOODPECKER   PLATE 48

Mulleripicus pulverulentus pulverulentus (Temminck, 1826)

1826 *Picus pulverulentus* Temminck, Pl. Col., livr. 66, pl. 389, (Java and Sumatra)

Description: Male—entire bird dark slate except for a red patch below the eyes and a yellow throat that often tends to be pinkish. The dark slate feathers of the head and neck have white tips. Female—similar to male but lacks the red patch below the eyes.
Soft Parts: Bill, upper mandible black with gray base, lower mandible gray; iris dark brown; feet black.

216

Measurements: Wing 235; tail 172; bill 65; tarsus 36.

Range: Balabac and Palawan.

SOOTY WOODPECKER   PLATE 48

Mulleripicus funebris funebris (Valenciennes, 1826)

1826   *Picus funebris* Valenciennes, Dict. Sci. Nat., **40**:179, (Philippines)

1949   *Mulleripicus funebris mayri* Gilliard, Auk, **66**:279, (Cape Engano, Luzon)

Description: Male—forehead, cheeks, and a patch around the eye red; back, wings, and tail glossy black; underparts black with some brown; small white spots on throat and neck. Female—similar to the male but lacks the red on the head.

Soft Parts: Bill white; iris yellow; feet black.

Measurements: Wing 160; tail 140; bill 37; tarsus 28.

Range: Catanduanes, Luzon, and Marinduque. (Endemic.)

Mulleripicus funebris parkesi Manuel, 1957

1957   *Mulleripicus funebris parkesi* Manuel, Phil. Journ. Sci., **86**:4, (Polillo)

Description: Differs from *funebris* by having the red forehead darker and covering a narrower area on the head.

Range: Polillo. (Endemic.)

Mulleripicus funebris fuliginosus Tweeddale, 1877

1877   *Mulleripicus fuliginosus* Tweeddale, Ann. Mag. Nat. His., **20**:534, (Surigao, Mindanao)

Description: Male—similar to *M. f. funebris* but dark gray, not black; lacks the red except for the malar region; white spots on neck are larger. Female—lacks red on the head; otherwise similar to the male.

Range: Leyte, Mindanao, and Samar. (Endemic.)

WHITE-BELLIED BLACK WOODPECKER   PLATE 48

Dryocopus javensis confusus (Stresemann, 1913)

1913   *Thriponax javensis confusus* Stresemann, Nov. Zool., **20**:318, (Mt. Arayat, Luzon)

Description: Male—forehead, crown, crest, and malar region bright scarlet; rest of bird black except for belly, which is buffy white. Female—same as male but having only red crest; rest of head is black.

Soft Parts: Bill, upper mandible black, lower mandible white; iris yellow; feet gray.

Measurements: Wing 205; tail 165; bill 50; tarsus 32.

Range: Central and southern Luzon. (Endemic.)

217

Dryocopus javensis estholterus Parkes, 1971

1971 *Dryocopus javensis estholterus* Parkes, Nemouria, 4:17, (Haight's Place, Benguet, Mt. Prov., Luzon)

Description: Differs from *confusus* by having white marks of throat and side of head reduced; interramal area (streaked with white in *confusus*) without white streaks; bill averages more slender.

Range: Northern Luzon. (Endemic.)

Dryocopus javensis mindorensis (Steere, 1890)

1890 *Thriponax Mindorensis* Steere, List Bds. Mamms. Steere Expd., p. 8, (Mindoro)

Description: Differs from *confusus* by having a white band on lower back; bill all black.

Range: Mindoro. (Endemic.)

Dryocopus javensis multilunatus (McGregor, 1907)

1907 *Thriponax multilunatus* McGregor, Phil. Journ. Sci., 2:285, (Isabella, Basilan)

Description: Differs from *confusus* by having throat feathers bordered with buff; outer primaries have a white spot at the tip.

Range: Basilan and Mindanao. (Endemic.)

Dryocopus javensis pectoralis (Tweeddale, 1878)

1878 *Thriponax pectoralis* Tweeddale, Proc. Zool. Soc. London, p. 340, (Leyte)

1960 *Dryocopus javensis samarensis* Parkes, Bull. Brit. Orn. Cl., 80:60, (Matuginao, Samar)

Description: Differs from *confusus* by having chin and throat white; ear-coverts and sides of neck with some white.

Range: Bohol, Calicoan, Leyte, Panaon, and Samar. (Endemic.)

Dryocopus javensis philippensis (Steere, 1890)

1890 *Thriponax philippensis* Steere, List Bds. Mamms. Steere Expd., p. 8, (Guimaras and Masbate)

Description: Differs from *mindorensis* by having white on outer primaries, wider malar red stripe, heavier bill, and paler lower mandible.

Range: Guimaras, Masbate, Negros, and Panay. (Endemic.)

Dryocopus javensis hargitti (Sharpe, 1884)

1884 *Thriponax hargitti* Sharpe, Ibis, p. 317, (Palawan)

Description: Differs from *philippensis* by having a larger patch of white on the lower back; male with less red on the face and sides of the face streaked with white.

Range: Palawan. (Endemic.)

218

Dryocopus javensis suluensis (W. Blasius, 1890)

1890 *Thriponax javensis* var. nov. *suluensis* W. Blasius, Journ. f. Orn., **38**:140, (Sulu Archipelago)

Description: Differs from *multilunatus* by being much smaller and lacking buffy margins to breast feathers; a concealed white patch on back.

Range: Sulu Archipelago. (Endemic.)

PYGMY WOODPECKER   PLATE 48

Dendrocopos maculatus validirostris (Blyth, 1849)

1849 *Picus validirostris* Blyth, Cat. Bds. Mus. As. Soc., p. 64, (no locality = Manila, Luzon)

1953 *Dendrocopus moluccensis igorotus* Salomonsen, Vid. Medd. Dansk nat. Foren., **115**:272, (Benguet, northern Luzon)

Description: Male—head blackish brown with a white stripe from eye to nape; a few red feathers on sides of crown; back barred with black and white; wings and tail deep brown; middle of throat white with black margins; rest of underparts buffy, the breast having black spots and the belly with streaks. Female—similar to male but lacks the red on the head.

Soft Parts: Bill black; iris brown; feet black.

Measurements: Wing 81; tail 43; bill 19; tarsus 14.

Range: Catanduanes, Lubang, Luzon, Marinduque, and Mindoro. (Endemic.)

Dendrocopos maculatus maculatus (Scopoli, 1786)

1786 *Picus maculatus* Scopoli, Del. Flor. et Faun. Insubr., p. 89, (Antigua, Panay)

Description: Differs from *validirostris* by having more red on sides of crown and joining at the nape; upperparts lighter brown; spots on chest not so dark.

Range: Cebu, Guimaras, Negros, and Panay. (Endemic.)

Dendrocopos maculatus leytensis (Steere, 1890)

1890 *Yungipicus Leytensis* Steere, List Bds. Mamms. Steere Expd., p. 9, (Leyte)

Description: Differs from *validirostris* by having the upperparts much darker; rump white; spots and stripes of the underparts much darker. In the male the red patches on the sides of the crown are much larger.

Range: Bohol, Leyte, and Samar. (Endemic.)

Dendrocopos maculatus fulvifasciatus (Hargitt, 1881)

1881 *Iyngipicus fulvifasciatus* Hargitt, Ibis, p. 598, (Basilan)

1890 *Yungipicus Basilanicus* Steere, List Bds. Mamms. Steere Expd., p. 9, (Basilan)

1934 *Dryobates moluccensis apo* Hachisuka, Bds. Phil. Ids., p. 235, (Mt. Apo, Mindanao)

Description: Differs from *leytensis* by having underparts darker buff with fewer spots and stripes.

Range: Basilan and Mindanao. (Endemic.)

Dendrocopos maculatus menagei (Bourns and Worcester, 1894)

1894 *Iyngipicus menagei* Bourns and Worcester, Occ. Papers Minn. Acad. Nat. Sci., 1:14, (Sibuyan)

Description: Differs from *maculatus* by having the upperparts darker and a pure white rump. In the male the red patches on the side of the crown are smaller.

Range: Sibuyan. (Endemic.)

Dendrocopos maculatus ramsayi (Hargitt, 1881)

1881 *Iyngipicus ramsayi* Hargitt, Ibis, p. 598, (Sulu Islands)

Description: Differs from other Philippine forms by being paler brown and breast a rich yellow, not buff; also spots and stripes much reduced.

Range: Bongao, Jolo, and Tawi Tawi. (Endemic.)

Dendrocopos maculatus siasiensis (Mearns, 1909)

1909 *Yungipicus siasiensis* Mearns, Proc. U. S. Nat. Mus., **36**:438, (Siasi Island)

Description: Differs from *ramsayi* by lacking the white margins of the primaries and secondaries and by having the golden yellow breast band reduced.

Range: Siasi. (Endemic.)

CRIMSON-BACKED WOODPECKER   PLATE 48

Chrysocolaptes lucidus haematribon (Wagler, 1827)

1827 *Picus haematribon* Wagler, Syst. Av., Picus, 95, (Luzon)

1949 *Chrysocolaptes lucidus ramosi* Gilliard, Auk, **66**:278, (Sorsogon, Luzon)

1952 *Chrysocolaptes lucidus montium* Salomonsen, Vid. Medd. Dansk nat. Foren., **114**: 350, (Abra Provence, North Luzon)

Description: Male—head, back, and wings dark red; tail brown; throat and breast black with white spots; underparts pale buff with brown bars. Female—similar to male but with black head spotted with white.

Soft Parts: Bill black; iris red; feet dark green.

Measurements: Wing 141; tail 90; bill 40; tarsus 27.

Range: Luzon and Marinduque. (Endemic.)

Chrysocolaptes lucidus grandis Hachisuka, 1930

1930 *Chrysocolaptes lucidus grandis* Hachisuka, Orn. Soc. Japan, suppl. 14:179, (Polillo)

Description: Differs from *haematribon* by having the white spots on the crown smaller; underparts browner and larger (wing 155; tail 102).

Range: Polillo. (Endemic.)

Chrysocolaptes lucidus rufopunctatus Hargitt, 1889

1889 *Chrysocolaptes rufopunctatus* Hargitt, Ibis, p. 231, (Panaon)

Description: Differs from *haematribon* by having upperparts brighter red and lower parts darker. In the female the head is more reddish.

Range: Bohol, Leyte, Panaon, and Samar. (Endemic.)

Chrysocolaptes lucidus lucidus (Scopoli, 1786)

1786 *Picus lucidus* Scopoli, Del. Flor. et Faun. Insubr., p. 89, (Zamboanga, Mindanao)

1877 *Chrysocolaptes maculiceps* Sharpe, Trans. Linn. Soc. London, 1:314, (Basilan)

Description: Differs from other forms by having mantle and wings golden yellow heavily washed with crimson; underparts olive-brown with yellowish spots.

Range: Basilan and Zamboanga Peninsula of Mindanao. (Endemic.)

Chrysocolaptes lucidus montanus Ogilvie-Grant, 1905

1905 *Chrysocolaptes montanus* Ogilvie-Grant, Bull. Brit. Orn. Cl., 16:16, (Mt. Apo, Mindanao)

Description: Differs from *C. l. lucidus* by lacking the crimson on the back and wings.

Range: Mindanao, except for the Zamboanga Peninsula. (Endemic.)

Chrysocolaptes lucidus xanthocephalus Walden and Layard, 1872

1872 *Chrysocolaptes xanthocephalus* Walden and Layard, Ibis, p. 99, (Negros)

Description: Differs from other forms by having back and wings bright red; top of head red in the male and bright golden yellow in the female; underneath much more yellow.

Range: Guimaras, Masbate, Negros, Panay, and Ticao. (Endemic.)

Chrysocolaptes lucidus erythrocephalus Sharpe, 1877

1877 *Chrysocolaptes erythrocephalus* Sharpe, Trans. Linn. Soc. London, 1:315, (Puerto Princesa, Palawan)

Description: Male—head, upper throat, back, and rump red; wing and mantle rich golden yellow; tail black; underparts whiter with dark edges. Female—similar to male but has olive-yellow head.

Range: Balabac, Calamianes, and Palawan. (Endemic.)

PLATE 48

A   WHITE-BELLIED BLACK WOODPECKER
    (Dryocopus javensis)—page 217

B   GREAT SLATY WOODPECKER
    (Mulleripicus pulverulentus)—page 216

C   PYGMY WOODPECKER
    (Dendrocopos maculatus)—page 219

D   THREE-TOED WOODPECKER
    (Dinopium javanense)—page 216

E   CRIMSON-BACKED WOODPECKER
    (Chrysocolaptes lucidus)—page 220

F   SOOTY WOODPECKER
    (Mulleripicus funebris)—page 217

G   WATTLED BROADBILL
    (Eurylaimus steerii), female—page 224

H   WATTLED BROADBILL
    (Eurylaimus steerii), male—page 224

PLATE 48

Family EURYLAIMIDAE   BROADBILLS

WATTLED BROADBILL   PLATE 48

Eurylaimus steerii steerii Sharpe, 1876

1876 *Eurylaimus Steerii* Sharpe, Nature, **14**:297, (Basilan)

Description: Male—crown reddish purple; nuchal collar white; mantle gray; lower back, rump, and tail chestnut; wings black with a yellowish white stripe in the secondaries; throat and sides of head black; rest of underparts pale lilac. Female—similar to male but with white underparts.

Soft Parts: Bill bluish; iris light orange; feet light blue; eye wattle blue.

Measurements: Wing 87; tail 60; bill 21; tarsus 19.

Range: Basilan and Zamboanga Peninsula on Mindanao. (Endemic.)

Eurylaimus steerii mayri Salomonsen, 1953

1953 *Eurylaimus steerei mayri* Salomonsen, Vid. Medd. Dansk nat. Foren., **115**:268, (Agay, Agusan Province, Mindanao)

Description: Differs from *E. s. steerii* by having a much darker crown; underparts paler with center of belly white; also smaller (wing 82; tail 54; bill 22).

Range: Mindanao, except Zamboanga Peninsula. (Endemic.)

Eurylaimus steerii samarensis (Steere, 1890)

1890 *Sarcophanops Samarensis* Steere, List Bds. Mamms. Steere Expd., p. 23, (Samar)

Description: Differs from *E. s. steerii* by having mantle reddish purple and the secondary stripe white and lilac, not yellow.

Range: Bohol, Leyte, and Samar. (Endemic.)

Family PITTIDAE   PITTAS

RED-BREASTED PITTA   PLATE 49

Pitta erythrogaster erythrogaster Temminck, 1823

1823 *Pitta erythrogaster* Temminck, Pl. Col., pl. 212, (Manila, Luzon)

1935 *Pitta erythrogastra yairocho* Hachisuka, Bds. Phil. Ids., p. 259, (Sibutu)

Description: Forehead and crown blackish brown; hind neck dark chestnut followed by a light blue collar; mantle and back dark green; rump and tail blue; wings blue; primaries black with a small white patch; throat black; chest blue with green on sides; rest of underparts scarlet.

224

Soft Parts: Bill black; iris dark brown; feet dark brown.

Measurements: Wing 94; tail 38; bill 18; tarsus 37.

Range: Found throughout the Philippines, except Palawan.

Pitta erythrogaster propinqua (Sharpe, 1877)

1877 *Brachyurus propinquus* Sharpe, Trans. Linn. Soc. London, 1:330, (Balabac)

Description: Differs from *P. e. erythrogaster* by having head with more chestnut and upperparts bluer; also, slightly smaller (wing 88; tail 34).

Range: Balabac and Palawan. (Endemic.)

Pitta erythrogaster thompsoni Ripley and Rabor, 1962

1962 *Pitta erythrogaster thompsoni* Ripley and Rabor, Postilla, 73:5, (Culion Island)

Description: Differs from *propinqua* by having the back, rump, tail, and scapulars paler blue.

Range: Culion Island. (Endemic.)

KOCH'S PITTA   PLATE 49

Pitta kochi Bruggemann, 1877

1877 *Pitta Kochi* Bruggemann, Abh. Naturwiss. Ver. Bremen, 5:65, (Luzon)

Description: Forehead, lores, and ear-coverts dark red-brown; crown rufous-brown; back olive-brown with some rufous; tail gray-blue; wings gray-blue with a white patch in the primaries; throat dark red with brown margins; breast reddish lilac with bluish sides; rest of underparts red.

Soft Parts: Bill dark brown; iris dark brown; feet slate.

Measurements: Wing 118; tail 56; bill 31; tarsus 53.

Range: Northern Luzon. (Endemic.)

BLACK-HEADED PITTA   PLATE 49

Pitta sordida sordida (P. L. S. Müller, 1776)

1776 *Turdus sordida* P. L. S. Müller, Natursyst., suppl., 1776:143, (Philippines)

1907 *Pitta atricapilla rothschildi* Parrot, Abhand. Bayen Akad. Wiss., p. 223,
    (Marinduque)

Description: Crown, neck, and throat black; back dark green, sometimes streaked with black; rump cobalt-blue; tail black; wings dark green with cobalt-blue shoulders; primaries white with black tips; breast and flanks dark green; center of belly black; lower belly and under tail-coverts scarlet.

Soft Parts: Bill black; iris brown; feet dark brown.

Measurements: Wing 101; tail 37; bill 19; tarsus 34.

Range: Found throughout the Philippines, except Palawan and Sibutu.

Pitta sordida mulleri (Bonaparte, 1850)

1850   *Brachyurus mulleri* Bonaparte, Consp. Av., **1**:256, (Borneo)

Description: Differs from *P. s. sordida* by being larger (wing 111; tail 43).

Range: Sibutu.

Pitta sordida palawanensis Parkes, 1960

1960   *Pitta sordida palawanensis* Parkes, Proc. Biol. Soc. Wash., **73**:57, (Puerto Princesa, Palawan)

Description: Differs from *P. s. sordida* by having wing-coverts and rump deeper blue; upperparts tend to be lighter green.

Range: Balabac and Palawan. (Endemic.)

STEERE'S PITTA   PLATE 49

Pitta steerii steerii (Sharpe, 1876)

1876   *Brachyurus steerii* Sharpe, Nature, **14**:297, (Dumalon, Mindanao)

Description: Head and neck black; back dark green; rump light cobalt-blue; tail black; wings dark green with light blue shoulders; throat white; breast and flanks light blue; center of belly blue-black; vent tuft red.

Soft Parts: Bill black; iris brown; feet brown.

Measurements: Wing 116; tail 38; bill 24; tarsus 45.

Range: Mindanao. (Endemic.)

Pitta steerii coelestis Parkes, 1971

1971   *Pitta steerii coelestis* Parkes, Bull. Brit. Orn. Cl., **91**:99, (Bonga, Samar)

Description: Differs from *P. s. steerii* by having blues purer, especially the rump and wing-coverts.

Range: Bohol, Leyte, and Samar. (Endemic.)

BLUE-WINGED PITTA   PLATE 49

Pitta brachyura moluccensis (P. L. S. Müller, 1776)

1776   *Turdus moluccensis* P. L. S. Müller, Natursyst., suppl., 1776:144, (Tenasserim)

1907   *Pitta fastosa* McGregor, Phil. Journ. Sci., **2**:286, (Isabella, Basilan)

Description: Forehead and crown brown; sides of head and hind neck black; back dark green; rump light blue; tail black; wings mostly black with bright blue wing-coverts; a white patch in the primaries; throat white; breast light yellow-orange, becoming darker on the belly; vent and under tail-coverts red.

Soft Parts: Bill dark horn color; iris dark brown; feet pinkish.

Measurements: Wing 190; tail 40; bill 28; tarsus 36.

Range: Basilan (once).

Family ALAUDIDAE   LARKS

BUSH LARK   PLATE 50

Mirafra javanica philippensis Ramsay, 1886

1886   *Mirafra philippensis* Ramsay, Ibis, p. 166, (Manila, Luzon)

Description: Upperparts dark brown mottled with buff; wing primaries and coverts have rufous edges; throat whitish; upper breast light buff with dark brown streaks; rest of underparts dark buffy.

Soft Parts: Bill tan; iris light brown; feet pinkish.

Measurements: Wing 69; tail 47; bill 10; tarsus 21.

Range: Luzon and Mindoro. (Endemic.)

Mirafra javanica mindanensis Hachisuka, 1931

1931   *Mirafra philippensis mindanensis* Hachisuka, Ois. et Rev. Fran. d'Orn., 1:471, (Mindanao)

Description: Differs from *philippensis* by having the upperparts darker, less rufous on the wing, and a larger wing (74).

Range: Mindanao and Negros. (Endemic.)

SMALL SKYLARK   PLATE 50

Alauda gulgula wolfei Hachisuka, 1930

1930   *Alauda arvensis wolfei* Hachisuka, Orn. Soc. Japan, suppl. 14:215, (Los Baños, Luzon)

Description: Upperparts have brown feathers with light brown margins; throat whitish; breast pale buff with dark brown spots; rest of underparts pale buff; outermost tail feathers white.

Soft Parts: Bill tan; iris light brown; feet pinkish.

Measurements: Wing 74; tail 52; bill 10; tarsus 28.

Range: Bohol, Luzon, Mindanao, Sibuyan, and Ticao. (Endemic.)

PLATE 49

A   KOCH'S PITTA
(Pitta kochi)—page 225

B   BLACK-HEADED PITTA
(Pitta sordida)—page 225

C   RED-BREASTED PITTA
(Pitta erythrogaster)—page 224

D   STEERE'S PITTA
(Pitta steerii)—page 226

E   BLUE-WINGED PITTA
(Pitta brachyura)—page 226

A

B

C

D

E

JOHN R. PEIRCE

PLATE 49

PLATE 50

A   BANK SWALLOW
       (Riparia riparia)—page 232

B   BARN SWALLOW
       (Hirundo rustica)—page 232

C   PACIFIC SWALLOW
       (Hirundo tahitica)—page 233

D   MOSQUE SWALLOW
       (Hirundo striolata)—page 233

E   GRAY-BREASTED SAND MARTIN
       (Riparia paludicola)—page 232

F   ASIATIC HOUSE MARTIN
       (Delichon dasypus)—page 233

G   SMALL SKYLARK
       (Alauda gulgula)—page 227

H   BUSH LARK
       (Mirafra javanica)—page 227

PLATE 50

Family HIRUNDINIDAE   SWALLOWS

GRAY-BREASTED SAND MARTIN   PLATE 50

Riparia paludicola tantilla Riley, 1935

1935   *Riparia chinensis tantilla* Riley, Proc. Biol. Soc. Wash., **48**:147, (Laoag River, Luzon)

Description: Upperparts pale brown; tail and wing primaries dark brown; underparts dirty white.
Soft Parts: Bill black; iris light brown; feet dark brown.
Measurements: Wing 94; tail 43; bill 6; tarsus 10.
Range: Luzon. (Endemic.)

BANK SWALLOW   PLATE 50

Riparia riparia ijimae (Lönnberg, 1908)

1908   *Clivicola riparia ijimae* Lönnberg, Journ. Coll. Sci. Imp. Univ. Tokyo, **23**:38, (Tretiya Padj, Sakhalin)

Description: Upperparts brown; rump with buff tips to feathers; underparts white with a wide brown band on breast.
Soft Parts: Bill dark brown; iris brown; feet dark brown.
Measurements: Wing 98; tail 41; bill 6; tarsus 12.
Range: Calayan and Palawan.

BARN SWALLOW   PLATE 50

Hirundo rustica gutturalis Scopoli, 1786

1786   *Hirundo gutturalis* Scopoli, Del. Flor. et Faun. Insubr., p. 96, (Antigua, Panay)
Description: Upperparts glossy greenish blue; tail and wing primaries dull black; chin and throat chestnut; upper breast black with a green gloss; rest of underparts white.
Soft Parts: Bill black; iris brown; feet dark brown.
Measurements: Wing 118; tail 81; bill 8; tarsus 10.
Range: Winters throughout the Philippines from eastern Asia.

Hirundo rustica saturata Ridgway, 1883

1883   *Hirundo saturata* Ridgway, Proc. U. S. Nat. Mus., **6**:95, (Petropavlovsk, Kamchatka)
Description: Differs from *gutturalis* by having the underparts light pinkish brown.
Range: Leyte and Luzon; a winter visitor from northeast Asia.

PACIFIC SWALLOW

PLATE 50

Hirundo tahitica abbotti (Oberholser, 1917)

1917   *Hypurolepis javanica abbotti* Oberholser, Proc. U. S. Nat. Mus., **98**:32, (Pulo Manguan, Anamba Islands)

1926   *Hypurolepis javanica mallopega* Oberholser, Journ. Wash. Acad. Sci., **16**:515, (Benguet, Luzon)

Description: Forehead dark rufous; crown dark brown; back and wing-coverts dark brown with a green gloss; wings and rump dark brown; tail dark brown with subterminal white spots; throat rufous; rest of underparts gray, feathers having dark shaft streaks.

Soft Parts: Bill black; iris brown; feet dark brown.

Measurements: Wing 116; tail 40; bill 8; tarsus 12.

Range: Found throughout the Philippines.

MOSQUE SWALLOW

PLATE 50

Hirundo striolata striolata Temminck and Schlegel, 1847

1847   *Hirundo striolata* Temminck and Schlegel, in Siebold's Faun. Jap., Aves, p. 33, (Java)

Description: Head, back, and wing-coverts black with a blue-green gloss; lower back and rump pale chestnut, feathers having dark shaft streaks; wings and tail dark brown; underparts white heavily streaked with dark brown; under tail-coverts dark brown with a greenish gloss.

Soft Parts: Bill black; iris dark brown; feet brown.

Measurements: Wing 123; tail 90; bill 8; tarsus 15.

Range: Batan, Bohol, Calayan, Camiguin North, Cebu, Luzon, Masbate, Mindoro, and Panay.

ASIATIC HOUSE MARTIN

PLATE 50

Delichon dasypus dasypus (Bonaparte, 1851)

1851   *Chelidon dasypus* Bonaparte, Consp. Av., **1**:343, (Borneo)

Description: Crown, sides of head, hind neck, and back glossy green-black; lower back and rump white; tail and wings dark brown; underparts white with a slight gray-brown band on the breast; tarsus and feet feathered.

Soft Parts: Bill black; iris dark brown; feet dark brown.

Measurements: Wing 103; tail 45; bill 6; tarsus 9.

Range: Calayan; a migrant from China.

Family CAMPEPHAGIDAE CUCKOO-SHRIKES

BARRED GRAYBIRD PLATE 51

Coracina striata striata (Boddaert, 1783)

1783 *Corvus striatus* Boddaert, Table Pl., enlum., p. 38, (Luzon)

Description: Male—all gray; lores, primaries, and tail black. Female—differs by having rump, lower breast, belly, and under tail-coverts heavily barred with black and white. Immature male—barred on rump. Immature female—completely barred on underparts and back.

Soft Parts: Bill black; iris yellow; feet black.

Measurements: Wing 162; tail 118; bill 23; tarsus 24.

Range: Lubang, Luzon, Marinduque, and Polillo. (Endemic.)

Coracina striata difficilis (Hartert, 1895)

1895 *Graucalus sumatrensis difficilis* Hartert, Nov. Zool., **2**:470, (Balabac)

Description: Male—differs from *C. s. striata* by having gray lores and being lighter gray overall. Female—the barring on the rump extends further up the lower back.

Range: Balabac, Calamianes, and Palawan. (Endemic.)

Coracina striata mindorensis (Steere, 1890)

1890 *Artamides Mindorensis* Steere, List Bds. Mamms. Steere Expd., p. 14, (Mindoro)

Description: Male—similar to *C. s. striata*. Female—differs by having no barring and lacks black lores found in males.

Range: Libagao, Mindoro, and Tablas. (Endemic.)

Coracina striata panayensis (Steere, 1890)

1890 *Artamides Panayensis* Steere, List Bds. Mamms. Steere Expd., p. 14, (Panay)

Description: Male—differs from *C. s. striata* by having black loral mark extending as a mask back over eyes; rump and belly barred with black and white. Female—differs by having barring extend further up the lower breast, sometimes all the way to the throat.

Range: Guimaras, Masbate, Negros, Panay, and Ticao. (Endemic.)

Coracina striata kochii (Kutter, 1882)

1882 *Graucalus Kochii* Kutter, Orn. Centralb., **7**:183, (Mindanao)

1890 *Artamides Mindanensis* Steere, List Bds. Mamms. Steere Expd., p. 14, (Mindanao, Samar)

234

Description: Male—differs from *C. s. striata* by having the rump, breast, belly, and under tail-coverts barred with black and white. Female—differs by having nasal tufts and lores white; rump, lower back, and underparts from chin to belly barred with black and white; under tail-coverts white.

Range: Basilan and Mindanao. (Endemic.)

Coracina striata cebuensis (Ogilvie-Grant, 1896)

1896 *Artamides cebuensis* Ogilvie-Grant, Ibis, p. 535, (Cebu)

Description: Male—differs from *C. s. striata* by having a black eye-ring. Female—differs by having an all gray rump as on the back.

Range: Cebu. (Extinct.)

Coracina striata guillemardi (Salvadori, 1886)

1886 *Graucalus guillemardi* Salvadori, Ibis, p. 154, (Lapac, Sulu Archipelago)

Description: Male—differs from *kochii* by having upper- and underparts all gray. Female—similar to male but has less black on head. This race is barely separable from *mindorensis* but is larger (wing 170 vs. 160) and has a darker gray head, thus less contrast with black face.

Range: Sulu Archipelago. (Endemic.)

Coracina striata boholensis Rand and Rabor, 1959

1959 *Coracina striata boholensis* Rand and Rabor, Fieldiana: Zoology, 39:276, (Bohol)

Description: Differs from *kochii* by having less barring on the rump and the underparts more heavily marked, especially on the under tail-coverts.

Range: Bohol, Leyte, and Samar. (Endemic.)

BLACK GRAYBIRD   PLATE 51

Coracina coerulescens coerulescens (Blyth, 1842)

1842 *Ceblepyris coerulescens* Blyth, Journ. As. Soc. Bengal, 11:463, (Luzon)

Description: Male—entire bird black with a greenish gloss; lores, primaries, and tail true black. Female—dark gray.

Soft Parts: Bill black; iris dark brown; feet black.

Measurements: Wing 128; tail 111; bill 19; tarsus 23.

Range: Luzon. (Endemic.)

Coracina coerulescens altera (Ramsay, 1881)

1881 *Edoliosoma alterum* Ramsay, Ibis, p. 34, (Cebu)

Description: Male—similar to *C. c. coerulescens*. Female—much lighter gray.

Range: Cebu. (Extinct.)

PLATE 51

A BARRED GRAYBIRD
      (Coracina s. striata), female—page 234

B BARRED GRAYBIRD
      (Coracina s. striata), male—page 234

C BLACK GRAYBIRD
      (Coracina coerulescens)—page 235

D SHARP-TAILED GRAYBIRD
      (Coracina mcgregori)—page 239

E WHITE-WINGED GRAYBIRD
      (Coracina ostenta)—page 239

F MOLUCCAN GRAYBIRD
      (Coracina morio)—page 238

PLATE 51

MOLUCCAN GRAYBIRD   PLATE 51

Coracina morio elusa (McGregor, 1905)

1905 *Edoliisoma elusum* McGregor, Bur. Govt. Lab., Manila, 34:19, (Balete, Mindoro)
Description: Male—nasal tufts, lores, sides of head, and throat black; crown, back, and rump blue-gray; primaries and tail black, outer rectrices with light gray tips; breast, belly, and under tail-coverts blue-gray. Female—lacks the black on the head and throat.
Soft Parts: Bill black; iris black; feet black.
Measurements: Wing 132; tail 104; bill 22; tarsus 21.
Range: Mindoro. (Endemic.)

Coracina morio everetti (Sharpe, 1893)

1893 *Edoliisoma everetti* Sharpe, Bull. Brit. Orn. Cl., 3:10, (Bongao, Sulu Islands)
Description: Differs from *elusa* by being smaller (wing 126 vs. 132; tail 102 vs. 104).
Range: Sulu Archipelago.

Coracina morio lecroyae Parkes, 1971

1971 *Coracina morio lecroyae* Parkes, Nemouria, 4:21, (Lamao, Bataan Prov., Luzon)
Description: Differs from *elusa* by being paler gray and having edges of remiges and wing-coverts much paler, especially in females—so much so that it may be whitish; wing and tail also shorter.
Range: Luzon. (Endemic.)

Coracina morio ripleyi Parkes, 1971

1971 *Coracina morio ripleyi* Parkes, Nemouria, 4:21, (Barrio Patok, Dagami, Mt. Lobi, Leyte)
Description: Male—differs from *mindanensis* by being paler gray. Female—has pale gray rump, not whitish. Terminal black band of central rectrices of both sexes narrower; wing and tail longer.
Range: Bohol, Leyte, and Samar. (Endemic.)

Coracina morio mindanensis (Tweeddale, 1878)

1878 *Volvocivora mindanensis* Tweeddale, Proc. Zool. Soc. London, p. 947, (Zamboanga, Mindanao)
Description: Male—differs from *elusa* by having the crown and rump lighter gray. Female—differs by having lower abdomen and under tail-coverts white.
Range: Basilan and Mindanao. (Endemic.)

238

SHARP-TAILED GRAYBIRD   PLATE 51

Coracina mcgregori (Mearns, 1907)

1907   *Malindangia mcgregori* Mearns, Phil. Journ. Sci., **2**:355, (Mt. Malindang, Mindanao)

1953   *Edolisoma mcgregori peterseni* Salomonsen, Vid. Medd. Dansk nat. Foren., **115**: 276, (Mt. Katanglad, Mindanao)

Description: Forehead black; crown gray; throat, sides of head, upper breast, and collar black; back, rump, and central rectrices gray; inner rectrices all black, outer rectrices black with white tips; wing-coverts white, primaries black; lower breast and thighs gray; belly and under tail-coverts white.

Soft Parts: Bill black; iris light brown; feet black.

Measurements: Wing 109; tail 98; bill 15; tarsus 21.

Range: Mindanao. (Endemic.)

WHITE-WINGED GRAYBIRD   PLATE 51

Coracina ostenta Ripley, 1952

1890   *Edoliisoma (Graucalus) panayensis* Steere, List Bds. Mamms. Steere Expd., p. 14, (Panay)

1952   *Coracina ostenta* Ripley, Condor, **54**:362, new name for *Edoliisoma (Graucalus) panayensis* Steere, 1890

Description: Male—forehead black; crown dark gray-black; back dark gray; rump blue-gray; tail black, outer rectrices with white tips; wing black, outer edges of coverts white forming a white stripe; sides of face and throat black; breast and belly dark blue-gray; under tail-coverts white. Female—differs by having a gray head and underparts lighter.

Soft Parts: Bill black; iris black; feet black.

Measurements: Wing 141; tail 130; bill 22; tarsus 23.

Range: Guimaras, Negros, and Panay. (Endemic.)

BLACK AND WHITE TRILLER   PLATE 52

Lalage melanoleuca melanoleuca (Blyth, 1861)

1861   *Pseudolalage melanoleuca* Blyth, Journ. As. Soc. Bengal, **30**:97, (Luzon)

Description: Male—forehead, crown, and upper back black with a green gloss; lower back and rump white with basal half of feathers gray that distorts the color; tail black with a green gloss, outer rectrices tipped with white; wings basically black with a green gloss, but wing-coverts, secondaries, and primaries have some white forming a stripe; underparts white. Female—differs by having gray head and underparts barred with gray.

Soft Parts: Bill black; iris dark brown; feet black.

Measurements: Wing 115; tail 82; bill 21; tarsus 23.

Range: Luzon and Mindoro. (Endemic.)

Lalage melanoleuca minor (Steere, 1890)

1890 *Pseudolalage minor* Steere, List Bds. Mamms. Steere Expd., p. 15, (Ayala, Mindanao)

Description: Differs from *L. m. melanoleuca* by having the underparts of the female darker gray.

Range: Leyte, Mindanao, and Samar. (Endemic.)

PIED TRILLER   PLATE 52

Lalage nigra chilensis (Meyen, 1834)

1834 *Ceblepyris chilensis* Meyen, Verh. K. Leop. Carol Akad. Naturf., **16**:74, (Manila, Luzon)

1919 *Lalage schisticeps* Neumann, Journ. f. Orn., **67**:333, (Culion); type a composite specimen

1922 *Lalage nigra mitifica* Bangs, Bull. Mus. Comp. Zool., **65**:80, (Lubang Island)

Description: Male—forehead and stripe over eye white; upper back black with a blue-green gloss; lower back and rump dark gray; tail has black feathers tipped with white; wings black with a white stripe; underparts gray-white. Female—upperparts gray-brown; underparts with fine dark gray barring.

Soft Parts: Bill black; iris black; feet black.

Measurements: Wing 91; tail 76; bill 15; tarsus 20.

Range: Found throughout the Philippines.

ASHY MINIVET   PLATE 52

Pericrocotus divaricatus divaricatus (Raffles, 1822)

1822 *Lanius divaricatus* Raffles, Trans. Linn. Soc. London, **13**:305, (Singapore)

1845 *Pericrocotus cinereus* Lafresnaye, Rev. et Mag. Zool., **8**:94, (Luzon)

Description: Male—forehead white; crown dark gray-black; back and rump gray; tail black, outer rectrices with terminal halves white; wings black; lores black; underparts gray-white. Female—differs by having gray head.

Soft Parts: Bill black; iris black; feet black.

Measurements: Wing 98; tail 100; bill 13; tarsus 15.

Range: Found throughout the Philippines as a winter visitor.

240

FIERY MINIVET   PLATE 52

Pericrocotus cinnamomeus igneus Blyth, 1846

1846 *P(ericrocotus) igneus* Blyth, Journ. As. Soc. Bengal, **15**:309, (Malacca)

Description: Head, throat, and upper back black with blue gloss; lower back and rump bright orange-red; tail black, outer rectrices dull orange-red; wings black with an orange-red patch in the secondaries; breast, belly, and under tail-coverts bright orange-red. Female—differs by having head and upper back gray; wings gray-black with orange-yellow patch; nasal tufts and underparts orange-yellow.
Soft Parts: Bill black; iris dark brown; feet black.
Measurements: Wing 76; tail 69; bill 12; tarsus 16.
Range: Palawan.

FLAME MINIVET   PLATE 52

Pericrocotus flammeus novus McGregor, 1904

1904 *Pericrocotus novus* McGregor, Bull. Phil. Mus., 3:13, (Irisan, Luzon)

Description: Male—head, throat, and upper back black with a bluish gloss; rump orange; tail black, outer rectrices orange, innermost tipped with orange; wings black with two orange patches; underparts orange. Female—above gray-black; rump, throat, wing patches, and underparts lemon-yellow.
Soft Parts: Bill black; iris dark brown; feet black.
Measurements: Wing 82; tail 78; bill 14; tarsus 16.
Range: Luzon and Negros. (Endemic.)

Pericrocotus flammeus leytensis Steere, 1890

1890 *Pericrocotus Leytensis* Steere, List Bds. Mamms. Steere Expd., p. 15, (Leyte)

Description: Male—differs from *novus* by having the orange-red much brighter. Female —browner above.
Range: Leyte and Samar. (Endemic.)

Pericrocotus flammeus johnstoniae Ogilvie-Grant, 1905

1905 *Pericrocotus johnstoniae* Ogilvie-Grant, Bull. Brit. Orn. Cl., **16**:18, (Mt. Apo, Mindanao)

Description: Male—differs from *leytensis* by being bright orange-yellow. Female—also brighter.
Range: Mt. Apo, Mindanao. (Endemic.)

PLATE 52

A   FLAME MINIVET
      (Pericrocotus flammeus), male—page 241

B   FLAME MINIVET
      (Pericrocotus flammeus), female—page 241

C   FIERY MINIVET
      (Pericrocotus cinnamomeus), male—page 241

D   FIERY MINIVET
      (Pericrocotus cinnamomeus), female—page 241

E   ASHY MINIVET
      (Pericrocotus divaricatus)—page 240

F   PIED TRILLER
      (Lalage nigra)—page 240

G   BLACK AND WHITE TRILLER
      (Lalage melanoleuca)—page 239

PLATE 52

Pericrocotus flammeus gonzalesi Ripley and Rabor, 1961

1961 *Pericrocotus flammeus gonzalesi* Ripley and Rabor, Postilla, 50:8, (Mt. Katanglad, Mindanao)

Description: Differs from *johnstoniae* by having the underparts richer orange-yellow.
Range: Mt. Katanglad, Mindanao. (Endemic.)

Pericrocotus flammeus marchesae Guillemard, 1885

1885 *Pericrocotus marchesae* Guillemard, Proc. Zool. Soc. London, p. 259, (Jolo)

Description: Differs from Mindanao forms by being much lighter in color in both sexes—orange replaced by lemon-yellow.
Range: Jolo. (Endemic.)

Family DICRURIDAE   DRONGOS

GRAY DRONGO   PLATE 53

Dicrurus leucophaeus leucophaeus Vieillot, 1817

1817 *Dicrurus leucophaeus* Vieillot, Nouv. Dict. d'Hist. Nat., **9**:587, ("Ceylon"; error = Java)

1890 *Buchanga palawanensis* Whitehead, Ibis, p. 47, (Taguso, Palawan)

1901 *Dicrurus leucophaeus* var. *whiteheadi* Dubois, Syn. Avium, **1**:530, new name for *Buchanga palawanensis* Whitehead, 1890

1919 *Dicrurus cineraceus rebaptizatus* Hartert, Nov. Zool., **26**:130, new name for *Buchanga palawanensis* Whitehead, 1890

Description: Upperparts steel-gray; wings and tail dark brown-black; underparts gray.
Soft Parts: Bill black; iris red; feet black.
Measurements: Wing 138; tail 141; bill 21; tarsus 16.
Range: Balabac and Palawan.

BALICASSIAO   PLATE 53

Dicrurus balicassius balicassius (Linnaeus, 1766)

1766 *Corvus balicassius* Linnaeus, Syst. Nat., **1**:157, (Philippines)

1909 *Dicrurus balicassius mindorensis* Mearns, Proc. U. S. Nat. Mus., **36**:447, (Mt. Halcon, Mindoro)

244

Description: All black with a brilliant green gloss slightly duller on lower abdomen and vent.

Soft Parts: Bill black; iris dark brown; feet black.

Measurements: Wing 141; tail 118; bill 33; tarsus 25.

Range: Lubang, central and southern Luzon, Marinduque, Mindoro, Polillo, and Verde. (Endemic.)

Dicrurus balicassius abraensis Vaurie, 1947

1947 *Dicrurus balicassius abraensis* Vaurie, Am. Mus. Novit., 1335:2, (Bucay, Abra Province, northern Luzon)

Description: Differs from *D. b. balicassius* by having a purplish gloss, a stronger bill, and a longer wing (154).

Range: Northern Luzon. Intergrades with *balicassius* in north-central Luzon (Nueva Ecija Province). (Endemic.)

Dicrurus balicassius mirabilis Walden and Layard, 1872

1872 *Dicrurus mirabilis* Walden and Layard, Ibis, p. 103, (Negros)

Description: Differs from *D. b. balicassius* by having a white lower breast and belly.

Range: Bantayan, Cebu, Guimaras, Masbate, Negros, Panay, and Ticao. (Endemic.)

CROW-BILLED DRONGO   PLATE 53

Dicrurus annectans (Hodgson, 1836)

1836 *Bhuchanga annectans* Hodgson, India Rev., 1:326, (Nepal)

Description: Entire bird black glossed with green; tail more deeply forked than that of *D. balicassius.*

Soft Parts: Bill black; iris maroon; feet black.

Measurements: Wing 142; tail 100; bill 27; tarsus 19.

Range: Sulu Island (once); a straggler from Borneo and eastern Asia.

SPANGLED   DRONGO   PLATE 53

Dicrurus hottentottus striatus Tweeddale, 1877

1877 *Dicrurus striatus* Tweeddale, Proc. Zool. Soc. London, p. 545, (Pasananca, Mindanao)

Description: All black with top of head, wings, tail, and ends of feathers on throat and chest glossed with green.

Soft Parts: Bill black; iris red; feet black.

Measurements: Wing 138; tail 105; bill 22; tarsus 24.

Range: Basilan and Mindanao. (Endemic.)

PLATE 53

A   SPANGLED DRONGO
      (Dicrurus hottentottus)—page 245

B   GRAY DRONGO
      (Dicrurus leucophaeus)—page 244

C   BALICASSIAO
      (Dicrurus b. balicassius)—page 244

D   CROW-BILLED DRONGO
      (Dicrurus annectans)—page 245

PLATE 53

Dicrurus hottentottus samarensis Vaurie, 1947

1947 *Dicrurus hottentottus samarensis* Vaurie, Am. Mus. Novit., 1335:1, (Bonga, Samar)

Description: Differs from *striatus* by having a shorter tail (95).

Range: Bohol, Leyte, Panaon, and Samar. (Endemic.)

Dicrurus hottentottus suluensis Hartert, 1902

1902 *Dicrurus suluensis* Hartert, Nov. Zool., **9**:441, (Maimbun, Sulu = Jolo)

Description: Differs from *palawanensis* by being smaller (wing 147; tail 135; bill 34).

Range: Marantua and Sulu Archipelago.

Dicrurus hottentottus palawanensis Tweeddale, 1878

1878 *Dicrurus palawanensis* Tweeddale, Proc. Zool. Soc. London, p. 614, (Puerto Princesa, Palawan)

1909 *Chibia cagayanensis* Mearns, Proc. U. S. Nat. Mus., **36**:447, (Cagayan)

Description: Differs from *striatus* by having the tail deeply forked and longer (147).

Range: Balabac, Cagayan Sulu, Calamianes, and Palawan. (Endemic.)

Dicrurus hottentottus cuyensis (McGregor, 1903)

1903 *Chibia cuyensis* McGregor, Bull. Phil. Mus., 1:5, (Cuyo)

1905 *Chibia worcesteri* McGregor, Bur. Govt. Lab., Manila, 34:26, (Semirara)

Description: Differs from *palawanensis* by having upperparts with a bluish gloss and a longer wing (152).

Range: Cuyo and Semirara. (Endemic.)

Dicrurus hottentottus menagei (Bourns and Worcester, 1894)

1894 *Chibia menagei* Bourns and Worcester, Occ. Papers Minn. Acad. Nat. Sci., 1:15, (Tablas)

Description: Differs from *palawanensis* by having a much longer tail (185).

Range: Tablas. (Endemic.)

Family ORIOLIDAE   ORIOLES

DARK-THROATED ORIOLE   PLATE 54

Oriolus xanthonotus samarensis Steere, 1890

1890 *Oriolus samarensis* Steere, List Bds. Mamms. Steere Expd., p. 17, (Samar)

Description: Crown and back yellowish green; tail dark olive, outer rectrices with a light yellow spot on tips; wings olive, primaries dark brown; bend of wing bright yellow; inner edge of primaries and under wing-coverts bright yellow; throat olive-gray with faint whitish streaks; breast and belly white heavily streaked with black; under tail-coverts yellow.

Soft Parts: Bill dull red; iris dark brown; feet slate.

Measurements: Wing 115; tail 80; bill 21; tarsus 20.

Range: Bohol, Leyte, eastern Mindanao, and Samar. (Endemic.)

Oriolus xanthonotus cinereogenys Bourns and Worcester, 1894

1894　*Oriolus cinereogenys* Bourns and Worcester, Occ. Papers Minn. Acad. Nat. Sci., 1:16, (Tawi Tawi, Bongao)

1894　*Oriolus poliogenys* Sharpe, Zool. Record, **31**:41, new name for *Oriolus cinereogenys* Bourns and Worcester, 1894

Description: Differs from *samarensis* by having gray ear-coverts and throat more distinctly streaked with white; streaks of underparts heavier; rump yellow.

Range: Bongao and Tawi Tawi. (Endemic.)

Oriolus xanthonotus basilanicus Ogilvie-Grant, 1896

1896　*Oriolus basilanicus* Ogilvie-Grant, Ibis, p. 532, (Basilan)

Description: Differs from *samarensis* by having the throat purer gray (less olive) and the edging to primaries and coverts gray not yellowish; inner edge of primaries and under wing-coverts yellowish white, not yellow.

Range: Basilan and western Mindanao. (Endemic.)

Oriolus xanthonotus persuasus Bangs, 1922—PLATE 54

1922　*Oriolus xanthonotus persuasus* Bangs, Bull. Mus. Comp. Zool., **65**:83, (Puerto Princesa, Palawan)

1941　*Oriolus xanthonotus palawanus* Hachisuka, Tori, **11**:89, (Puerto Princesa, Palawan)

Description: Differs from other races by having head, neck, throat, wings, and tail black; back rich golden yellow.

Range: Calamianes and Palawan. (Endemic.)

Oriolus xanthonotus steerii Sharpe, 1877

1877　*Oriolus steerii* Sharpe, Cat. Bds. Brit. Mus., **3**:213, (Negros and Basilan = Negros)

1894　*Oriolus nigrostriatus* Bourns and Worcester, Occ. Papers Minn. Acad. Nat. Sci., 1:16, (Negros and Masbate)

Description: Differs from *samarensis* by having chin and throat gray; rump slightly lighter; yellow on outer rectrices more extensive.

Range: Masbate and Negros. (Endemic.)

Oriolus xanthonotus assimilis Tweeddale, 1878

1878   *Oriolus assimilis* Tweeddale, Proc. Zool. Soc. London, p. 760, (Cebu)

Description: Differs from *steerii* by being generally darker; also slightly larger than *samarensis* (wing 120). Differs from other races by having wings gray, not green (except lesser coverts); tail blackish gray, with small yellow spot on tip of outer rectrices.

Range: Cebu. (Extinct.)

Oriolus xanthonotus albiloris Ogilvie-Grant, 1894—PLATE 54

1894   *Oriolus albiloris* Ogilvie-Grant, Bull. Brit. Orn. Cl., 3:49, (northern Luzon)

Description: Upperparts light olive-green; lores and chin white; underparts yellow, somewhat darker on chest and vaguely streaked with olive-yellow on abdomen; tail with blackish subterminal spots.

Soft Parts: Bill dark red; iris dark red; feet gray.

Measurements: Wing 115; tail 78; bill 21; tarsus 22.

Range: Bataan Peninsula and northern Luzon. (Endemic.)

ISABELLA   ORIOLE   PLATE 54

Oriolus isabellae Ogilvie-Grant, 1894

1894   *Oriolus isabellae* Ogilvie-Grant, Bull. Brit. Orn. Cl., 4:2, (northern Luzon)

Description: Upperparts olive-yellow; wings and tail olive-brown; underparts yellow.

Soft Parts: Bill gray; iris dark red; feet gray.

Measurements: Wing 116; tail 98; bill 26; tarsus 23.

Range: Bataan Peninsula and northern Luzon. (Endemic.)

BLACK-NAPED   ORIOLE   PLATE 54

Oriolus chinensis chinensis Linnaeus, 1766

1766   *Oriolus chinensis* Linnaeus, Syst. Nat., 1:160, ("China"= Manila)

1877   *Oriolus suluensis* Sharpe, Cat. Bds. Brit. Mus., 3:205, (Si Butu)

1878   *Oriolus chinensis palawanensis* Tweeddale, Proc. Zool. Soc. London, p. 616, (Puerto Princesa, Palawan)

1927   *Oriolus chinensis yamamurae* Kuroda, Tori, 5:257, (Basilan)

1949   *Oriolus chinensis fugaensis* Gilliard, Proc. Biol. Soc. Wash., **62**:156, (Fuga Island, off the coast of northern Luzon)

1949   *Oriolus chinensis sorsogonensis* Gilliard, Proc. Biol. Soc. Wash., **62**:157, (Sorsogon, southern Luzon)

Description: Forehead golden yellow; lores, crown, and neck black; mantle, back, and rump golden yellow; wings black; tail black tipped with yellow; outer rectrices half yellow; underparts rich golden yellow.

Soft Parts: Bill pink; iris light red; feet black.

Measurements: Wing 162; tail 115; bill 35; tarsus 28.

Range: Luzon, south to Palawan and Sulu Archipelago. (Endemic.)

Family CORVIDAE   CROWS

LITTLE   CROW   PLATE 54

Corvus enca pusillus Tweeddale, 1878

1878   *Corvus pusillus* Tweeddale, Proc. Zool. Soc. London, p. 622, (Puerto Princesa, Palawan)

Description: All black with grayish gloss. Feathers of back, neck, and breast with white base.

Soft Parts: Bill black; iris brown; feet black.

Measurements: Wing 246; tail 138; bill 52; tarsus 44.

Range: Balabac, Mindoro, and Palawan. (Endemic.)

Corvus enca samarensis Steere, 1890

1890   *Corvus Samarensis* Steere, List Bds. Mamms. Steere Expd., p. 23, (Samar)

Description: Differs from *pusillus* by being smaller (wing 226) and having deeper bill (20 vs. 18); also slightly darker plumage, more intensely black, with bluish gloss; bases of neck feathers grayish white.

Range: Mindanao and Samar. (Endemic.)

Corvus enca sierramadrensis Rand and Rabor, 1961

1961   *Corvus enca sierramadrensis* Rand and Rabor, Fieldiana: Zoology, **39**:577, (San Pascua, Cagayan Prov., Luzon)

Description: Differs from *samarensis* by having the bill shorter (48) and more slender; also more intensely black; concealed feather bases grayer.

Range: Northeastern Luzon. (Endemic.)

PLATE 54

A   DARK-THROATED ORIOLE
(Oriolus xanthonotus persuasus), male—page 249

B   DARK-THROATED ORIOLE
(Oriolus xanthonotus persuasus), female—page 249

C   DARK-THROATED ORIOLE
(Oriolus xanthonotus albiloris)—page 250

D   ISABELLA ORIOLE
(Oriolus isabellae)—page 250

E   BLACK-NAPED ORIOLE
(Oriolus chinensis)—page 250

F   LARGE-BILLED CROW
(Corvus macrorhynchos)—page 254

G   LITTLE CROW
(Corvus enca)—page 251

PLATE 54

LARGE-BILLED CROW

PLATE 54

Corvus macrorhynchos philippinus (Bonaparte, 1853)

1853 *Cornix philippinus* Bonaparte, Compt. Rend. Acad. Sci. Paris, **37**:830, (Philippines)

Description: All black with a slight purplish gloss.
Soft Parts: Bill black; iris dark brown; feet black.
Measurements: Wing 298; tail 216; bill 61; tarsus 61.
Range: Found throughout the Philippines, except Palawan. (Endemic.)

Family PARIDAE

TITMICE

ELEGANT TITMOUSE

PLATE 55

Parus elegans elegans Lesson, 1831

1831 *Parus elegans* Lesson, Traité d'Orn., p. 456, (no locality = Manila, Luzon)
1840 *Parus quadrivittatus* Lafresnaye, Rev. et. Mag. Zool., **3**:129, ("In Manilla out in India" = Manila)
1916 *Pardaliparus elegans panayensis* Mearns, Proc. U. S. Nat. Mus., **51**:57, (Panay)

Description: Male—top of head black with a blue gloss; a spot of yellow on the hind neck; mantle black with white spots; lower back and rump yellowish gray; tail feathers black with white tips, outer rectrices with a white patch in the center of the outer web; wings black with two bars formed by the white tips of the coverts; throat black; cheeks yellow; breast and belly yellow with grayish flanks. Female—similar to male but much duller.
Soft Parts: Bill black; iris black; feet dark gray.
Measurements: Wing 65; tail 44; bill 9; tarsus 17.
Range: Southern Luzon, Mindoro, and Panay. (Endemic.)

Parus elegans edithae (McGregor, 1907)

1907 *Pardaliparus edithae* McGregor, Phil. Journ. Sci., **2**:294, (Calayan Island)

Description: Differs from *P. e. elegans* by having cheek patch whitish, white spots on back and wing-coverts reduced, and a longer wing (70) and bill (9.5).
Range: Babuyan Islands. (Endemic.)

Parus elegans montigenus (Hachisuka, 1930)

1930 *Pardaliparus elegans montigenus* Hachisuka, Orn. Soc. Japan, suppl. 14:200, (Haight's Place, Baguio, Luzon)

Description: Male—differs from *P. e. elegans* by having fewer spots, thus appearing darker on upperparts; yellow of cheeks and underparts paler. Female—more spotted on upper back, grayer, with less yellow on lower back.

Range: Northern Luzon. (Endemic.)

Parus elegans gilliardi Parkes, 1958

1958   *Parus elegans gilliardi* Parkes, Proc. Biol. Soc. Wash., **71**:98, (Lamao, Bataan Province, Luzon)

Description: Differs from *P. e. elegans* by having yellow spots on mantle and white spots on coverts; tail is larger, with yellow edges. Wing slightly larger (68). Females are brighter yellow dorsally, with blacker throat and wings.

Range: Bataan Peninsula, Luzon. (Endemic.)

Parus elegans visayanus (Hachisuka, 1930)

1930   *Pardaliparus elegans visayanus* Hachisuka, Orn. Soc. Japan, suppl. 14:201, (Danao, Cebu)

Description: Male—differs from *P. e. elegans* by having fewer spots on the wings and more on the back; rump is gray; flanks dark greenish gray. Female—grayer on flanks.

Range: Cebu. (Endemic.)

Parus elegans albescens (McGregor, 1907)

1907   *Pardaliparus albescens* McGregor, Phil. Journ. Sci., **2**:293, (Ticao)

1916   *Pardaliparus elegans guimarasensis* Mearns, Proc. U. S. Nat. Mus., **51**:58, (Guimaras)

Description: Male—differs from *P. e. elegans* by having more white on the back and larger spots on the wings. Female—more yellow dorsally, with duller crown and throat patch.

Range: Guimaras, Masbate, Negros, and Ticao. (Endemic.)

Parus elegans mindanensis (Mearns, 1905)

1905   *Pardaliparus elegans mindanensis* Mearns, Proc. Biol. Soc. Wash., **18**:8, (Mt. Apo, Mindanao)

Description: Differs from other races by having blacks less intense, seemingly washed with yellow; back has fewer spots and wing spots are smaller; primaries and secondaries have yellow margins. All white spots of wings and tail are washed or edged with yellow.

Range: Mindanao and Samar (once). (Endemic.)

Parus elegans suluensis (Mearns, 1916)

1916   *Pardaliparus elegans suluensis* Mearns, Proc. U. S. Nat. Mus., **51**:59, (Sulu = Jolo)

255

PARIDAE

Description: Differs from *mindanensis* by being slightly smaller and having fewer white spots on the back. All yellows are paler.
Range: Jolo and Tawi Tawi. (Endemic.)

Parus elegans bongaoensis Parkes, 1958

1958 *Parus elegans bongaoensis* Parkes, Proc. Biol. Soc. Wash., **71**:105, (Bongao Island)
Description: Differs from *suluensis* by being smaller and having darker upperparts; lower back blackish green, darker than any other race. Wing edgings greenish, not yellowish.
Range: Bongao Island. (Endemic.)

PALAWAN TITMOUSE   PLATE 55

Parus amabilis Sharpe, 1877

1877 *Parus amabilis* Sharpe, Trans. Linn. Soc. London, **1**:338, (Balabac)
Description: Male—head, neck, and throat black with a blue gloss; upper back light yellow; lower back and rump gray; tail black with a white tip; outer halves of outer rectrices are white; wings black with white patches in the secondaries and coverts, forming broad bars; underparts pale yellow. Female—back green; crown and throat duller, the latter washed with yellow.
Soft Parts: Bill black; iris brown; feet gray.
Measurements: Wing 73; tail 48; bill 9; tarsus 16.
Range: Balabac and Palawan. (Endemic.)

WHITE-FRONTED TITMOUSE   PLATE 55

Parus semilarvatus semilarvatus (Salvadori, 1865)

1865 *Melaniparus semilarvatus* Salvadori, Atti. Soc. Ital. Sci. Nat. Milano, **8**:375, ("Himalayas"; error= Mt. Arayat, Luzon)
Description: Forehead and lores white; upperparts black with a bluish gloss; underparts dull black. Has a concealed white spot on the nape.
Soft Parts: Bill black; iris brown; feet black.
Measurements: Wing 77; tail 48; bill 12; tarsus 17.
Range: Central and southern Luzon. (Endemic.)

Parus semilarvatus snowi Parkes, 1971

1971 *Parus semilarvatus snowi* Parkes, Nemouria, 4:26, (Barrio Disulap, San Mariano, Isabela Province, Luzon)

256

Description: Differs from *P. s. semilarvatus* by being duller. Male—most noticeably duller above and below; concealed white patch on nape more extensive. Female—an obvious white nape and browner below.

Range: Northern Luzon. (Endemic.)

Parus semilarvatus nehrkorni (Blasius, 1890)

1890 *Micropus nehrkorni* Blasius, Journ. f. Orn., **38**:147, (Davao, Mindanao)

Description: Differs from *P. s. semilarvatus* by having a white patch in the primaries and secondaries.

Range: Mindanao. (Endemic.)

Family SITTIDAE   NUTHATCHES

VELVET-FRONTED NUTHATCH   PLATE 55

Sitta frontalis oenochlamys (Sharpe, 1877)

1877 *Dendrophila oenochlamys* Sharpe, Trans. Linn. Soc. London, **1**:338, (Guimaras)

1930 *Callisitta frontalis cebuensis* Hachisuka, Contrib. Bds. Phil., 2:203, (Toledo, Cebu)

1930 *Callisitta frontalis insignis* Hachisuka, Contrib. Bds. Phil., 2:202, (Cadiz, Negros)

Description: Male—forehead and stripe behind eye black; crown blue; back and rump lilac-blue; tail blue; wing primaries and secondaries black, coverts blue; lores white; underparts pinkish buff. Female—similar to male but lacks black stripe behind the eye.

Soft Parts: Bill yellow; iris yellow; feet brown.

Measurements: Wing 75; tail 44; bill 15; tarsus 16.

Range: Cebu, Guimaras, Negros, and Panay. (Endemic.)

Sitta frontalis mesoleuca (Ogilvie-Grant, 1894)

1894 *Dendrophila mesoleuca* Ogilvie-Grant, Bull. Brit. Orn. Cl., **3**:49, (mountains of northern Luzon)

Description: Differs from *oenochlamys* by having upper back, chin, and throat much paler.

Range: Northwestern Luzon. (Endemic.)

Sitta frontalis isarog Rand and Rabor, 1967

1967 *Sitta frontalis isarog* Rand and Rabor, Fieldiana: Zoology, **51**:89, (Curry, Pili, Camarines Sur, Luzon)

Description: Differs from *mesoleuca* by having the upperparts darker blue and the underparts darker cinnamon-buff.

Range: Northeastern, eastern, and southern Luzon. (Endemic.)

Sitta frontalis lilacea (Whitehead, 1897)

1897 *Dendrophila lilacea* Whitehead, Bull. Brit. Orn. Cl., **6**:49, (Samar)

Description: Differs from *oenochlamys* by having the black of the forehead extending further up the crown; upperparts duller blue; underparts richer lilac.

Range: Leyte and Samar. (Endemic.)

Sitta frontalis apo (Hachisuka, 1930)

1930 *Callisitta frontalis apo* Hachisuka, Contrib. Bds. Phil., 2:203, (Mt. Apo, Mindanao)

Description: Differs from *lilacea* by having the upperparts darker blue and the underparts darker lilac.

Range: Mindanao, except Zamboanga Peninsula. (Endemic.)

Sitta frontalis zamboanga Rand and Rabor, 1957

1957 *Sitta frontalis zamboanga* Rand and Rabor, Fieldiana: Zoology, **42**:16, (Mt. Malindang, Mindanao)

Description: Differs from *apo* by having the underparts darker.

Range: Basilan and Zamboanga Peninsula of Mindanao. (Endemic.)

Sitta frontalis palawana Hartert, 1905

1905 *Sitta frontalis palawana* Hartert, Bull. Brit. Orn. Cl., **16**:11, (Puerto Princesa, Palawan)

Description: Differs from *oenochlamys* by having a red bill and by being slightly darker below.

Range: Balabac and Palawan. (Endemic.)

Family RHABDORNITHIDAE   CREEPERS

STRIPED-HEADED CREEPER   PLATE 55

Rhabdornis mysticalis mysticalis (Temminck, 1825)

1825 *Meliphaga mysticalis* Temminck, Pl. Col., pl. 335, (Manila, Luzon)
1911 *Rhabdornis longirostris* McGregor, Phil. Journ. Sci., **6**:45, (Cadiz, Negros)

Description: Male—top of head and upperback black with white stripes; lower back, wings, and tail gray with white shaft streaks; cheeks and sides of neck black; a white stripe extends from behind the eye; throat and center of breast and belly white; flanks heavily striped with black. Female—browner back than male.

Soft Parts: Bill black; iris brown; feet black.

Measurements: Wing 81; tail 50; bill 21; tarsus 19.

Range: Luzon, Masbate, Negros, and Panay. (Endemic.)

Rhabdornis mysticalis minor Ogilvie-Grant, 1896

1896 *Rhabdornis minor* Ogilvie-Grant, Bull. Brit. Orn. Cl., **6**:17, (Samar)

Description: Differs from *R. m. mysticalis* by being smaller (bill 18). Female—slightly redder brown.

Range: Bohol, Dinagat, Leyte, Mindanao, and Samar. (Endemic.)

PLAIN-HEADED CREEPER   PLATE 55

Rhabdornis inornatus inornatus Ogilvie-Grant, 1896

1896 *Rhabdornis inornatus* Ogilvie-Grant, Bull. Brit. Orn. Cl., **6**:18, (Samar)

Description: Upperparts brown; wings and tail darker; eye stripe white; lores and ear-coverts dark brown; underparts white with brown stripes.

Soft Parts: Bill black; iris brown; feet black.

Measurements: Wing 92; tail 54; bill 18; tarsus 21.

Range: Samar. (Endemic.)

Rhabdornis inornatus grandis Salomonsen, 1953

1952 *Rhabdornis longirostris* Salomonsen, Vid. Medd. Dansk nat. Foren., **114**:356, (Kainay, Abra Province, Luzon)

1953 *Rhabdornis grandis* Salomonsen, Dansk Orn. Foren. Tidsskrift, **47**:139, new name for *Rhabdornis longirostris* Salomonsen, 1952

Description: Differs from *R. i. inornatus* by being larger (wing 99; tail 68; bill 26; tarsus 23).

Range: Northern Luzon. (Endemic.)

Rhabdornis inornatus rabori Rand, 1950

1950 *Rhabdornis inornatus rabori* Rand, Nat. His. Misc., 59:2, (Lake Balinsasayo, Negros)

Description: Differs from *R. i. inornatus* by having the crown and upper back grayer; lores and ear-coverts gray.

Range: Negros. (Endemic.)

PLATE 55

A   VELVET-FRONTED NUTHATCH
      (Sitta frontalis)—page 257

B   STRIPED-HEADED CREEPER
      (Rhabdornis mysticalis)—page 258

C   PLAIN-HEADED CREEPER
      (Rhabdornis inornatus)—page 259

D   ELEGANT TITMOUSE
      (Parus elegans)—page 254

E   PALAWAN TITMOUSE
      (Parus amabilis)—page 256

F   WHITE-FRONTED TITMOUSE
      (Parus semilarvatus)—page 256

G   WHITE-FRONTED TITMOUSE
      (Parus semilarvatus)—page 256

PLATE 55

Rhabdornis inornatus alaris Rand, 1948

1948 *Rhabdornis inornatus alaris* Rand, Fieldiana: Zoology, **31**:204, (Mt. McKinley, Mindanao)

1957 *Rhabdornis inornatus zamboanga* Rand and Rabor, Fieldiana: Zoology, **42**:16, (Mt. Malindang, Mindanao)

Description: Differs from *R. i. inornatus* by having the crown browner; wing-coverts with less white; underparts heavily streaked.

Range: Mindanao. (Endemic.)

Family TIMALIIDAE   BABBLERS

ASHY-HEADED GROUND-BABBLER   PLATE 56

Trichastoma cinereiceps (Tweeddale, 1878)

1878 *Drymocataphus cinereiceps* Tweeddale, Proc. Zool. Soc. London, p. 617, (Puerto Princesa, Palawan)

Description: Top of head and hind neck gray; back, rump, tail, and wing-coverts dark chestnut; primaries dark brown; sides of face light gray; chin and throat white; upper breast, flanks, and thighs light chestnut; lower breast and belly white; under tail-coverts light chestnut.

Soft Parts: Bill, upper mandible black, lower mandible whitish; iris brown; feet pinkish.

Measurements: Wing 70; tail 35; bill 18; tarsus 28.

Range: Balabac and Palawan. (Endemic.)

BAGOBO BABBLER   PLATE 56

Leonardina woodi (Mearns, 1905)

1905 *Leonardia woodi* Mearns, Proc. Biol. Soc. Wash., **18**:2, (Mt. Apo, Mindanao)

Description: Top of head, back, and wings chestnut-brown; tail dark brown; sides of head dark gray; chin and throat white; breast and belly slate-gray; under tail-coverts olive-brown.

Soft Parts: Bill black; iris red-brown; feet black.

Measurements: Wing 88; tail 87; bill 20; tarsus 36.

Range: Mindanao. (Endemic.)

RED-HEADED TREE-BABBLER

PLATE 56

Malacopteron palawanense Büttikofer, 1895

1878   *Trichostoma rufifrons* Tweeddale, Proc. Zool. Soc. London, p. 616, (Puerto Princesa, Palawan)

1895   *Malacopteron palawanense* Büttikofer, Notes Leyden Mus., **17**:104, new name for *Trichostoma rufifrons* Tweeddale, 1878

Description: Forehead chestnut; top of head, back, and wings olive-brown; tail bright chestnut; sides of head gray; chin and throat white; breast and flanks whitish with an olive-brown wash; belly white; under tail-coverts pale rufous.

Soft Parts: Bill black; iris light yellow; feet black.

Measurements: Wing 89; tail 77; bill 22; tarsus 26.

Range: Balabac and Palawan. (Endemic.)

STREAKED GROUND-BABBLER

PLATE 56

Ptilocichla mindanensis mindanensis (Blasius, 1890)

1890   *Ptilopyga mindanensis* Blasius, Braunschweig. Anz., **87**:877, (Davao, Mindanao)

1890   *Ptilocichla (?) Mindanensis* Steere, List Bds. Mamms. Steere Expd., p. 18, (Ayala, Mindanao)

Description: Top of head blackish brown with light shaft streaks; rest of upperparts fulvous-brown; eyebrow stripe, chin, and throat white; breast and belly white with heavy blackish brown stripes.

Soft Parts: Bill, upper mandible black, lower mandible black with a yellow base; iris redbrown; feet dark brown.

Measurements: Wing 74; tail 50; bill 22; tarsus 26.

Range: Mindanao. (Endemic.)

Ptilocichla mindanensis minuta Bourns and Worcester, 1894

1894   *Ptilocichla minuta* Bourns and Worcester, Occ. Papers Minn. Acad. Nat. Sci., 1: 24, (Samar)

Description: Differs from *P. m. mindanensis* by having upperparts darker brown and shaft streaks on the back more pronounced; also smaller (wing 71; tail 47).

Range: Leyte and Samar. (Endemic.)

Ptilocichla mindanensis fortichi Rand and Rabor, 1957

1957   *Ptilocichla mindanensis fortichi* Rand and Rabor, Fieldiana: Zoology, **42**:13, (Cantaub, Sierra Bullones, Bohol)

Description: Differs from *minuta* by having the margins of the crown and back feathers black; lower back and rump darker; contrast between the blackish brown and white on the underparts is greater.

Range: Bohol. (Endemic.)

Ptilocichla mindanensis basilanica Steere, 1890

1890   *Ptiocichla* [sic] *Basilanica* Steere, List Bds. Mamms. Steere Expd., p. 18, (Basilan)

Description: Differs from *P. m. mindanensis* by having upperparts light reddish brown with pale shaft streaks.

Range: Basilan. (Endemic.)

FALCATED   GROUND-BABBLER   PLATE 56

Ptilocichla falcata Sharpe, 1877

1877   *Ptilocichla falcata* Sharpe, Trans. Linn. Soc. London, 1:332, (Puerto Princesa, Palawan)

Description: Forehead light chestnut; crown and hind neck dark chestnut; back and rump feathers extremely long with light shaft streaks and dark blackish brown margins; wings and tail chestnut; lores and ear-coverts dark brown; cheeks, chin, and throat white; breast and belly blackish brown with white shaft streaks.

Soft Parts: Bill buff; iris brown; feet dark brown.

Measurements: Wing 90; tail 71; bill 22; tarsus 33.

Range: Balabac and Palawan. (Endemic.)

LUZON   WREN-BABBLER   PLATE 56

Napothera rabori mesoluzonica duPont, 1971

1971   *Napothera rabori mesoluzonica* duPont, Nemouria, 3:3, (Barrio Saray, Pakil, Laguna, Luzon)

Description: Crown, hind neck, and back dark red-brown with black margins to feathers; elongated fluffy rump feathers and tail dark red-brown; primary wing-coverts black terminated with a white spot; rest of wing dark brown with outer red-brown margins to feathers; feathers of face gray with white shaft streaks; chin and throat white with a black jugular stripe on either side; breast dark gray; center of belly white; flanks chestnut; thighs and under tail-coverts dull red-brown.

Soft Parts: Bill, upper mandible blackish brown, lower mandible gray; iris brown; feet light brown.

Measurements: Wing 98; tail 84; bill 25; tarsus 32.

Range: Known only from the type locality. (Endemic.)

Napothera rabori sorsogonensis Rand and Rabor, 1967

1967 *Napothera sorsogonensis* Rand and Rabor, Fieldiana: Zoology, **51**:86, (Mt. Bulusan, San Rogue, Bulusan, Sorsogon Province, Luzon)

Description: Differs from *mesoluzonica* by having the upperparts lighter and the black margins to the feathers all but absent; gray breast band narrower; flanks and under tail-coverts paler.

Range: Known only from the type locality. (Endemic.)

Napothera rabori rabori Rand, 1960

1960 *Napothera rabori* Rand, Fieldiana: Zoology, **39**:377, (Tabbug, Pagudpud, Ilocos Norte, Luzon)

Description: Differs from *mesoluzonica* by having wider black margins to the feathers of the upperparts, giving an overall darker appearance; chestnut and red-brown underparts much darker.

Range: Known only from the type locality. (Endemic.)

PYGMY TREE-BABBLER   PLATE 57

Stachyris plateni plateni (Blasius, 1890)

1890 *Mixornis Plateni* Blasius, Braunschweig. Anz., **87**:877, (Davao, Mindanao)

Description: Top of head dark brown, forehead almost black, and both with white shaft streaks; a short crest is not prominent; back brown with obscure light shaft streaks; rump, wings, and tail brown; throat chestnut-brown with white shaft streaks becoming heavier on chin; breast, belly, and under tail-coverts pale gray.

Soft Parts: Bill blue-black; iris, outer ring red, inner ring light yellow; feet black.

Measurements: Wing 57; tail 46; bill 11; tarsus 15.

Range: Mindanao. (Endemic.)

Stachyris plateni pygmaea (Ogilvie-Grant, 1896)—PLATE 57

1896 *Zosterornis pygmaeus* Ogilvie-Grant, Bull. Brit. Orn. Cl., **6**:18, (Samar)

Description: Differs from *S. p. plateni* by being gray instead of brown, with light shaft streaks.

Range: Leyte and Samar. (Endemic.)

BLACK-CROWNED TREE-BABBLER   PLATE 57

Stachyris capitalis nigrocapitata (Steere, 1890)

1890 *Mixornis nigrocapitatus* Steere, List Bds. Mamms. Steere Expd., p. 17, (Samar and Leyte)

Description: Forehead and crown black; nape grayish chestnut; back gray with light shaft streaks; rump gray; wings and tail dark olive-brown; outer rectrices tipped with white; cheeks gray; throat yellow with rufous stripes on the sides; breast and belly pale gray with a yellowish wash.

Soft Parts: Bill black; iris red-brown; feet olive-brown.

Measurements: Wing 68; tail 60; bill 16; tarsus 20.

Range: Leyte and Samar. (Endemic.)

Stachyris capitalis affinis (McGregor, 1907)

1907   *Zosterornis affinis* McGregor, Phil. Journ. Sci., 2:292, (Lamao, Bataan Province, Luzon)

Description: Differs from *nigrocapitata* by having the upperparts more olive, the throat with rufous on the yellow, and the underparts heavily washed with olive-yellow.

Range: Southern Luzon. (Endemic.)

Stachyris capitalis dennistouni (Ogilvie-Grant, 1895)

1895   *Zosterornis dennistouni* Ogilvie-Grant, Bull. Brit. Orn. Cl., 5:2, (Cape Engaño, Luzon)

Description: Differs from *affinis* by having the forehead and crown bright yellow and the underparts much yellower.

Range: Northern Luzon. (Endemic.)

Stachyris capitalis boholensis Rand and Rabor, 1957

1957   *Stachyris nigrocapitata boholensis* Rand and Rabor, Fieldiana: Zoology, 42:14, (Cantaub, Sierra Bullones, Bohol)

Description: Differs from *nigrocapitata* by having reduced rufous stripes on the sides of the throat, the yellow of throat not streaked, and less chestnut on the nape.

Range: Bohol. (Endemic.)

Stachyris capitalis capitalis (Tweeddale, 1877)

1877   *Mixornis (?) capitalis* Tweeddale, Ann. Mag. Nat. His., 20:535, (Dinagat)

Description: Differs from *nigrocapitata* by having the forehead and crown chestnut and the back slightly darker gray.

Range: Dinagat, Mindanao, and Panaon. (Endemic.)

Stachyris capitalis isabelae Parkes, 1963

1963   *Stachyris capitalis isabelae* Parkes, Auk, 80:543, (Isabela, Basilan)

Description: Differs from *S. c. capitalis* by having more prominent shaft streaks on the crown and back; upperparts slightly duller; wing-coverts with pale shaft streaks. Wing longer (71.5 vs. 67.5).

Range: Basilan. (Endemic.)

ROUGH-TEMPLED TREE-BABBLER PLATE 57

Stachyris speciosa (Tweeddale, 1878)

1878 *Dasycrotapha speciosa* Tweeddale, Proc. Zool. Soc. London, p. 114, (Valencia, Negros)

Description: Forehead yellow; center of crown black; hind crown light olive-yellow followed by a black collar on the hind neck; back olive-gray with light shaft streaks; rump, wings, and tail olive-brown; lores, eye-ring, chin, and feathers at base of bill yellow; tufts above eye bright orange; ear-coverts black with white shaft streaks; throat yellow with large black spots; breast and belly olive.

Soft Parts: Bill light orange; iris red; feet olive.

Measurements: Wing 70; tail 58; bill 17; tarsus 18.

Range: Negros. (Endemic.)

WHITEHEAD'S TREE-BABBLER PLATE 57

Stachyris whiteheadi (Ogilvie-Grant, 1894)

1894 *Zosterornis whiteheadi* Ogilvie-Grant, Bull. Brit. Orn. Cl., **3**:50, ("mountains of northern Luzon" = Benguet)

1967 *Stachyris whiteheadi sorsogonensis* Rand and Rabor, Fieldiana: Zoology, **51**:88, (Mt. Bulusan, San Roque, Sorsogon Province, Luzon)

Description: Forehead, lores, sides of head, and chin dark chestnut; eye-ring white; crown and hind neck gray; back, wings, and tail olive; underparts olive-yellow.

Soft Parts: Bill black; iris brown; feet olive.

Measurements: Wing 68; tail 52; bill 16; tarsus 24.

Range: Luzon. (Endemic.)

STRIPED TREE-BABBLER PLATE 58

Stachyris striata (Ogilvie-Grant, 1894)

1894 *Zosterornis striatus* Ogilvie-Grant, Bull. Brit. Orn. Cl., **4**:ii, (Isabela Province, Luzon)

Description: Underparts olive-brown, crown somewhat grayer; eyebrow stripe black;

lores and eye-ring white; chin and throat white with a dark brown malar stripe; rest of underparts white washed with olive with heavy dark brown streaks.

Soft Parts: Bill black; iris light brown; feet dull olive.

Measurements: Wing 62; tail 51; bill 15; tarsus 17.

Range: Northern Luzon. (Endemic.)

NEGROS TREE-BABBLER   PLATE 58

Stachyris nigrorum Rand and Rabor, 1952

1952 *Stachyris nigrorum* Rand and Rabor, Nat. His. Misc., 100:1, (Cuernos de Negros, Negros Oriental, Negros)

Description: Nostril feathers white followed by a black band that extends over eyes; eye-ring white; crown, back, wings, and tail olive-brown; sides of head and throat whitish with a black patch below the eye; breast and belly olive-yellow with dull brown stripes.

Soft Parts: Bill black; iris unrecorded; feet gray-black.

Measurements: Wing 68; tail 54; bill 17; tarsus 22.

Range: Negros (highlands). (Endemic.)

PALAWAN TREE-BABBLER   PLATE 58

Stachyris hypogrammica Salomonsen, 1962

1962 *Stachyris hypogrammica* Salomonsen, (1961), Dansk Orn. Foren. Tidsskrift, **55**: 219, (Mt. Mataling, Palawan)

Description: Top of head dull orange-buff; back, wings, and tail olive-green; sides of head gray; throat whitish; breast and belly olive-yellow streaked with black.

Soft Parts: Bill black; iris unrecorded; feet olive.

Measurements: Wing 70; tail 56; bill 17; tarsus 21.

Range: Palawan. (Endemic.)

GRAY-FACED TIT-BABBLER   PLATE 58

Macronous gularis woodi (Sharpe, 1877)

1877 *Mixornis Woodi* Sharpe, Trans. Linn. Soc. London, 1:331, (Puerto Princesa, Palawan)

Description: Crown dark rufous; back gray-brown washed with rufous; rump, wings, and tail rufous; sides of face gray; throat light yellow with fine black streaks; breast and belly olive-gray.

Soft Parts: Bill black; iris orange; feet olive.

Measurements: Wing 62; tail 59; bill 15; tarsus 18.

Range: Balabac and Palawan. (Endemic.)

Macronous gularis cagayanensis (Guillemard, 1885)

1885   *Mixornis cagayanensis* Guillemard, Proc. Zool. Soc. London, p. 419, (Cagayan Sulu)

Description: Differs from *woodi* by having the crown streaked with black, all upperparts rufous-brown, cheeks dark brown with white streaks, and the throat white with black spots.

Range: Cagayan Sulu. (Endemic.)

BROWN   TIT-BABBLER   PLATE 58

Macronous striaticeps mindanensis Steere, 1890

1890   *Macronous Mindanensis* Steere, List Bds. Mamms. Steere Expd., p. 17, (Ayala, Mindanao)

1905   *Macronous mindanensis montanus* Mearns, Proc. Biol. Soc. Wash., **18**:4, (Mt. Apo, Mindanao)

1930   *Macronous striaticeps boholensis* Hachisuka, Orn. Soc. Japan, suppl. 14:193, (Tagbilaran, Bohol)

1934   *Minodoria striaticeps cumingi* Hachisuka, Tori, **8**:38, ("Manila"; error = Samar)

1951   *Macronous striaticeps mearnsi* Deignan, Bull. Raffles Mus., **23**:128, new name for *Macronous mindanensis montanus* Mearns, 1905

Description: Top of head black with white shaft streaks; rest of upperparts dark rufous; throat whitish; breast and belly buff-gray; under tail-coverts chestnut. There is a great deal of variation in this species.

Soft Parts: Bill black, tip of lower mandible gray; iris dirty white; feet gray.

Measurements: Wing 62; tail 61; bill 16; tarsus 20.

Range: Bohol, Leyte, Mindanao, and Samar. (Endemic.)

Macronous striaticeps striaticeps Sharpe, 1877

1877   *Macronous striaticeps* Sharpe, Trans. Linn. Soc. London, 1:331, (Malamaui Islet, Basilan)

Description: Differs from *mindanensis* by being darker on the sides of the head and neck, with light shaft streaks; throat whiter.

Range: Basilan and Malamaui. (Endemic.)

Macronous striaticeps kettlewelli Guillemard, 1885

1885   *Macronous kettlewelli* Guillemard, Proc. Zool. Soc. London, p. 262, (Lukatlapas, Jolo, Sulu Archipelago)

Description: Differs from *M. s. striaticeps* by being paler. Top of the head is brown, back has pale shaft streaks, and throat is darker.

Range: Sulu Archipelago. (Endemic.)

PLATE 56

A   ASHY-HEADED GROUND-BABBLER
     (*Trichastoma cinereiceps*)—page 262

B   BAGOBO BABBLER
     (*Leonardina woodi*)—page 262

C   RED-HEADED TREE-BABBLER
     (*Malacopteron palawanense*)—page 263

D   STREAKED GROUND-BABBLER
     (*Ptilocichla mindanensis*)—page 263

E   FALCATED GROUND-BABBLER
     (*Ptilocichla falcata*)—page 264

F   LUZON WREN-BABBLER
     (*Napothera rabori*)—page 264

270

PLATE 56

PLATE 57

A   PYGMY TREE-BABBLER
     (Stachyris p. plateni)—page 265

B   PYGMY TREE-BABBLER
     (Stachyris plateni pygmaea)—page 265

C   BLACK-CROWNED TREE-BABBLER
     (Stachyris capitalis)—page 265

D   ROUGH-TEMPLED TREE-BABBLER
     (Stachyris speciosa)—page 267

E   WHITEHEAD'S TREE-BABBLER
     (Stachyris whiteheadi)—page 267

272

A

B

C

D

E

SANDSTRÖM

PLATE 57

PLATE 58

A   PALAWAN TREE-BABBLER
        (Stachyris hypogrammica)—page 268

B   STRIPED TREE-BABBLER
        (Stachyris striata)—page 267

C   GRAY-FACED TIT-BABBLER
        (Macronous gularis)—page 268

D   NEGROS TREE-BABBLER
        (Stachyris nigrorum)—page 268

E   BROWN TIT-BABBLER
        (Macronous striaticeps)—page 269

F   MINIATURE TIT-BABBLER
        (Micromacronus leytensis)—page 276

PLATE 58

MINIATURE TIT-BABBLER PLATE 58

Micromacronus leytensis leytensis Amadon, 1962

1962 *Micromacronus leytensis* Amadon, Condor, **64**:3, (east side of Mt. Lobi, Leyte)

Description: Male—crown olive-green with black tips to feathers; wing-coverts bright olive-green; wings and tail black with an olive-green gloss; rump and midflank areas have specialized feathers made up of a few barbs on elongated white shafts that extend beyond the tail; lores and superciliary stripe yellow; underparts bright yellow. Female—duller yellow.

Soft Parts: Bill black; iris red; tarsus greenish gray; feet straw-yellow.

Measurements: Wing 41; tail 29; bill 9.5; tarsus 15.

Range: Leyte. (Endemic.)

Micromacronus leytensis sordidus Ripley and Rabor, 1968

1968 *Micromacronus leytensis sordidus* Ripley and Rabor, Proc. Biol. Soc. Wash., **81**:
33, (Mt. Matutum, Tupi, Cotabato Province, Mindanao)

Description: Differs from *M. l. leytensis* by being slightly darker and larger (wing 47; tail 31).

Range: Mindanao. (Endemic.)

Family PYCNONOTIDAE BULBULS

BLACK-HEADED BULBUL PLATE 59

Pycnonotus atriceps atriceps (Temminck, 1822)

1822 *Turdus atriceps* Temminck, Pl. Col., livr. 25, pl. 147, (Java and Sumatra = Java)

Description: Head, neck, and throat black with a purplish green gloss; back and wing-coverts olive; lower back feathers black with olive tips; primaries black; tail has olive base becoming black toward tip and terminating in yellow; breast dark olive; belly and under tail-coverts olive-yellow.

Soft Parts: Bill black; iris bright blue; feet black.

Measurements: Wing 78; tail 70; bill 15; tarsus 14.

Range: Palawan.

WATTLED BULBUL PLATE 59

Pycnonotus urostictus urostictus (Salvadori, 1870)

1870 *Brachypus urostictus* Salvadori, Atti. R. Accad. Sci. Torino, 5:509, (Philippine Islands = Luzon)

Description: Crown and crest gray; back, rump, wings, and tail olive-brown; outer rectrices tipped with white; throat and breast olive-brown; belly and under tail-coverts white.

Soft Parts: Bill black; iris dark brown; feet black.

Measurements: Wing 83; tail 76; bill 15; tarsus 16.

Range: Catanduanes, central and southern Luzon, Panaon, and Polillo. (Endemic.)

Pycnonotus urostictus ilokensis Rand and Rabor, 1967

1967   *Pycnonotus urostictus ilokensis* Rand and Rabor, Fieldiana: Zoology, **51**:86, (Balaoi, Pagudpud, Ilocos Norte, Luzon)

Description: Differs from *P. u. urostictus* by having darker underparts and less white on the tips of the rectrices.

Range: Northern Luzon. (Endemic.)

Pycnonotus urostictus atricaudatus Parkes, 1967

1967   *Pycnonotus urostictus atricaudatus* Parkes, Bull. Brit. Orn. Cl., **87**:24, (San Isidro, Samar)

Description: Differs from *P. u. urostictus* by having rectrices much blacker and more white on the tips, especially the central pair.

Range: Bohol, Leyte, and Samar. (Endemic.)

Pycnonotus urostictus philippensis (Hachisuka, 1934)

1934   *Poliolophus urostictus philippensis* Hachisuka, Tori, **8**:220, (Dinagat)

Description: Differs from *P. u. urostictus* by having paler underparts, especially the breast; tail spots large, as in *atricaudatus*.

Range: Dinagat, Mindanao, and Siargao. (Endemic.)

Pycnonotus urostictus basilanicus (Steere, 1890)

1890   *Poliolophus Basilanicus* Steere, List Bds. Mamms. Steere Expd., p. 19, (Basilan)

Description: Differs from *philippensis* by having a more olive back and the white extending further into the breast.

Range: Basilan. (Endemic.)

OLIVE-BROWN BULBUL   PLATE 59

Pycnonotus plumosus cinereifrons (Tweeddale, 1878)

1878   *Brachypus cinereifrons* Tweeddale, Proc. Zool. Soc. London, p. 617, (Puerto Princesa, Palawan)

Description: Crown olive-brown with gray tips to feathers; rest of upperparts olive-brown, but tail has a slight rufous wash; throat and breast olive-gray; belly pale olive-brown.

Soft Parts: Bill black; iris brown; feet brown.

Measurements: Wing 86; tail 81; bill 18; tarsus 20.

Range: Calamianes and Palawan. (Endemic.)

YELLOW-VENTED BULBUL   PLATE 59

Pycnonotus goiavier goiavier (Scopoli, 1786)

1786   *Muscicapa Goiavier* Scopoli, Del. Flor. et Faun. Insubr., p. 96, (Manila, Luzon)

Description: Forehead and center of crown brown bordered with dark brown on sides; rest of upperparts brown; stripe over eye and throat white; breast and belly gray streaked with brown; vent and under tail-coverts yellow.

Soft Parts: Bill black; iris dark brown; feet black.

Measurements: Wing 85; tail 86; bill 18; tarsus 19.

Range: Luzon, Marinduque, Mindoro, Negros, and Panay. (Endemic.)

Pycnonotus goiavier samarensis Rand and Rabor, 1960

1960   *Pycnonotus goiavier samarensis* Rand and Rabor, Fieldiana: Zoology, **35**:346, (Matuguinao, Samar)

Description: Differs from *P. g. goiavier* by having heavier streaks on the breast and darker flanks; also, smaller wing (80).

Range: Bohol, Cebu, Samar, and Ticao. (Endemic.)

Pycnonotus goiavier suluensis Mearns, 1909

1909   *Pycnonotus goiavier suluensis* Mearns, Proc. U. S. Nat. Mus., **36**:470, (Jolo)

Description: Differs from *goiavier* in slightly paler crown and definitely paler ear-coverts.

Range: Basilan, Mindanao, and Sulu Archipelago. (Endemic.)

WHITE-THROATED BULBUL   PLATE 59

Criniger bres frater Sharpe, 1877

1877   *Criniger frater* Sharpe, Trans. Linn. Soc. London, 1:334, (Puerto Princesa, Palawan)

Description: Top of head brown; back and rump olive-green; wings and tail brown; sides of head light gray; chin and throat gray; breast and belly golden yellow with olive tinge on flanks.

Soft Parts: Bill brown; iris red-brown; feet pale brown.

Measurements: Wing 109; tail 99; bill 22; tarsus 19.

Range: Balabac, Calamianes, and Palawan. (Endemic.)

OLIVE BULBUL

PLATE 60

Hypsipetes palawanensis (Tweeddale, 1878)

1878 *Criniger palawanensis* Tweeddale, Proc. Zool. Soc. London, p. 618, (Puerto Princesa, Palawan)

1888 *Iole striaticeps* Sharpe, Ibis, p. 200, (Palawan)

Description: Top of head, back, rump and wing-coverts olive-brown; wing primaries and tail dark rufous-brown; throat yellow-gray; breast olive; belly, vent, and under tail-coverts yellow; flanks olive.

Soft Parts: Bill black; iris yellow; feet brown.

Measurements: Wing 82; tail 79; bill 17; tarsus 19.

Range: Palawan. (Endemic.)

PHILIPPINE BULBUL

PLATE 60

Hypsipetes philippinus philippinus (J. R. Forster, 1795)

1795 *(Turdus) philippinus* J. R. Forster, Faunula Indica, p. 8, (Luzon)

1832 *G(algulus) philippinensis* Kittlitz, Kupfert. Naturg. Vögel, 1:8, (Luzon)

1844 *Hypsipetes philippensis* Strickland, Ann. Mag. Nat. His., 13:413, (Manila, Luzon)

1855 *Philedon gularis* "Cuvier" Pucheran, Arch. Mus. Hist. Nat., 7:344, (Luzon)

1916 *Iole philippinus saturatior* Hartert, Bull. Brit. Orn. Cl., 36:58, (Davao, Mindanao)

Description: Crown gray; back, rump, wings, and tail olive-brown; throat rufous with pale shaft streaks; breast rufous-brown; belly and under tail-coverts dirty white; thighs olive.

Soft Parts: Bill black; iris dark brown; feet dark brown.

Measurements: Wing 98; tail 91; bill 21; tarsus 18.

Range: Banton, Bohol, Cebu, Leyte, Luzon, Marinduque, eastern Mindanao, Panaon, Polillo, and Samar. (Endemic.)

PLATE 59

A   WHITE-THROATED BULBUL
      (Criniger bres)—page 278

B   OLIVE-BROWN BULBUL
      (Pycnonotus plumosus)—page 277

C   WATTLED BULBUL
      (Pycnonotus urostictus)—page 276

D   YELLOW-VENTED BULBUL
      (Pycnonotus goiavier)—page 278

E   BLACK-HEADED BULBUL
      (Pycnonotus atriceps)—page 276

PLATE 59

PLATE 60

A   OLIVE BULBUL
      (Hypsipetes palawanensis)—page 279

B   MOTTLED-BREASTED BULBUL
      (Hypsipetes siquijorensis)—page 284

C   PHILIPPINE BULBUL
      (Hypsipetes philippinus)—page 279

D   CHESTNUT-EARED BULBUL
      (Hypsipetes amaurotis)—page 286

E   PLAIN-THROATED BULBUL
      (Hypsipetes everetti)—page 285

PLATE 60

Hypsipetes philippinus guimarasensis (Steere, 1890)

1890   *Iole Guimarasensis* Steere, List Bds. Mamms. Steere Expd., p. 19, (Panay, Guimaras, Negros)

Description: Differs from *H. p. philippinus* by having a duller rufous throat; also, larger bill and substantially larger wing (112).
Range: Guimaras, Masbate, Negros, Panay, Ticao, and Verde. (Endemic.)

Hypsipetes philippinus mindorensis (Steere, 1890)

1890   *Iole Mindorensis* Steere, List Bds. Mamms. Steere Expd., p. 19, (Mindoro)
1890   *Jole schmackeri* Hartert, Journ. f. Orn., **38**:155, (Mt. Halcon, Mindoro)

Description: Differs from *philippinus* by having a deep olive throat and breast; rest of underparts also darker.
Range: Mindoro and Semirara Group. (Endemic.)

ZAMBOANGA   BULBUL

Hypsipetes rufigularis Sharpe, 1877

1877   *Hypsipetes rufigularis* Sharpe, Trans. Linn. Soc. London, **1**:335, (Malamaui Islet, Isabela, Basilan)

Description: Similar to *H. philippinus* (Plate 60) but differs by having a darker crown and being much larger (wing 125).
Range: Basilan and Mindanao (Lake Lanao and west). (Endemic.)

MOTTLED-BREASTED   BULBUL   PLATE 60

Hypsipetes siquijorensis siquijorensis (Steere, 1890)

1890   *Iole Siquijorensis* Steere, List Bds. Mamms. Steere Expd., p. 19, (Siquijor)

Description: Top of head very dark brown; rest of upperparts brown; throat and upper breast gray with heavy brown streaks; rest of underparts gray.
Soft Parts: Bill, upper mandible black, lower mandible dark brown; iris dark brown; feet black.
Measurements: Wing 130; tail 121; bill 30; tarsus 23.
Range: Siquijor. (Endemic.)

Hypsipetes siquijorensis monticola (Bourns and Worcester, 1894)

1894   *Iole monticola* Bourns and Worcester, Occ. Papers Minn. Acad. Nat. Sci., 1:25, (Cebu)

Description: Differs from *H. s. siquijorensis* by having a paler crown, more rufous back, and whiter throat; also, somewhat smaller.
Range: Cebu. (Extinct.)

Hypsipetes siquijorensis cinereiceps (Bourns and Worcester, 1894)

1894 *Iole cinereiceps* Bourns and Worcester, Occ. Papers Minn. Acad. Nat. Sci., 1:25, (Tablas and Romblon)

Description: Differs from *H. s. siquijorensis* by having the top of the head gray and the throat and upper breast white.
Range: Romblon and Tablas. (Endemic.)

PLAIN-THROATED BULBUL   PLATE 60

Hypsipetes everetti everetti (Tweeddale, 1877)

1877 *Criniger Everetti* Tweeddale, Ann. Mag. Nat. His., **20**:535, (Surigao, Mindanao)
Description: Upperparts olive-green; chin yellowish; throat and upper breast brown washed with yellow; rest of underparts yellow.
Soft Parts: Bill black; iris dark brown; feet black.
Measurements: Wing 120; tail 96; bill 26; tarsus 19.
Range: Dinagat and eastern and central Mindanao. (Endemic.)

Hypsipetes everetti samarensis Rand and Rabor, 1959

1959 *Hypsipetes everetti samarensis* Rand and Rabor, Auk, **76**:102, (San Isidro, Samar)
Description: Differs from *H. e. everetti* by having the upper- and underparts much duller.
Range: Leyte and Samar. (Endemic.)

Hypsipetes everetti haynaldi (Blasius, 1890)

1890 *Criniger Haynaldi* Blasius, Journ. f. Orn., **38**:143, (Jolo)
Description: Differs from *H. e. everetti* by being duller and having the upperparts browner, the underparts darker, and the wing shorter (110).
Range: Sulu Archipelago. (Endemic.)

Hypsipetes everetti catarmanensis Rand and Rabor, 1969

1969 *Hypsipetes everetti catarmanensis* Rand and Rabor, Fieldiana: Zoology, **51**:160, (Mt. Catarman, Camiguin South)
Description: Differs from *H. e. everetti* by having the crown brownish black and all other parts darker; also a longer wing (129).
Range: Camiguin South. (Endemic.)

CHESTNUT-EARED BULBUL   PLATE 60

Hypsipetes amaurotis batanensis Mearns 1907

1907   *Hypsipetes batanensis* Mearns, Phil. Journ. Sci., **2**:357, (Batan, northern Luzon)

Description: Top of head and hind neck gray-cinnamon; rest of upperparts dark rufous-brown; chin gray; ear-coverts and upper throat chestnut; breast and belly motley gray-brown.

Soft Parts: Bill dark brown; iris red-brown; feet dark brown.

Measurements: Wing 129; tail 128; bill 28; tarsus 25.

Range: Batan. (Endemic.)

Hypsipetes amaurotis fugensis Ogilvie-Grant, 1895

1895   *Hypsipetes fugensis* Ogilvie-Grant, Bull. Brit. Orn. Cl., **5**:2, (Fuga Island)

Description: Differs from *batanensis* by having the forehead grayer and being smaller overall.

Range: Calayan and Fuga. (Endemic.)

Hypsipetes amaurotis camiguinensis McGregor, 1907

1907   *Hypsipetes camiguinensis* McGregor, Phil. Journ. Sci., **2**:347, (Camiguin Island)

Description: Differs from *batanensis* by being slightly smaller and having grayer flanks.

Range: Camiguin North. (Endemic.)

Family IRENIDAE   LEAFBIRDS

BLACK-WINGED IORA   PLATE 61

Aegithina tiphia aequanimis Bangs, 1922

1922   *Aegithina tiphia aequanimis* Bangs, Bull. Mus. Comp. Zool., **65**:81, (Puerto Princesa, Palawan)

Description: Male—forehead golden yellow; crown and upper back light olive; lower back olive; wings black with large white spots in wing-coverts; tail black; throat and breast golden yellow; belly light yellow. Female—more olive, especially wings, tail, and underparts.

Soft Parts: Bill black, margins whitish; iris light yellow; feet black.

Measurements: Wing 64; tail 55; bill 17; tarsus 19.

Range: North Borneo and Palawan.

286

YELLOW-BILLED LEAFBIRD
PLATE 61

Chloropsis flavipennis flavipennis (Tweeddale, 1878)

1878 *Phyllornis flavipennis* Tweeddale, Proc. Zool. Soc. London, p. 761, (Cebu)

Description: Upperparts bright green; outer margins of primaries pale yellow; chin yellow-green; rest of underparts green.

Soft Parts: Bill black; iris dark brown; feet black.

Measurements: Wing 96; tail 78; bill 20; tarsus 18.

Range: Cebu and Leyte. (Endemic.)

Chloropsis flavipennis mindanensis Salomonsen, 1953

1953 *Chloropsis flavipennis mindanensis* Salomonsen, Vid. Medd. Dansk nat. Foren., **115**:270, (Agay, Agusan Province, Mindanao)

Description: Differs from *C. f. flavipennis* by being slightly larger (wing 102; bill 22).

Range: Mindanao. (Endemic.)

PALAWAN LEAFBIRD
PLATE 61

Chloropsis palawanensis (Sharpe, 1877)

1877 *Phyllornis palawanensis* Sharpe, Trans. Linn. Soc. London, **1**:333, (Puerto Princesa, Palawan)

Description: Top of head, back, rump, and wing-coverts bright green; primaries black with blue margins; tail dark green; lores and base of bill bright blue-green; chin and throat orange-yellow; rest of underparts bright grass-green.

Soft Parts: Bill black; iris brown; feet black.

Measurements: Wing 91; tail 79; bill 20; tarsus 19.

Range: Balabac, Calamianes, and Palawan. (Endemic.)

PALAWAN FAIRY BLUEBIRD
PLATE 61

Irena puella tweeddalei Sharpe, 1877

1877 *Irena tweeddalei* Sharpe, Cat. Bds. Brit. Mus., **3**:268, (Balabac)

Description: Male—top of head, back, rump, wing-coverts, and upper and under tail-coverts bright turquoise-blue; all other parts black. Female—dull blue-green.

Soft Parts: Bill black; iris dark red; feet black.

Measurements: Wing 129; tail 99; bill 26; tarsus 16.

Range: Balabac, Calamianes, and Palawan. (Endemic.)

PLATE 61

A   PHILIPPINE FAIRY BLUEBIRD
     (Irena cyanogaster)—page 290

B   YELLOW-BILLED LEAFBIRD
     (Chloropsis flavipennis)—page 287

C   BLACK-WINGED IORA
     (Aegithina tiphia), male—page 286

D   BLACK-WINGED IORA
     (Aegithina tiphia), female—page 286

E   PALAWAN FAIRY BLUEBIRD
     (Irena puella), male—page 287

F   PALAWAN FAIRY BLUEBIRD
     (Irena puella), female—page 287

G   PALAWAN LEAFBIRD
     (Chloropsis palawanensis)—page 287

288

PLATE 61

PHILIPPINE FAIRY BLUEBIRD   PLATE 61

Irena cyanogaster cyanogaster Vigors, 1831

1831   *Irena cyanogaster* Vigors, Proc. Zool. Soc. London, p. 97, (Manila, Luzon)

Description: Male—crown, rump, wing-coverts, and under tail-coverts cobalt-blue; rest of the bird black tinged with blue. Female—similar to male but much duller.

Soft Parts: Bill black; iris dark red; feet black.

Measurements: Wing 134; tail 118; bill 27; tarsus 19.

Range: Luzon and Polillo. (Endemic.)

Irena cyanogaster ellae Steere, 1890

1890   *Irena Ellae* Steere, List Bds. Mamms. Steere Expd., p. 18, (Catbalogan, Samar)

Description: Male—differs from *I. c. cyanogaster* by having the cobalt parts brighter and the rest of the bird pure black.

Range: Leyte and Samar. (Endemic.)

Irena cyanogaster melanochlamys Sharpe, 1877

1877   *Irena melanochlamys* Sharpe, Cat. Bds. Brit. Mus., 3:226, (Basilan)

Description: Differs from *ellae* by having dark blue lower underparts in the male and female.

Range: Basilan. (Endemic.)

Irena cyanogaster hoogstraali Rand, 1948

1948   *Irena cyanogaster hoogstraali* Rand, Fieldiana: Zoology, **31**:203, (Burung-kot, Upi Municipality, Cotabato Province, Mindanao)

Description: Differs from *melanochlamys* by having the upperparts much duller blue and by lacking the purplish tinge.

Range: Mindanao. (Endemic.)

Family TURDIDAE   THRUSHES

BLUE SHORTWING   PLATE 62

Brachypteryx montana poliogyna Ogilvie-Grant, 1895

1895   *Brachypteryx poliogyna* Ogilvie-Grant, Bull. Brit. Orn. Cl., **4**:40, (Lepanto, northern Luzon)

Description: Male—upperparts dark blue; eyebrow stripe white; lores black; underparts dark blue shading to gray on lower belly. Female—similar to male but with a dark chestnut head and neck; throat paler chestnut.

Soft Parts: Bill black; iris dark brown; feet black.

Measurements: Wing 66; tail 47; bill 14; tarsus 29.

Range: Northern and central Luzon and Mindoro. (Endemic.)

Brachypteryx montana andersoni Rand and Rabor, 1967

1967 *Brachypteryx montana andersoni* Rand and Rabor, Fieldiana: Zoology, **51**:86, (Mt. Isarog, southern Luzon)

Description: Female—differs from *poliogyna* by having the crown darker brown, belly darker gray, and under tail-coverts slate colored.

Range: Known only from the type locality. (Endemic.)

Brachypteryx montana sillimani Ripley and Rabor, 1962

1962 *Brachypteryx montana sillimani* Ripley and Rabor, Postilla, **73**:6, (Magtaguimbong, Mt. Mantalingajan, Palawan)

Description: Differs from *poliogyna* by having the blue of the upper- and underparts much brighter and by having a longer bill (17).

Range: Palawan. (Endemic.)

Brachypteryx montana brunneiceps Ogilvie-Grant, 1896

1896 *Brachypteryx brunneiceps* Ogilvie-Grant, Ibis, p. 526, (Negros)

Description: Male—differs from *poliogyna* by having the top of head and throat blue-black. Female—underparts darker; also smaller (wing ♂ 64; tail 44).

Range: Negros. (Endemic.)

Brachypteryx montana malindangensis Mearns, 1909

1909 *Brachypteryx malindangensis* Mearns, Proc. U. S. Nat. Mus., **36**:441, (Mt. Malindang, Mindanao)

Description: Differs from *mindanensis* by having upperparts much darker and the white eyebrows reduced.

Range: Mt. Malindang, Mindanao. (Endemic.)

Brachypteryx montana mindanensis Mearns, 1905

1905 *Brachypteryx mindanensis* Mearns, Proc. Biol. Soc. Wash., **18**:3, (Mt. Apo, Mindanao)

Description: Differs from *brunneiceps* by being larger (wing 70; tail 62).

Range: Mt. Apo, Mindanao. (Endemic.)

PLATE 62

A   BLUE SHORTWING
      (Brachypteryx montana), male—page 290

B   BLUE SHORTWING
      (Brachypteryx montana), female—page 290

C   RUBY-THROAT
      (Erithacus calliope), female—page 294

D   RUBY-THROAT
      (Erithacus calliope), male—page 294

E   DYAL THRUSH
      (Copsychus saularis), female—page 294

F   DYAL THRUSH
      (Copsychus saularis), male—page 294

G   BLACK SHAMA
      (Copsychus cebuensis)—page 296

H   PALAWAN SHAMA
      (Copsychus niger)—page 295

I   WHITE-EYEBROWED SHAMA
      (Copsychus luzoniensis), male—page 295

J   WHITE-EYEBROWED SHAMA
      (Copsychus luzoniensis), female—page 295

K   PHILIPPINE WATER REDSTART
      (Rhyacornis bicolor)—page 294

PLATE 62

RUBY-THROAT   PLATE 62

Erithacus calliope (Pallas, 1776)

1776   *Motacilla Calliope* Pallas, Reise Versch. Prov. Russ. Reichs, **3**:697, (between the
          Yenisei and Lena Rivers)

Description: Male—top of head and upperparts olive-brown; eye stripe white; lores black; malar patch white; chin and throat bright red bordered with black; breast dark gray; center of belly and under tail-coverts white; flanks olive-brown. Female—similar to male but with paler lores and whitish throat.

Soft Parts: Bill dark brown; iris brown; feet light brown.

Measurements: Wing 81; tail 65; bill 13; tarsus 30.

Range: Found throughout the Philippines wintering from northeast Asia.

PHILIPPINE   WATER   REDSTART   PLATE 62

Rhyacornis bicolor (Ogilvie-Grant, 1894)

1894   *Chimarrhornis* [sic] *bicolor* Ogilvie-Grant, Bull. Brit. Orn. Cl., **3**:49, (northern
          Luzon)

Description: Male—head, back, throat, and breast dark blue; rump and tail bright chestnut; lores black; belly and under tail-coverts chestnut. Female—much duller than male and with a brown tail.

Soft Parts: Bill black; iris dark brown; feet black.

Measurements: Wing 77; tail 58; bill 14; tarsus 25.

Range: Northern Luzon. (Endemic.)

DYAL   THRUSH   PLATE 62

Copsychus saularis deuteronymus Parkes, 1963

1962   *Copsychus saularis heterogynus* Parkes, Postilla, 63:3, (Pangil, Laguna, Luzon)

1963   *Copsychus saularis deuteronymus* Parkes, Bull. Brit. Orn. Cl., **83**:50, new name
          for *Copsychus saularis heterogynus* Parkes, 1962

Description: Male—head, back, rump, throat, and upper breast black with a blue gloss; wings dull black with a white stripe; tail black; rest of underparts white. Female—similar to the male but black is replaced with gray; white underparts heavily washed with buff.

Soft Parts: Bill black; iris black; feet black.

Measurements: Wing 90; tail 86; bill 17; tarsus 26.

Range: Luzon. (Endemic.)

Copsychus saularis mindanensis (Boddaert, 1783)

1783 *Turdus mindanensis* Boddaert, Table Pl., enlum., p. 38, (Philippine Islands
 = Mindanao)

Description: Female—differs from *deuteronymus* by having the white underparts only slightly washed with buff. Bills in this form get larger from north to south approaching the Sulus (on Sanga Sanga, bill = 18).

Range: Basilan, Bohol, Cebu, Mindanao, Mindoro, Negros, Samar, Sibuyan, Siquijor, Sulu Archipelago, and Ticao. (Endemic.)

WHITE-EYEBROWED SHAMA   PLATE 62

Copsychus luzoniensis luzoniensis (Kittlitz, 1832)

1832 *Turdus luzoniensis* Kittlitz, Kupfert. Naturg. Vögel, 1:7, (Luzon)

Description: Male—head, back, and throat black; long superciliary stripe white; lower back and rump chestnut; wing black with a white patch; tail black, outer rectrices tipped with white; underparts white; thighs buffy. Female—similar to male but black is replaced with brown.

Soft Parts: Bill black; iris black; feet pinkish.

Measurements: Wing 76; tail 75; bill 16; tarsus 26.

Range: Catanduanes, Luzon, and Marinduque. (Endemic.)

Copsychus luzoniensis parvimaculata (McGregor, 1910)

1910 *Kittacincla parvimaculata* McGregor, Phil. Journ. Sci., 5:112, (Polillo)

Description: Differs from *C. l. luzoniensis* by having much smaller white tips to the rectrices.

Range: Polillo. (Endemic.)

Copsychus luzoniensis superciliaris (Bourns and Worcester, 1894)

1894 *Cittocincla superciliaris* Bourns and Worcester, Occ. Papers Minn. Acad. Nat. Sci., 1:23, (Masbate, Negros, Ticao)

Description: Differs from *C. l. luzoniensis* by lacking chestnut rump and having a wider and more prominent superciliary stripe.

Range: Masbate, Negros, Panay, and Ticao. (Endemic.)

PALAWAN SHAMA   PLATE 62

Copsychus niger (Sharpe, 1877)

1877 *Cittocincla niger* Sharpe, Trans. Linn. Soc. London, 1:335, (Palawan)

Description: Male—all black with a blue gloss, except for lower flank, under tail-coverts, and outer rectrices, which are white. Female—similar to male but having black duller and having buffy white on lower abdomen.

Soft Parts: Bill black; iris dark brown; feet black.

Measurements: Wing 92; tail 109; bill 18; tarsus 25.

Range: Balabac, Calamianes, and Palawan. (Endemic.)

BLACK SHAMA   PLATE 62

Copsychus cebuensis (Steere, 1890)

1890 *Cittocincla cebuensis* Steere, List Bds. Mamms. Steere Expd., p. 20, (Cebu)

Description: All black with a blue gloss. A wattle around the eye. Female—somewhat duller.

Soft Parts: Bill black; iris dark brown; feet blackish.

Measurements: Wing 88; tail 111; bill 16; tarsus 26.

Range: Cebu. (Endemic.)

PIED   CHAT   PLATE 63

Saxicola caprata caprata (Linnaeus, 1766)

1766 *Motacilla Caprata* Linnaeus, Syst. Nat., **1**:335, (Luzon)

Description: Male—all black with a bluish gloss, except rump, wing-coverts, and under tail-coverts, which are white; tips of thigh feathers are also white. Female—upperparts brown with black mottling; rump rufous; tail dark brown; underparts pale gray-brown with a rufous wash; vent tufts rufous.

Soft Parts: Bill black; iris dark brown; feet black.

Measurements: Wing 66; tail 48; bill 12; tarsus 19.

Range: Luzon, Marinduque, Mindoro, and Ticao. (Endemic.)

Saxicola caprata randi Parkes, 1960

1960 *Saxicola caprata randi* Parkes, Proc. Biol. Soc. Wash., **73**:59, (Bondo, Siaton, Negros)

Description: Female—differs from *S. c. caprata* by having upperparts darker and the throat paler and more grayish; underparts with heavy black shaft streaks.

Range: Bohol, Cebu, Negros, and Siquijor. (Endemic.)

Saxicola caprata anderseni Salomonsen, 1953

1953 *Saxicola caprata anderseni* Salomonsen, Vid. Medd. Dansk nat. Foren., **115**:260, (Del Monte, Bukidnon Province, Mindanao)

296

Description: Female—differs from *S. c. caprata* by being much paler and grayer underneath; in many birds the dark shaft streaks of the breast feathers are almost absent.

Range: Mindanao. (Endemic.)

WHEATEAR   PLATE 63

Oenanthe oenanthe oenanthe (Linnaeus, 1758)

1758   *Motacilla oenanthe* Linnaeus, Syst. Nat., 1:186, (Sweden)

Description: Forehead and eye stripe white; top of head and back gray; rump white; wings dark brown; basal half of tail is white and terminal half is black; lores and ear-coverts black; underparts white with a pinkish wash.

Soft Parts: Bill black; iris dark brown; feet black.

Measurements: Wing 97; tail 57; bill 15; tarsus 27.

Range: Calayan (once); a visitor from Asia.

BLUE   ROCK   THRUSH   PLATE 63

Monticola solitarius philippensis (P. L. S. Müller, 1776)

1776   *Turdus Philippensis* P. L. S. Müller, Natursyst., suppl., 1776:145, (Philippines)

Description: Male—upperparts, throat, and upper breast blue; wings and tail brown-black; lower breast, belly, and under tail-coverts dark chestnut. Female—top of head and mantle gray-brown mottled with black and egg-shell white; lower back and rump blue-gray mottled with black; wings and tail black; underparts rufous-buff heavily mottled with black.

Soft Parts: Bill black; iris dark brown; feet black.

Measurements: Wing 114; tail 85; bill 23; tarsus 27.

Range: Found throughout the Philippines; a winter visitor.

KUHL'S   GROUND   THRUSH   PLATE 63

Zoothera interpres interpres (Temminck, 1826)

1826   *Turdus interpres* Temminck, Pl. Col., livr. 78, pl. 458, (Java and Sumatra)

1934   *Geokichla interpres minima* Hachisuka, Tori, **8**:221, (Basilan)

Description: Top of head and hind neck bright chestnut; back, rump, wings, and tail dark gray-brown; wings with large white spots; lores, ear-coverts, and chin white; throat black; breast white with black spots; belly and under tail-coverts white.

Soft Parts: Bill dark brown; iris dark brown; feet pinkish.

Measurements: Wing 112; tail 63; bill 18; tarsus 27.

Range: Basilan and Sulu Archipelago.

PLATE 63

A   SUNDA GROUND THRUSH
      (Zoothera andromedae)—page 300

B   PIED CHAT
      (Saxicola caprata), female—page 296

C   PIED CHAT
      (Saxicola caprata), male—page 296

D   WHEATEAR
      (Oenanthe oenanthe)—page 297

E   ASHY GROUND THRUSH
      (Zoothera cinerea)—page 300

F   BLUE ROCK THRUSH
      (Monticola solitarius), female—page 297

G   BLUE ROCK THRUSH
      (Monticola solitarius), male—page 297

H   GOLDEN GROUND THRUSH
      (Zoothera dauma)—page 300

I   KUHL'S GROUND THRUSH
      (Zoothera interpres)—page 297

PLATE 63

ASHY GROUND THRUSH
PLATE 63

Zoothera cinerea (Bourns and Worcester, 1894)

1894 *Geocichla cinerea* Bourns and Worcester, Occ. Papers Minn. Acad. Nat. Sci., 1:23, (Mindoro)

Description: Upperparts dark bluish gray; wings with two white bars, outer rectrices tipped with white; lores and chin white; sides of throat and breast heavily spotted with black; belly white with a few large black spots becoming more numerous on the flanks; under tail-coverts white.

Soft Parts: Bill black; iris dark brown; feet white.

Measurements: Wing 111; tail 71; bill 20; tarsus 30.

Range: Luzon and Mindoro. (Endemic.)

SUNDA GROUND THRUSH
PLATE 63

Zoothera andromedae (Temminck, 1826)

1826 *Myiothera andromedae* Temminck, Pl. Col., livr. 66, pl. 392, (Java and Sumatra)

1907 *Geocichla mindanensis* Mearns, Phil. Journ. Sci., **2**:359, (Mt. Malindang, Mindanao)

Description: Top of head, back, and rump dark gray, some feathers having black tips; wings and tail brown-black; lores and eye-ring white; malar patch and ear-coverts' feathers white with black tips; chin white with a black stripe on sides; throat and upper breast dark gray; center of lower breast, belly, and under tail-coverts white; flank feathers white with black margins.

Soft Parts: Bill dark brown; iris dark brown; feet dark brown.

Measurements: Wing 119; tail 65; bill 26; tarsus 29.

Range: Luzon, Mindanao, and Mindoro.

GOLDEN GROUND THRUSH
PLATE 63

Zoothera dauma aurea (Holandre, 1825)

1825 *Turdus aureus* Holandre, Ann. Moselle, p. 60, (Metz, France)

Description: Top of head, back, and rump feathers golden brown with dark brown tips; wing-coverts dark brown with golden tips; primaries dark brown with pale outer margins; tail dark brown, central rectrices dark golden, and outer rectrices tipped with white; chin white; feathers of sides of face, throat, and upper breast golden buff with dark brown tips; feathers of lower breast, belly, and flanks white with dark brown tips; under tail-coverts white.

Soft Parts: Bill dark brown; iris olive-brown; feet yellow-brown.

Measurements: Wing 164; tail 110; bill 29; tarsus 34.

Range: Luzon, Mindoro, and Palawan; a winter visitor.

ISLAND THRUSH   PLATE 64

Turdus poliocephalus thomassoni (Seebohm, 1894)

1894 *Merula thomassoni* Seebohm, Bull. Brit. Orn. Cl., 3:51, (mountains of northern
Luzon)

Description: Top of head, neck, throat, and upper breast brown; rest of bird dark
brown-black. Female—dark brown.

Soft Parts: Bill yellow; iris dark brown; feet yellow.

Measurements: Wing 124; tail 101; bill 24; tarsus 32.

Range: Northern Luzon. (Endemic.)

Turdus poliocephalus mayonensis (Mearns, 1907)

1907 *Merula mayonensis* Mearns, Phil. Journ. Sci., 2:358, (Mt. Mayon, Albay Province,
Luzon)

Description: Differs from *thomassoni* by having the head, neck, and throat uniform dark
brown-black like the rest of the bird.

Range: Southern Luzon. (Endemic.)

Turdus poliocephalus mindorensis Ogilvie-Grant, 1896

1896 *Turdus mindorensis* Ogilvie-Grant, Ibis, p. 465, (Mindoro)

Description: Head and neck light brown; rest of upperparts dark brown; chin and throat
light brown; upper breast, sides of breast, and flanks dark chestnut; center of breast and
belly white.

Range: Mindoro. (Endemic.)

Turdus poliocephalus nigrorum Ogilvie-Grant, 1896

1896 *Turdus nigrorum* Ogilvie-Grant, Ibis, p. 544, ("Volcano of Canloon"= Mt. Canlaon, Negros)

Description: Upperparts brown; underparts brown, paler on breast and belly.

Range: Negros. (Endemic.)

Turdus poliocephalus malindangensis (Mearns, 1907)

1907 *Merula malindangensis* Mearns, Phil. Journ. Sci., 2:357, (Mt. Malindang, Mindanao)

Description: Upperparts dark brown; chin and throat pale brown; sides of breast, flanks, and under tail-coverts brown; center of breast and belly white.
Range: Mt. Malindang, Mindanao. (Endemic.)

Turdus poliocephalus katanglad Salomonsen, 1953

1953   *Turdus poliocephalus katanglad* Salomonsen, Vid. Medd. Dansk nat. Foren., **115**: 277, (Mt. Katanglad, Mindanao)

Description: Upperparts dark brown; top of head and neck lighter; chin and throat light brown; breast with a dark brown band; sides of breast and flanks dark chestnut; center of breast and belly white.
Range: Mt. Katanglad, Mindanao. (Endemic.)

Turdus poliocephalus kelleri (Mearns, 1905)

1905   *Merula kelleri* Mearns, Proc. Biol. Soc. Wash., **18**:6, (Mt. Apo, Mindanao)

Description: Entire bird dark brown with a light brown head, neck, chin, and throat.
Range: Mt. Apo, Mindanao. (Endemic.)

JAPANESE BROWN THRUSH   PLATE 64

Turdus chrysolaus chrysolaus Temminck, 1831

1831   *Turdus chrysolaus* Temminck, Pl. Col., livr. 87, pl. 537, (Japan)

Description: Upperparts olive-brown; chin and throat white; male has head, face, and throat streaked with dark brown (light brown in females); breast and flanks bright rufous; belly and under tail-coverts white.
Soft Parts: Bill dark brown, base of lower mandible yellowish; iris dark brown; feet light brown.
Measurements: Wing 117; tail 90; bill 18; tarsus 28.
Range: Calayan and Luzon; a winter visitor from eastern Asia.

PALE THRUSH   PLATE 64

Turdus pallidus Gmelin, 1789

1789   *Turdus pallidus* Gmelin, Syst. Nat., **1**:815, (Siberia)

Description: Top of head pale gray-brown; rest of upperparts pale brown; wings and tail dark brown, outer rectrices with white ends; chin white; throat white with rufous-gray streaks; breast rufous-gray; belly pale gray; under tail-coverts white.
Soft Parts: Bill dark brown, base of lower mandible yellowish; iris dark brown; feet light brown.

Measurements: Wing 122; tail 90; bill 20; tarsus 33.

Range: Calayan; a visitor from eastern Asia.

DUSKY THRUSH   PLATE 64

Turdus obscurus Gmelin, 1789

1789   *Turdus obscurus* Gmelin, Syst. Nat., **1**:816, (Siberia)

Description: Head and neck olive-gray; chin and stripe above and below eye white; back, rump, wings, and tail olive-brown; chin white; throat gray; breast and flanks bright rufous; belly and under tail-coverts white.

Soft Parts: Bill dark brown, base of lower mandible yellowish; iris dark brown; feet light brown.

Measurements: Wing 125; tail 91; bill 21; tarsus 29.

Range: Calayan, Guimaras, Luzon, Mindanao, and Negros; a visitor from Asia.

Family SYLVIIDAE   OLD WORLD WARBLERS

YELLOW-BREASTED WREN-WARBLER   PLATE 65

Gerygone sulphurea simplex Cabanis, 1872

1872   *Gerygone simplex* Cabanis, Journ. f. Orn., **20**:316, (Luzon)

1905   *Gerygone rhizophorae* Mearns, Proc. Biol. Soc. Wash., **18**:7, (Mindanao)

Description: Upperparts dark olive-brown; lores white; underparts yellowish.

Soft Parts: Bill black; iris dark brown; feet black.

Measurements: Wing 52; tail 35; bill 12; tarsus 16.

Range: Bohol, Cebu, Lubang, Luzon, Mindanao, Mindoro, Negros, Sulu Archipelago, and Verde.

BUSH-WARBLER   PLATE 65

Cettia diphone canturians (Swinhoe, 1860)

1860   *Arundinax canturians* Swinhoe, Ibis, p. 52, (Shanghai, China)

Description: Crown dark rufous-brown; rest of upperparts olive-brown; wings rufous-brown; superciliary white; underparts gray-white; flanks and under tail-coverts buffy. Female—similar to male but much smaller.

Soft Parts: Bill horn color; iris chestnut; feet buffy white.

Measurements: Wing ♂76, ♀63; tail ♂77, ♀61; bill 14; tarsus 26.

Range: Luzon; a winter visitor from Siberia.

PLATE 64

A   ISLAND THRUSH
     (Turdus poliocephalus nigrorum), Negros—page 301

B   ISLAND THRUSH
     (Turdus poliocephalus mindorensis), Mindoro—page 301

C   ISLAND THRUSH
     (Turdus poliocephalus thomassoni), Northern Luzon—page 301

D   DUSKY THRUSH
     (Turdus obscurus)—page 303

E   JAPANESE BROWN THRUSH
     (Turdus chrysolaus)—page 302

F   PALE THRUSH
     (Turdus pallidus)—page 302

PLATE 64

PLATE 65

A   BUSH-WARBLER
     (Cettia diphone)—page 303

B   YELLOW-BREASTED WREN-WARBLER
     (Gerygone sulphurea)—page 303

C   RUSSET SCRUB WARBLER
     (Bradypterus luteoventris)—page 308

D   MOUNTAIN BUSH-WARBLER
     (Cettia montana)—page 308

E   LONG-TAILED GROUND WARBLER
     (Bradypterus caudatus)—page 309

A

B

C

D

E

SANDSTRÖM

PLATE 65

Cettia diphone seebohmi Ogilvie-Grant, 1894

1894 *Cettia seebohmi* Ogilvie-Grant, Ibis, p. 507, (northern Luzon)

Description: Differs from *canturians* by having the upperparts more rufous, the lores darker, and the underparts grayer. Both sexes are the same size (similar in size to the female of *canturians*).

Range: Mountains of northern Luzon. (Endemic.)

Cettia diphone borealis Campbell, 1892

1892 *Cettia minuta borealis* Campbell, Ibis, p. 235, (Chemulpo, Korea)

Description: Differs from *canturians* by having upperparts paler rufous and underparts lighter buff; it has, on the average, a longer wing; bill is smaller and more slender.

Range: Luzon; a winter visitor from Siberia.

MOUNTAIN BUSH-WARBLER   PLATE 65

Cettia montana palawana Ripley and Rabor, 1962

1962 *Cettia montana palawana* Ripley and Rabor, Postilla, 73:10, (Mt. Mantalingajan, Palawan)

Description: Upperparts dark chestnut-brown; throat olive-gray; rest of underparts olive-buff; flanks and under tail-coverts olive-brown.

Soft Parts: Unrecorded.

Measurements: Wing 53; tail ♂57, ♀51; bill 15; tarsus 21.

Range: Palawan. (Endemic.)

RUSSET SCRUB WARBLER   PLATE 65

Bradypterus luteoventris seebohmi Ogilvie-Grant, 1895

1895 *Bradypterus luteoventris seebohmi* Ogilvie-Grant, Bull. Brit. Orn. Cl., 4:40, (northern Luzon)

Description: Upperparts dark rufous-brown; chin, throat, center of breast, and belly whitish; sides of throat and flanks gray-brown.

Soft Parts: Bill, upper mandible black, lower mandible flesh color; iris brown; feet flesh color.

Measurements: Wing 51; tail 62; bill 11; tarsus 20.

Range: Northern Luzon. (Endemic.)

LONG-TAILED GROUND WARBLER PLATE 65

Bradypterus caudatus caudatus (Ogilvie-Grant, 1895)

1895 *Pseudotharrhaleus caudatus* Ogilvie-Grant, Bull. Brit. Orn. Cl., 4:40, (northern Luzon)

Description: Upperparts dark brown; tail dark chestnut-brown; lores gray-white; chin and throat white streaked with gray; breast dark gray; belly and under tail-coverts dark brown.

Soft Parts: Bill, upper mandible black, lower mandible whitish; iris light brown; feet dark brown.

Measurements: Wing 64; tail 87; bill 16; tarsus 26.

Range: Northern Luzon. (Endemic.)

Bradypterus caudatus unicolor (Hartert, 1904)

1904 *Pseudotharrhaleus unicolor* Hartert, Bull. Brit. Orn. Cl., 14:74, (Mt. Apo, Mindanao)

1905 *Pseudotharrhaleus griseipectus* Mearns, Proc. Biol. Soc. Wash., 18:2, (Mt. Apo, Mindanao)

Description: Differs from *B. c. caudatus* by having the upperparts darker, the underparts more rufous, and the tail shorter (80).

Range: Mt. Apo, Mindanao. (Endemic.)

Bradypterus caudatus malindangensis (Mearns, 1909)

1909 *Pseudotharrhaleus malindangensis* Mearns, Proc. U. S. Nat. Mus., 36:441, (Mt. Malindang, Mindanao)

Description: Differs from *unicolor* by having the sides of the face darker brown and the throat whiter.

Range: Mt. Malindang, Mindanao. (Endemic.)

STRIATED CANEGRASS WARBLER PLATE 66

Megalurus palustris forbesi Bangs, 1919

1919 *Megalurus palustris forbesi* Bangs, Proc. New Eng. Zool. Cl., 7:5, (Baguio, Luzon)

Description: Crown and hind neck buffy with faint shaft streaks; back and wing-coverts dark brown with buffy margins; tail brownish; chin and throat white; breast pale buff with fine black streaks; belly white, washed with buff; flanks and under tail-coverts buffy. Immature—upperparts more reddish and underparts strongly washed with yellow.

Soft Parts: Bill, upper mandible dark brown, lower mandible whitish; iris brown; feet pinkish brown.

Measurements: Wing 99; tail 138; bill 22; tarsus 37.

Range: Luzon to Mindanao. (Endemic.)

RUFOUS-CAPPED CANEGRASS WARBLER   PLATE 66

Megalurus timoriensis tweeddalei McGregor, 1908

1877   *Megalurus ruficeps* Tweeddale, Ann. Mag. Nat. His., **20**:94, ("Monte Alban" = Montalban, Rizal Prov., Luzon)

1908   *Megalurus tweeddalei* McGregor, Phil. Journ. Sci., **3**:283, new name for *Megalurus ruficeps* Tweeddale, 1877, preoccupied

Description: Crown pale rufous; back and wings olive-brown with buffy margins to feathers, giving a streaked appearance; tail rufous-brown; superciliary white; chin, throat, and central parts of breast and belly white; flanks and under tail-coverts buffy.

Soft Parts: Bill, upper mandible black, lower mandible greenish; iris brown; feet light brown.

Measurements: Wing 78; tail 136; bill 19; tarsus 29.

Range: Luzon, Marinduque, Panay, Tablas, and Ticao. (Negros and Samar specimens are intermediate with *alopex*.) (Endemic.)

Megalurus timoriensis mindorensis Salomonsen, 1953

1953   *Megalurus timoriensis mindorensis* Salomonsen, Vid. Medd. Dansk nat. Foren., **115**:265, (Mt. Halcon, Mindoro)

Description: Differs from *tweeddalei* by having the crown darker rufous and the rest of the upperparts darker.

Range: Mindoro. (Endemic.)

Megalurus timoriensis alopex Parkes, 1970

1970   *Megalurus timoriensis alopex* Parkes, Bull. Brit. Orn. Cl., **90**:111, (Tacloban Airstrip, Leyte)

Description: Differs from *tweeddalei* by having the crown richer rufous, the general color more rufescent, and the superciliary buffy and indistinct; also smaller (tail 116; bill 16).

Range: Bohol, Cebu, and Leyte. (Endemic.)

Megalurus timoriensis crex Salomonsen, 1953

1953   *Megalurus timoriensis crex* Salomonsen, Vid. Medd. Dansk nat. Foren., **115**:261, (Mt. Katanglad, Mindanao)

Description: Differs from *alopex* by having the crown darker, the tail blackish brown, the upperparts less reddish, and the superciliary grayer; also smaller (wing 69; tail 110).
Range: Mindanao. (Endemic.)

COMMON FANTAIL WARBLER   PLATE 67

Cisticola juncidis tinnabulans (Swinhoe, 1859)

1859 *Calamanthella tinnabulans* Swinhoe, J. Roy. As. Soc. N. China Br., p. 225, (N. W. Formosa)

Description: Crown, back, and wing-coverts striped with dark brownish black and buff; rump pale rufous; tail dark brown barred with black; outer rectrices tipped with white; underparts white, except flanks and thighs, which are bright buff.
Soft Parts: Bill black; iris yellowish brown; feet red-brown.
Measurements: Wing 48; tail 47; bill 11; tarsus 20.
Range: Bohol, Culion, Leyte, Luzon, Mindanao, Mindoro, and Sulu. (Endemic.)

Cisticola juncidis brunneiceps (Temminck and Schlegel, 1850)

1850 *Salicaria (Cisticola) brunneiceps* Temminck and Schlegel, in Siebold's Faun. Jap., Aves, p. 134, (Japan)

1930 *Cisticola juncidis mcgregori* Hachisuka, Orn. Soc. Japan, suppl. 14:196, (Batan Islands)

Description: Differs from *tinnabulans* in being larger (wing 56), somewhat darker, and less reddish brown.
Range: Japan, south to Batan Island.

Cisticola juncidis nigrostriatus Parkes, 1971

1971 *Cisticola juncidis nigrostriatus* Parkes, Nemouria, 4:29, (Palawan)

Description: Similar to *tinnabulans* but dorsal streaks browner and blacker, with edgings less reddish and rump less rufescent; underparts whiter.
Range: Palawan.

GOLDEN-HEADED FANTAIL WARBLER   PLATE 67

Cisticola exilis semirufa Cabanis, 1872

1872 *Cisticola semirufa* Cabanis, Journ. f. Orn., **20**:316, (Luzon)

Description: Crown chestnut; upperparts buffy brown streaked with dark brown; chin, throat, breast, and flanks rufous; belly white. In winter, male has streaked crown.
Soft Parts: Bill black; iris light brown; feet yellow-brown.
Measurements: Wing 44; tail 33; bill 11; tarsus 18.
Range: Found throughout the Philippines, except Palawan.

PLATE 66

A   RUFOUS-CAPPED CANEGRASS WARBLER
       (Megalurus timoriensis)—page 310

B   STRIATED CANEGRASS WARBLER
       (Megalurus palustris)—page 309

C   GRAY'S GRASSHOPPER WARBLER
       (Locustella fasciolata)—page 316

D   ASIATIC GRASSHOPPER WARBLER
       (Locustella certhiola)—page 316

E   STREAKED GRASSHOPPER WARBLER
       (Locustella lanceolata)—page 316

F   GREAT REED WARBLER
       (Acrocephalus arundinaceus)—page 317

G   SPECKLED REED WARBLER
       (Acrocephalus sorghophilus)—page 317

A

B

D

C

E

F

G

PLATE 66

SANDSTRÖM

PLATE 67

A   MOUNTAIN LEAF WARBLER
     (*Phylloscopus trivirgatus*)—page 317

B   PHILIPPINE LEAF WARBLER
     (*Phylloscopus olivaceus*)—page 319

C   DUBOIS' LEAF WARBLER
     (*Phylloscopus cebuensis*)—page 319

D   ARCTIC WILLOW WARBLER
     (*Phylloscopus borealis*)—page 320

E   YELLOW-BREASTED FLYCATCHER WARBLER
     (*Seicercus montis*)—page 320

F   COMMON FANTAIL WARBLER
     (*Cisticola juncidis*)—page 311

G   GOLDEN-HEADED FANTAIL WARBLER
     (*Cisticola exilis*)—page 311

314

A

B

C

D

E

F

G

SANDSTRÖM

PLATE 67

GRAY'S GRASSHOPPER WARBLER

PLATE 66

Locustella fasciolata (J. E. Gray, 1860)

1860 *Acrocephalus fasciolatus* J. E. Gray, Proc. Zool. Soc. London, p. 349, (Batjan, Moluccas)

Description: Upperparts dark rufous-brown; superciliary gray; chin and center of throat white; sides of throat and breast gray; center of belly white; flanks and under tail-coverts buffy brown.

Soft Parts: Bill, upper mandible blackish, lower mandible flesh color; iris brown; feet flesh color.

Measurements: Wing 81; tail 74; bill 18; tarsus 26.

Range: Winters throughout the Philippines from Asia.

ASIATIC GRASSHOPPER WARBLER

PLATE 66

Locustella certhiola ochotensis (Middendorff, 1853)

1853 *Sylvia (Locustella) Ochotensis* Middendorff, Sib. Reise, 2:185, (Udskoe Ostrog, lower Uda River, Okhotsk Sea)

Description: Upperparts brown; tail faintly barred with dark brown and tipped with white; chin, throat, and belly white; breast, flanks, and under tail-coverts pale buff.

Soft Parts: Bill, upper mandible dark brown, lower mandible flesh color; iris brown; feet flesh color.

Measurements: Wing 69; tail 53; bill 14; tarsus 24.

Range: Batan, Bohol, Calayan, Luzon, Marinduque, Mindanao, Mindoro, and Romblon; a visitor from Siberia.

STREAKED GRASSHOPPER WARBLER

PLATE 66

Locustella lanceolata (Temminck, 1840)

1840 *Sylvia lanceolata* Temminck, Man. d' Orn., 4:614, (Russia)

Description: Upperparts brown streaked with black; tail dark brown; lores and eye-ring buffy; chin whitish; throat and breast white washed with buff and streaked with dark brown; center of belly whitish; flanks and under tail-coverts dark buff streaked with dark brown.

Soft Parts: Bill, upper mandible dark brown, lower mandible flesh color; iris brown; feet whitish.

Measurements: Wing 63; tail 41; bill 11; tarsus 18.

Range: Calayan, Luzon, and Palawan; a visitor from Asia.

316

SPECKLED REED WARBLER PLATE 66

Acrocephalus sorghophilus (Swinhoe, 1863)

1863 *Calamodyta sorghophila* Swinhoe, Proc. Zool. Soc. London, p. 293, (Amoy, Fukien)

Description: Upperparts yellowish brown faintly streaked with dark brown; upper tail-coverts and tail rufous-brown; superciliary buffy with a blackish brown stripe above; underparts whitish washed with buff, heavier on the breast and flanks.

Soft Parts: Bill, upper mandible dark brown, lower mandible flesh color; iris yellow-brown; feet dark brown.

Measurements: Wing 59; tail 55; bill 13; tarsus 23.

Range: Luzon; a visitor from China.

GREAT REED WARBLER PLATE 66

Acrocephalus arundinaceus orientalis (Temminck and Schlegel, 1847)

1847 *Salicaria turdina orientalis* Temminck and Schlegel, in Siebold's Faun. Jap., Aves, p. 50, (Japan)

Description: Upperparts olive-brown, tinged with rufous on the rump and upper tail-coverts; tail dark brown; underparts white; superciliary gray-white; flanks and under tail-coverts washed with buff.

Soft Parts: Bill, upper mandible dark brown, lower mandible flesh color; iris brown; feet dark brown.

Measurements: Wing 86; tail 73; bill 19; tarsus 29.

Range: Batan, Bohol, Calayan, Cebu, Luzon, Mindanao; Mindoro, and Palawan; a migrant from Asia.

Acrocephalus arundinaceus harterti Salomonsen, 1928

1928 *Acrocephalus stentoreus harterti* Salomonsen, Orn. Monatsb., **36**:119, (Laguna de Bai, Luzon)

Description: Differs from *orientalis* by being smaller (wing 74; tail 71; bill 18; tarsus 23); flanks and under tail-coverts more rufous.

Range: Bohol and Luzon. (Endemic.)

MOUNTAIN LEAF WARBLER PLATE 67

Phylloscopus trivirgatus nigrorum (Moseley, 1891)

1891 *Cryptolopha nigrorum* Moseley, Ibis, p. 47, (Negros)

1958 *Phylloscopus trivirgatus benguetensis* Ripley and Rabor, Bull. Peabody Mus. Nat. Hist., **13**:64, (Benguet, Luzon)

Description: Upperparts dark olive-green; tail dark olive-brown; central rectrices edged with yellow and outer rectrices white; superciliary yellowish; underparts yellow-gray; purer yellow on belly and under tail-coverts.

Soft Parts: Bill, upper mandible dark brown, lower mandible whitish; iris brown; feet flesh color.

Measurements: Wing 55; tail 44; bill 10; tarsus 19.

Range: Luzon, Mindoro, and Negros. (Endemic.)

Phylloscopus trivirgatus diuatae Salomonsen, 1953

1953 *Phylloscopus trivirgatus diuatae* Salomonsen, Vid. Medd. Dansk nat. Foren., **115**: 243, (Diuata Mts., Agusan Province, Mindanao)

Description: Differs from *nigrorum* by having the crown slightly darker, superciliary brighter, and underparts lighter, especially the belly.

Range: Diuata Mountains, northeastern Mindanao. (Endemic.)

Phylloscopus trivirgatus mindanensis (Hartert, 1903)

1903 *Cryptolopha mindanensis* Hartert, Bull. Brit. Orn. Cl., **14**:12, (Mt. Apo, Mindanao)

Description: Differs from *diuatae* by having the upperparts olive-brown, superciliary buffy, and underparts more olive-yellow.

Range: Mt. Apo, Mindanao. (Endemic.)

Phylloscopus trivirgatus malindangensis (Mearns, 1909)

1909 *Cryptolopha malindangensis* Mearns, Proc. U. S. Nat. Mus., **36**:440, (Mt. Malindang, Mindanao)

Description: Two color phases in this race—one with white superciliary, cheeks, and underparts and a brownish gray crown; other with yellow superciliary and cheeks, much yellow below, and more greenish crown.

Range: Mt. Malindang and Zamboanga Peninsula. (Endemic.)

Phylloscopus trivirgatus flavostriatus Salomonsen, 1953

1953 *Phylloscopus trivirgatus flavostriatus* Salomonsen, Vid. Medd. Dansk nat. Foren., **115**:244, (Mt. Katanglad, Mindanao)

Description: Differs from *malindangensis* by having the crown darker olive, superciliary buffy, and underparts gray-white streaked with yellow.

Range: Mt. Katanglad and mountains of Misamis Oriental Province, Mindanao. (Endemic.)

Phylloscopus trivirgatus petersoni Salomonsen, 1962

1962 *Phylloscopus trivirgatus petersoni* Salomonsen, Dansk Orn. Foren. Tidsskrift, **56**: 133, (Mt. Mataling, Palawan)

Description: Differs from *nigrorum* by having a yellowish spot in the nape and the underparts bright yellow.

Range: Palawan. (Endemic.)

PHILIPPINE LEAF WARBLER   PLATE 67

Phylloscopus olivaceus (Moseley, 1891)

1891 *Abrornis olivacea* Moseley, Ibis, p. 47, (Samar)

Description: Upperparts olive-green, rump lighter; superciliary yellow; chin and throat whitish; breast and belly gray-white washed with yellow; under tail-coverts yellow.

Soft Parts: Bill, upper mandible black, lower mandible yellowish; iris brown; feet blackish.

Measurements: Wing 60; tail 50; bill 14; tarsus 18.

Range: Leyte, Mindanao, Negros, Samar, and Sulu Archipelago. (Endemic.)

DUBOIS' LEAF WARBLER   PLATE 67

Phylloscopus cebuensis cebuensis (Dubois, 1900)

1894 *Cryptolopha flavigularis* Bourns and Worcester, Occ. Papers Minn. Acad. Nat. Sci., 1:23, (Cebu)

1900 *Cryptolopha cebuensis* Dubois, Syn. Avium, p. 286, new name for *Cryptolopha flavigularis* Bourns and Worcester, 1894

Description: Upperparts olive-green; superciliary, sides of face, chin, and throat yellow; breast and belly gray-white; under tail-coverts light yellow.

Soft Parts: Bill, upper mandible black, lower mandible yellowish; iris brown; feet black.

Measurements: Wing 56; tail 44; bill 13; tarsus 18.

Range: Cebu and Negros. (Endemic.)

Phylloscopus cebuensis luzonensis Rand and Rabor, 1952

1952 *Phylloscopus olivaceus luzonensis* Rand and Rabor, Nat. His. Misc., 107:3, (Massisiat, Abra Province, Luzon)

Description: Differs from *P. c. cebuensis* by having the upperparts slightly darker, sides of face and throat duller yellow, and under tail-coverts darker yellow.

Range: Northern Luzon. (Endemic.)

Phylloscopus cebuensis sorsogonensis Rand and Rabor, 1967

1967 *Phylloscopus cebuensis sorsogonensis* Rand and Rabor, Fieldiana: Zoology, 51:88, (Mt. Bulusan, Sorsogon Prov., Luzon)

Description: Differs from *luzonensis* by having the face brighter yellow.
Range: Southern Luzon. (Endemic.)

ARCTIC WILLOW WARBLER PLATE 67

Phylloscopus borealis borealis (Blasius, 1858)

1858 *Phyllopneuste borealis* Blasius, Naumannia, p. 313, (Okhotsk Sea)

Description: Upperparts olive-brown; superciliary gray-white; streak through eye brownish; underparts gray-white.
Soft Parts: Bill, upper mandible dark brown with a yellow tip, lower mandible orange-yellow with a dusky tip; iris dark brown; feet flesh color.
Measurements: Wing 66; tail 48; bill 14; tarsus 20.
Range: Winters throughout the Philippines from northeastern Siberia. Three other races—*P. b. hylebata* Swinhoe, 1860; *P. b. transbaicalicus* Portenko, 1938; and *P. b. kennicotti* (Baird, 1869)—reach the Philippines during the winter, but banded specimens must be caught to determine the exact race.

Phylloscopus borealis xanthodryas (Swinhoe, 1863)

1863 *Phyllopneuste xanthodryas* Swinhoe, Proc. Zool. Soc. London, p. 296, (Amoy, China)

Description: Differs from *P. b. borealis* by being greener above, yellower below, and larger (wing 70).
Range: Winters throughout the Philippines from Siberia.

YELLOW-BREASTED FLYCATCHER WARBLER PLATE 67

Seicercus montis xanthopygius (Whitehead, 1893)

1893 *Cryptolopha xanthopygia* Whitehead, Bull. Brit. Orn. Cl., 1:31, (Kina Balu, North Borneo)

Description: Top of head and sides of face chestnut, a dark brown stripe running from the bill over the eyes to the hind neck on either side of the crown; back, wings, and tail olive-green, wings having two yellow bars; lores yellowish; eye-ring white; underparts bright yellow.
Soft Parts: Bill, upper mandible dark brown, lower mandible flesh color; iris yellow-brown; feet flesh color.
Measurements: Wing 47; tail 40; bill 9; tarsus 17.
Range: Palawan.

320

MOUNTAIN   TAILOR-BIRD

PLATE 68

Orthotomus cucullatus philippinus (Hartert, 1897)

1897   *Phyllergates philippinus* Hartert, Nov. Zool., 4:517, (Luzon)

Description: Top of head orange; back, wings, and tail olive-green; sides of head gray with a white line extending behind the eye; chin, throat, and breast gray-white; breast and under tail-coverts yellow.

Soft Parts: Bill brown; iris brown; feet light brown.

Measurements: Wing 46; tail 46; bill 15; tarsus 19.

Range: Luzon. (Endemic.)

Orthotomus cucullatus heterolaemus (Mearns, 1905)

1905   *Phyllergates heterolaemus* Mearns, Proc. Biol. Soc. Wash., **18**:86, (Mindanao)

Description: Differs from *philippinus* by having top of head, face, chin, and throat orange-rufous.

Range: Mindanao. (Endemic.)

Orthotomus cucullatus viridicollis Salomonsen, 1962

1962   *Orthotomus cucullatus viridicollis* Salomonsen, Dansk Orn. Foren. Tidsskrift, **56**:
133, (Mt. Mataling, Palawan)

Description: Differs from *philippinus* by having top of head darker, superciliary line yellow, green of upperparts darker, and yellow of underparts more extensive.

Range: Palawan. (Endemic.)

LUZON   TAILOR-BIRD

PLATE 68

Orthotomus derbianus Moore, 1854

1854   *Orthotomus derbianus* Moore, Proc. Zool. Soc. London, p. 309, (Philippines?
= Luzon)

Description: Top of head chestnut; back and rump gray, rump with greenish wash; wings blackish with yellow-green edgings and coverts; tail dull chestnut, darker at base; chin, throat, breast, and flanks gray streaked with white in male and white streaked with gray in female; belly whitish; thighs chestnut; under tail-coverts dull yellowish gray.

Soft Parts: Bill, upper mandible dark brown, lower mandible paler; iris orange-brown; feet brownish.

Measurements: Wing 50; tail 51; bill 17; tarsus 20.

Range: Central and southern Catanduanes and Luzon. (Endemic.) One record from Palawan (stray?).

PLATE 68

A   MOUNTAIN TAILOR-BIRD
       (*Orthotomus cucullatus*)—page 321

B   LUZON TAILOR-BIRD
       (*Orthotomus derbianus*)—page 321

C   COMMON TAILOR-BIRD
       (*Orthotomus atrogularis*)—page 324

D   BLACK-HEADED TAILOR-BIRD
       (*Orthotomus nigriceps*)—page 325

E   WHITE-EARED TAILOR-BIRD
       (*Orthotomus cinereiceps*)—page 325

F   RUFOUS-CROWNED TAILOR-BIRD
       (*Orthotomus sericeus*)—page 326

G   ASHY TAILOR-BIRD
       (*Orthotomus sepium*)—page 326

A

B

C

D

E

F

G

SANDSTRÖM

PLATE 68

COMMON TAILOR-BIRD   PLATE 68

Orthotomus atrogularis chloronotus Ogilvie-Grant, 1895

1895   *Orthotomus chloronotus* Ogilvie-Grant, Bull. Brit. Orn. Cl., **5**:2, (Cape Engano, N. E. Luzon)

Description: Top of head dark chestnut; back and rump green; tail chestnut with greenish base and edges; wings dark brown edged with yellowish green; underparts dark gray streaked with white; thighs chestnut; under tail-coverts yellow-green.

Soft Parts: Bill, upper mandible horn color, lower mandible yellowish; iris light brown; feet pinkish brown.

Measurements: Wing 51; tail 52; bill 17; tarsus 21.

Range: Northern and central Luzon. (Endemic.)

Orthotomus atrogularis castaneiceps Walden, 1872

1872   *Orthotomus castaneiceps* Walden, Ann. Mag. Nat. His., **10**:252, (Guimaras)

1890   *Orthotomus Panayensis* Steere, List Bds. Mamms. Steere Expd., p. 20, (Panay)

Description: Differs from *chloronotus* by having upper back gray and tail more heavily washed with green; underparts white, less streaked with gray. Females—whiter, less gray below.

Range: Guimaras, Masbate, Panay, and Ticao. (Endemic.)

Orthotomus atrogularis rabori Parkes, 1960

1960   *Orthotomus atrogularis heterolaemus* Parkes, Bull. Brit. Orn. Cl., **80**:77, (Lake Balinsasayo, Negros)

1960   *Orthotomus atrogularis rabori* Parkes, Bull. Brit. Orn. Cl., **81**:33, new name for *Orthotomus atrogularis heterolaemus* Parkes, 1960

Description: Differs from *castaneiceps* by having upperparts grayer and throat more heavily streaked.

Range: Negros. (Endemic.)

Orthotomus atrogularis frontalis Sharpe, 1877

1877   *Orthotomus frontalis* Sharpe, Ibis, p. 112, (Zamboanga, Mindanao)

1952   *Orthotomus atrogularis davao* Salomonsen, Vid. Medd. Dansk nat. Foren., **114**: 353, (Limot, Mati, Davao Province, Mindanao)

Description: Differs from *chloronotus* by having the sides of the head and crown gray, tail olive-green, and chin and belly whiter. Wing 45.

Range: Bohol, Dinagat, Leyte, Mindanao, and Samar. (Endemic.)

Orthotomus atrogularis mearnsi McGregor, 1907

1907 *Orthotomus mearnsi* McGregor, Phil. Journ. Sci., 2:289, (Basilan)

Description: Differs from *frontalis* by having the chestnut forehead extending back to the center of the crown.

Range: Basilan. (Endemic.)

BLACK-HEADED TAILOR-BIRD   PLATE 68

Orthotomus nigriceps samarensis Steere, 1890

1890 *Orthotomus Samarensis* Steere, List Bds. Mamms. Steere Expd., p. 20, (Samar)

Description: Head, face, and throat black; chin white; back, rump, and wings dark olive-green; tail dark chestnut; breast and belly yellowish.

Soft Parts: Bill, upper mandible brownish black, lower mandible pinkish brown; iris light brown; feet flesh color.

Measurements: Wing 45; tail 38; bill 17; tarsus 22.

Range: Bohol, Leyte, and Samar. (Endemic.)

Orthotomus nigriceps nigriceps Tweeddale, 1877

1877 *Orthotomus nigriceps* Tweeddale, Proc. Zool. Soc. London, p. 828, (Butuan, Mindanao)

Description: Differs from *samarensis* by having white lores and superciliary, greenish chestnut tail, and gray breast and belly.

Range: Mindanao. (Endemic.)

WHITE-EARED TAILOR-BIRD   PLATE 68

Orthotomus cinereiceps Sharpe, 1877

1877 *Orthotomus cinereiceps* Sharpe, Ibis, p. 113, (Basilan)

Description: Top of head gray, rest of upperparts olive-green; ear-coverts white; chin and throat black; center of breast and belly gray; flanks and under tail-coverts olive-green.

Soft Parts: Bill, upper mandible whitish, lower mandible light brown; iris brown; feet light brown.

Measurements: Wing 50; tail 57; bill 18; tarsus 22.

Range: Basilan and Mindanao. (Endemic.)

RUFOUS-CROWNED TAILOR-BIRD   PLATE 68

Orthotomus sericeus nuntius Bangs, 1922

1922   *Orthotomus ruficeps nuntius* Bangs, Bull. Mus. Comp. Zool., **65**:82, (Cagayan de
      Sulu=Cagayan Sulu)

Description: Crown rufous; back gray; wings brown; tail chestnut, grayer at base; underparts white with grayish flanks and chestnut thighs.

Soft Parts: Bill, upper mandible light brown, lower mandible whitish; iris light brown;
feet light brown.

Measurements: Wing 50; tail 47; bill 17; tarsus 21.

Range: Balabac, Cagayan Sulu, Calamianes, Palawan, and Sulu Islands.

ASHY TAILOR-BIRD   PLATE 68

Orthotomus sepium cagayanensis Riley, 1935

1935   *Orthotomus cineraceus cagayanensis* Riley, Proc. Biol. Soc. Wash., **48**:147,
      (Cagayan Sulu)

Description: Male—forehead, sides of head, and chin rufous; top of head rufous-gray;
back gray; underparts lighter gray; tail chestnut-brown; wings brown. Female—whitish
below.

Soft Parts: Bill, upper mandible brown, lower mandible whitish; iris brown; feet light
brown.

Measurements: Wing 48; tail 44; bill 17; tarsus 19.

Range: Cagayan Sulu. (Endemic.)

Family MUSCICAPIDAE   OLD WORLD FLYCATCHERS

BLUE FANTAIL   PLATE 69

Rhipidura superciliaris superciliaris (Sharpe, 1877)

1877   *Hypothymis superciliaris* Sharpe, Trans. Linn. Soc. London, **1**:326, (Isabela, Basi-
      lan)

Description: Top of head dark blue-black; back and rump dull greenish blue; wings and
tail black with bright blue outer margins; lores and superciliary stripe bright cobalt-blue;
chin, throat, and flanks blue-gray; breast and belly gray with a light bluish wash.

Soft Parts: Bill black; iris brown; feet black.

Measurements: Wing 76; tail 80; bill 12; tarsus 15.

Range: Basilan and northern Mindanao. (Endemic.)

Rhipidura superciliaris apo Hachisuka, 1930

1930 *Rhipidura superciliaris apo* Hachisuka, Orn. Soc. Japan, suppl. 14:184, (Mt. Apo, Mindanao)

Description: Differs from *R. s. superciliaris* by being darker, especially the blue on the wings and tail.

Range: 4000', Mt. Apo and southeastern Mindanao. (Endemic.)

Rhipidura superciliaris samarensis (Steere, 1890)

1890 *Hypothymis Samarensis* Steere, List Bds. Mamms. Steere Expd., p. 16, (Samar, Leyte = Catbalogan, Samar)

Description: Differs from *R. s. superciliaris* by having the crown blue-black and the rest of the upperparts darker.

Range: Bohol, Leyte, and Samar. (Endemic.)

BLUE-HEADED FANTAIL   PLATE 69

Rhipidura cyaniceps cyaniceps (Cassin, 1855)

1855 *Muscipeta cyaniceps* Cassin, Proc. Acad. Nat. Sci. Phila., **7**:438, ("Philippines" = Mt. Makiling, Laguna Prov., Luzon)

Description: Head, upper back, throat, and breast gray-blue; back, scapulars, and outer tail feathers chestnut; primaries and two central tail feathers black; belly and under tail-coverts chestnut.

Soft Parts: Bill black; iris dark brown; feet brown.

Measurements: Wing 78; tail 87; bill 9; tarsus 18.

Range: Northeastern, central, and southern Luzon.

Rhipidura cyaniceps pinicola Parkes, 1958

1958 *Rhipidura cyaniceps pinicola* Parkes, Am. Mus. Novit., 1891:2, (Mt. Benguet, northern Luzon)

Description: Differs from *R. c. cyaniceps* by being smaller (wing 74; tail 83) and also much paler.

Range: Northwestern Luzon. (Endemic.)

Rhipidura cyaniceps sauli Bourns and Worcester, 1894

1894 *Rhipidura sauli* Bourns and Worcester, Occ. Papers Minn. Acad. Nat. Sci., 1:26, (Tablas)

Description: Differs from *R. c. cyaniceps* by being much larger (wing 84; tail 91) and also by having a "deep chestnut" belly which is not apparent on old specimens now in museums.

Range: Tablas. (Endemic.)

Rhipidura cyaniceps albiventris (Sharpe, 1877)

1877 *Philentoma albiventris* Sharpe, Trans. Linn. Soc. London, 1:325, (Guimaras)

Description: Differs from *R. c. cyaniceps* by having a white belly.

Range: Guimaras, Masbate, Negros, Panay, and Ticao. (Endemic.)

BLACK AND CINNAMON FANTAIL   PLATE 69

Rhipidura nigrocinnamomea hutchinsoni Mearns, 1907

1907 *Rhipidura hutchinsoni* Mearns, Phil. Journ. Sci., 2:357, (Mt. Bliss, Malindang Group, Mindanao, 5750')

Description: Head, chin, and throat black, except for a small white line running from over the eyes and across the forehead; back, rump, scapulars, and tail chestnut; primaries black; underparts pale chestnut.

Soft Parts: Bill black; iris dark brown; feet black.

Measurements: Wing 74; tail 83; bill 12; tarsus 12.

Range: Northern Mindanao. (Endemic.)

Rhipidura nigrocinnamomea nigrocinnamomea Hartert, 1903

1903 *Rhipidura nigrocinnamomea* Hartert, Bull. Brit. Orn. Cl., 14:12, (8000', Mt. Apo, Mindanao)

Description: Differs from *hutchinsoni* by having the upper breast white.

Range: Mt. Apo, Mindanao. (Endemic.)

MALAYSIAN FANTAIL   PLATE 69

Rhipidura javanica nigritorquis Vigors, 1831

1831 *Rhipidura nigritorquis* Vigors, Proc. Zool. Soc. London, p. 97, (Manila)

Description: Top of head dark brown-black; back, rump, wings, and tail gray-brown, outer rectrices tipped with white; lores black; superciliary stripe white; chin and upper throat white; lower throat black-brown, forming a band; rest of underparts white.

Soft Parts: Bill black; iris dark brown; feet black.

Measurements: Wing 87; tail 105; bill 16; tarsus 22.

Range: Found throughout the Philippines. (Endemic.)

WHITE-THROATED JUNGLE FLYCATCHER   PLATE 69

Rhinomyias gularis albigularis Bourns and Worcester, 1894

1894 *Rhinomyias albigularis* Bourns and Worcester, Occ. Papers Minn. Acad. Nat. Sci., 1:27, (Negros, Guimaras = Bais, Negros)

Description: Top of head brown, becoming reddish brown on back and wings; tail-coverts and tail chestnut; lores dark brown; indistinct eye-stripe light brown; chin and throat white; breast band brown; belly white.

Soft Parts: Bill black; iris brown; feet pale pinkish cobalt.

Measurements: Wing 87; tail 63; bill 19; tarsus 22.

Range: Guimaras and Negros. (Endemic.)

RUFOUS-TAILED JUNGLE FLYCATCHER PLATE 69

Rhinomyias ruficauda samarensis (Steere, 1890)

1890   *Setaria Samarensis* Steere, List Bds. Mamms. Steere Expd., p. 16, (Mindanao, Samar = Catbalogan, Samar)

1909   *Rhinomyias ruficauda mindanensis* Mearns, Proc. U. S. Nat. Mus., **36**:439, (Pantar, Mindanao)

Description: Upperparts rufous-brown; upper tail-coverts and tail rufous; lores and ear-coverts gray; throat white; breast and belly gray-white with an indistinct olive-brown breast band.

Soft Parts: Bill black; iris brown; feet dark gray-black.

Measurements: Wing 72; tail 59; bill 17; tarsus 16.

Range: Leyte, eastern Mindanao, and Samar. (Endemic.)

Rhinomyias ruficauda ruficauda (Sharpe, 1877)

1877   *Setaria ruficauda* Sharpe, Trans. Linn. Soc. London, **1**:327, (Isabela, Basilan)

1932   *Rhinomyias ruficauda basilanica* Hachisuka, Bull. Brit. Orn. Cl., **52**:110, (Basilan)

Description: Differs from *samarensis* by having the face and underparts much grayer and having no trace of a breast band.

Range: Basilan. (Endemic.)

Rhinomyias ruficauda boholensis Rand and Rabor, 1957

1957   *Rhinomyias ruficauda boholensis* Rand and Rabor, Fieldiana: Zoology, **42**:14, (Cantaub, Sierra Bullones, Bohol)

Description: Differs from *samarensis* by having the upperparts more olive-brown, underparts lighter, and breast band less distinct.

Range: Bohol. (Endemic.)

Rhinomyias ruficauda zamboanga Rand and Rabor, 1957

1957   *Rhinomyias ruficauda zamboanga* Rand and Rabor, Fieldiana: Zoology, **42**:15, (Diway, Dapiak, Zamboanga, Mindanao)

Description: Differs from *samarensis* by having the upperparts darker, especially the tail.

Range: Western Mindanao and Zamboanga Peninsula. (Endemic.)

Rhinomyias ruficauda occularis Bourns and Worcester, 1894

1894 *Rhynomyias occularis* Bourns and Worcester, Occ. Papers Minn. Acad. Nat. Sci.,
1:28, (Sulu, Tawi Tawi = Sulu)

Description: Differs from *mindanensis* by having a very prominent rufous eye-ring and
by being somewhat larger.

Range: Pangamian, Sulu, and Tawi Tawi. (Endemic.)

GOODFELLOW'S JUNGLE FLYCATCHER PLATE 69

Rhinomyias goodfellowi Ogilvie-Grant, 1905

1905 *Rhinomyias goodfellowi* Ogilvie-Grant, Bull. Brit. Orn. Cl., **16**:17, (Mt. Apo,
Mindanao)

Description: Male—top of head, back, and rump dark blue-gray; wings and tail dark
brown; lores and eye-ring black; superciliary stripe white; chin and throat white; breast
pale olive-brown; belly whitish with an olive-brown wash. Female—similar to male but
much duller and browner.

Soft Parts: Bill black; iris red-brown; feet dark gray.

Measurements: Wing 92; tail 75; bill 18; tarsus 23.

Range: Mindanao. (Endemic.)

LUZON JUNGLE FLYCATCHER PLATE 69

Rhinomyias insignis Ogilvie-Grant, 1895

1895 *Rhinomyias insignis* Ogilvie-Grant, Bull. Brit. Orn. Cl., 4:40, (Mt. Data, Luzon)

Description: Upperparts olive-brown; rump, tail, and wing margins with more rufous;
sides of face dark gray-brown; superciliary stripe, chin, and central throat white; sides of
throat dark reddish brown; breast band dull olive-orange; flanks burnt orange; belly and
under tail-coverts white.

Soft Parts: Bill black; iris light brown; feet plumbous.

Measurements: Wing 95; tail 75; bill 16; tarsus 28.

Range: Northern Luzon. (Endemic.)

NARCISSUS FLYCATCHER PLATE 70

Ficedula narcissina narcissina (Temminck, 1835)

1835 *Muscicapa narcissina* Temminck, Pl. Col., livr. 3, pl. 577, (Japan)

330

Description: Male—top of head and upper back black; lower back and rump bright orange; wings black with a white patch in the wing-coverts; tail black; a yellow stripe extends from the bill, above lores, and over and behind the eye; chin and throat orange; breast and belly deep yellow; under tail-coverts white. Female—upperparts olive-brown, except tail-coverts and tail, which are dull rufous; throat whitish; breast whitish mottled with olive-brown; belly whitish with a yellow wash; under tail-coverts white.

Soft Parts: Bill black; iris dark red-brown; feet bluish.

Measurements: Wing 76; tail 52; bill 11; tarsus 12.

Range: Calayan, Cebu, Luzon, Mindanao, and Negros; a migrant from eastern Asia.

BLACK AND ORANGE FLYCATCHER   PLATE 70

Ficedula mugimaki (Temminck, 1835)

1835   *Muscicapa Mugimaki* Temminck, Pl. Col., livr. 97, pl. 577, (Japan)

Description: Upperparts dark olive-brown; underparts dull orange, becoming paler on belly; under tail-coverts white. In spring the upperparts are almost black and the underparts a brighter orange.

Soft Parts: Bill dark pink; iris dark brown; feet pinkish.

Measurements: Wing 77; tail 50; bill 9; tarsus 16.

Range: Winters on Luzon, Mindanao, and Negros; a migrant from eastern Asia.

THICKET FLYCATCHER   PLATE 70

Ficedula hyperythra luzoniensis (Ogilvie-Grant, 1894)

1894   *Muscicapula luzoniensis* Ogilvie-Grant, Ibis, p. 505, (La Trinidad, Benguet, northern Luzon)

1935   *Muscicapula hyperythra mindorensis* Hachisuka, Bds. Phil. Ids., p. 299, (Mt. Dulangan, Mindoro)

1947   *Muscicapa hyperythra trinitatis* Deignan, Proc. Biol. Soc. Wash., **60**:166, new name for *Muscicapula luzoniensis* Ogilvie-Grant, 1894; not *Muscicapa luzoniensis* Gmelin, 1789

Description: Male—upperparts dark gray-blue; wings and tail dark brown; lores black; a partially concealed white stripe over eyes; chin white; throat and breast dull orange; belly white. Female—differs from male by having olive-brown upperparts, becoming rufous toward tail; primary margins and tail rufous.

Soft Parts: Bill black; iris dark brown; feet pale bluish.

Measurements: Wing 58; tail 50; bill 11; tarsus 18.

Range: Luzon and Mindoro. (Endemic.)

PLATE 69

A   BLUE-HEADED FANTAIL
    (Rhipidura cyaniceps)—page 327

B   BLUE FANTAIL
    (Rhipidura superciliaris)—page 326

C   WHITE-THROATED JUNGLE FLYCATCHER
    (Rhinomyias gularis)—page 328

D   BLACK AND CINNAMON FANTAIL
    (Rhipidura nigrocinnamomea)—page 328

E   MALAYSIAN FANTAIL
    (Rhipidura javanica)—page 328

F   RUFOUS-TAILED JUNGLE FLYCATCHER
    (Rhinomyias ruficauda)—page 329

G   LUZON JUNGLE FLYCATCHER
    (Rhinomyias insignis)—page 330

H   GOODFELLOW'S JUNGLE FLYCATCHER
    (Rhinomyias goodfellowi)—page 330

PLATE 69

PLATE 70

A   NARCISSUS FLYCATCHER
(Ficedula narcissina), male—page 330

B   NARCISSUS FLYCATCHER
(Ficedula narcissina), female—page 330

C   THICKET FLYCATCHER
(Ficedula hyperythra)—page 331

D   BLACK AND ORANGE FLYCATCHER
(Ficedula mugimaki)—page 331

E   LITTLE SLATY FLYCATCHER
(Ficedula basilanica), male—page 337

F   LITTLE SLATY FLYCATCHER
(Ficedula basilanica), female—page 337

G   PALAWAN FLYCATCHER
(Ficedula platenae)—page 338

H   LITTLE PIED FLYCATCHER
(Ficedula westermanni)—page 338

I   VAURIE'S FLYCATCHER
(Ficedula crypta)—page 337

PLATE 70

Ficedula hyperythra calayensis (McGregor, 1921)

1921 *Muscicapula calayensis* McGregor, Phil. Journ. Sci., **18**:76, (Calayan Island)

Description: Differs from *luzoniensis* by having underparts much darker, especially the throat and breast.

Range: Calayan Island. (Endemic.)

Ficedula hyperythra nigrorum (Whitehead, 1897)

1897 *Muscicapula nigrorum* Whitehead, Bull. Brit. Orn. Cl., **6**:43, (Mt. Canlaon, Negros)

Description: Male—differs from *luzoniensis* by having the white chin more extensive and the upperparts a richer blue. Female—differs by having grayer upperparts.

Range: Negros. (Endemic.)

Ficedula hyperythra montigena (Mearns, 1905)

1905 *Muscicapula montigena* Mearns, Proc. Biol. Soc. Wash., **18**:8, (Mt. Apo, Mindanao)

Description: Male—differs from *nigrorum* by having the entire underparts dark orange-rufous; upperparts grayer and tail chestnut. Female—more extensive orange-rufous on underparts.

Range: Mt. Apo and Mt. Katanglad, Mindanao. (Endemic.)

Ficedula hyperythra daggayana deSchauensee and duPont, 1962

1962 *Ficedula hyperythra daggayana* deSchauensee and duPont, Proc. Acad. Nat. Sci. Phila., **114**:166, (Daggayan, Misamis Oriental, Mindanao)

Description: Male—differs from *montigena* by having the lower back grayer, upper tail-coverts olive, tail dark olive-gray instead of chestnut, flanks deeper orange-rufous, and chin orange-rufous.

Range: Mountains on northern coast of Mindanao. (Endemic.)

Ficedula hyperythra malindangensis Rand and Rabor, 1957

1957 *Ficedula hyperythra malindangensis* Rand and Rabor, Fieldiana: Zoology, **42**:14, (Mt. Malindang, Mindanao)

Description: Male—differs from *daggayana* by having the lower back grayer, tail gray, chin white, and flanks paler orange-rufous.

Range: Mt. Malindang, Mindanao. (Endemic.)

LITTLE SLATY FLYCATCHER   PLATE 70

Ficedula basilanica basilanica (Sharpe, 1877)

1877 *Dendrobiastes basilanica* Sharpe, Trans. Linn. Soc. London, 1:332, (Basilan)

1890 *Muscicapula mindanensis* Blasius, Braunschweig. Anz., 87:877, (Davao, Mindanao)

Description: Male—upperparts dark blue-gray; tail-coverts and tail dark blue-black; wing primaries dark brown; stripe behind eye white; underparts white; flanks gray. Female—upperparts red-brown; eye-ring pale chestnut; underparts white washed with rufous.

Soft Parts: Bill black; iris black; feet dark gray.

Measurements: Wing 65; tail 44; bill 14; tarsus 20.

Range: Basilan and Mindanao. (Endemic.)

Ficedula basilanica samarensis (Bourns and Worcester, 1894)

1894 *Muscicapula samarensis* Bourns and Worcester, Occ. Papers Minn. Acad. Nat. Sci., 1:26, (Samar = Catbalogan, Samar)

Description: Differs from *F. b. basilanica* by having top of the head dark black-brown, stripe behind eye more conspicuous, and rest of upperparts darker, especially the wings.

Range: Leyte and Samar. (Endemic.)

VAURIE'S FLYCATCHER   PLATE 70

Ficedula crypta crypta (Vaurie, 1951)

1951 *Muscicapa crypta* Vaurie, Am. Mus. Novit., 1543:1, (Mt. McKinley, Mindanao)

Description: Top of head dark brown; back and wing-coverts rufous-brown; tail-coverts and tail chestnut; lores grayish; ear-coverts orange-brown; chin and throat white; breast band pale olive-brown; belly white.

Soft Parts: Bill dark brown; feet pearl-pink.

Measurements: Wing 63; tail 43; bill 14; tarsus 16.

Range: Mindanao. (Endemic.)

Ficedula crypta disposita (Ripley and Marshall, 1967)

1967 *Muscicapa bonthaina disposita* Ripley and Marshall, Proc. Biol. Soc. Wash., 80:243, (Zambales Mts., above Crow Valley, Tarlac Province, Luzon)

Description: Differs from *F. c. crypta* by having the tail paler with blackish tips to outer feathers, the breast more olive-brown, and more olive on upperparts.

Range: Known only from the type locality. (Endemic.)

PALAWAN FLYCATCHER PLATE 70

Ficedula platenae (Blasius, 1888)

1888 *Siphia platenae* Blasius, Braunschweig. Anz., **52**:467, (Puerto Princesa, Palawan)

1888 *Siphia erithacus* Sharpe, Ibis, p. 199, (Palawan)

1906 *Cyornis paraguae* McGregor, Condor, **8**:29, new name for *Siphia erithacus* Sharpe, 1888, preoccupied

Description: Upperparts rufous-brown; tail-coverts and tail bright chestnut; lores gray; throat whitish; sides of throat and breast pale orange; belly white.

Soft Parts: Bill black; iris blackish brown; feet slate.

Measurements: Wing 65; tail 45; bill 12; tarsus 20.

Range: Palawan. (Endemic.)

LITTLE PIED FLYCATCHER PLATE 70

Ficedula westermanni westermanni (Sharpe, 1888)

1888 *Muscicapula westermanni* Sharpe, Proc. Zool. Soc. London, p. 270, (Batang, Patang, Perak)

1930 *Muscicapula melanoleuca apo* Hachisuka, Orn. Soc. Japan, suppl. 14:183, (Mt. Apo, Mindanao)

1952 *Muscicapa westermanni rabori* Ripley, Proc. Biol. Soc. Wash., **65**:73, (Irisan, Benguet, Luzon)

Description: Male—crown, sides of head, and back black; wings black with a white stripe; tail, central rectrices black, remainder basal half white, terminal half black; superciliary stripe and underparts white. Female—upperparts gray; tail brownish; underparts white washed with gray.

Soft Parts: Bill black; iris dark brown; feet black.

Measurements: Wing 58; tail 40; bill 11; tarsus 14.

Range: Luzon, Mindanao, Negros, and Panay. (Endemic.)

Ficedula westermanni palawanensis (Ripley and Rabor, 1962)

1962 *Muscicapa westermanni palawanensis* Ripley and Rabor, Postilla, 73:8, (Mt. Mantalingajan, Palawan)

Description: Differs from *F. w. westermanni* by having the upperparts of the female darker gray and also by having slightly larger wing (♂ 59) and tail (♂ 43).

Range: Palawan. (Endemic.)

JAPANESE BLUE FLYCATCHER

PLATE 71

Ficedula cyanomelana cyanomelana (Temminck, 1829)

1829 *Muscicapa cyanomelana* Temminck, Pl. Col., pl. 470, (Japan)

Description: Male—top of head cobalt-blue; back, rump, and wing-coverts blue-green; primaries black with blue edges; tail, basal half white, terminal half black with blue edges; lores, sides of head, throat, and breast black; belly and under tail-coverts white. Female—upperparts olive-gray, tail with a slight rufous wash; chin, center of throat, belly, and under tail-coverts white; rest of underparts gray-brown.

Soft Parts: Bill dark brown; iris dark brown; feet brown.

Measurements: Wing 95; tail 65; bill 12; tarsus 20.

Range: Balabac and Palawan; a visitor from Japan.

BLUE-BREASTED FLYCATCHER

PLATE 71

Cyornis herioti herioti Ramsay, 1886

1886 *Cyornis herioti* Ramsay, Ibis, p. 159, (Manila)

1896 *Siphia enganensis* Ogilvie-Grant, Bull. Brit. Orn. Cl., 5:2, (Cape Engano, north Luzon)

Description: Male—forehead and eye stripe dull cobalt-blue; lores black; upperparts dull blue; throat and breast dull blue; flanks light rufous; belly and under tail-coverts white. Female—top of head and hind neck gray-brown; back brown; wings and tail rufous; lores dark brown; throat and breast pale rufous; belly and under tail-coverts white.

Soft Parts: Bill black; iris brown; feet black.

Measurements: Wing 79; tail 68; bill 16; tarsus 19.

Range: Northern and central Luzon. (Endemic.)

Cyornis herioti camarinensis (Rand and Rabor, 1967)

1967 *Muscicapa herioti camarinensis* Rand and Rabor, Fieldiana: Zoology, 51:88, (Mt. Isarog, Camarines Sur, Luzon)

Description: Differs from *C. h. herioti* by having the throat and breast dull rufous.

Range: Southern Luzon. (Endemic.)

HILL BLUE FLYCATCHER

PLATE 71

Cyornis lemprieri Sharpe, 1884

1884 *Cyornis lemprieri* Sharpe, Ibis, p. 319, (south Palawan)

1888 *Siphia ramsayi* Blasius, Braunschweig. Anz., 52:467, (Palawan)

Description: Male—upperparts blue; superciliary, margins of wing-coverts on the bend of the wing, primary and secondary outer margins, and tail margins dull cobalt-blue; malar stripe dark blue-black; chin and upper throat whitish with a pale rufous wash; breast rufous; belly and under tail-coverts whitish. Female—upperparts olive-brown; tail-coverts and tail chestnut; lores dark brown; line above lores and small patch beneath the eyes buffy white; underparts same as male.
Soft Parts: Bill black; iris dark brown; feet black.
Measurements: Wing 77; tail 70; bill 18; tarsus 18.
Range: Balabac, Calamianes, and Palawan. (Endemic.)

MANGROVE BLUE FLYCATCHER PLATE 71

Cyornis rufigaster simplex Blyth, 1870

1870 *Cyornis simplex* Blyth, Ibis, p. 165, ("Borneo"=Luzon)
1947 *Muscicapa rufigastra simplicior* Deignan, Proc. Biol. Soc. Wash., **60**:167, new name for *Cyornis simplex* Blyth, 1870

Description: Male—forehead and eyebrow dull cobalt-blue; upperparts dull blue; lores, malar region, ear-coverts, and chin dark blue-black; throat pale orange-rufous; breast orange-rufous; belly and under tail-coverts white. Female—same as male, but lores and chin white.
Soft Parts: Bill black; iris brown; feet bluish.
Measurements: Wing 72; tail 65; bill 14; tarsus 19.
Range: Luzon, Marinduque, and Polillo. (Endemic.)

Cyornis rufigaster mindorensis Mearns, 1907

1907 *Cyornis mindorensis* Mearns, Phil. Journ. Sci., **2**:356, (Rio Baco, Mindoro)
Description: Differs from *simplex* by having the under tail-coverts orange-rufous.
Range: Mindoro. (Endemic.)

Cyornis rufigaster philippinensis Sharpe, 1877

1877 *Cyornis philippinensis* Sharpe, Trans. Linn. Soc. London, **1**:325, (Panay)
Description: Differs from *simplex* by having the upperparts a much darker and duller blue; underparts are also darker, especially the breast.
Range: Basilan, Bohol, Cebu, Leyte, Masbate, Mindanao, Negros, Panay, Romblon, Samar, Siquijor, and Sulu Archipelago. (Endemic.)

Cyornis rufigaster litoralis Stresemann, 1925

1925 *Cyornis rufigastra litoralis* Stresemann, Orn. Monatsb., **33**:50, (Puerto Princesa, Palawan)

Description: Differs from *simplex* by having the upperparts a darker gray-blue; underparts also darker.

Range: Palawan. (Endemic.)

SOOTY FLYCATCHER   PLATE 72

Muscicapa sibirica sibirica Gmelin, 1789

1789 *Muscicapa sibirica* Gmelin, Syst. Nat., 1:936, (Lake Baikal)

Description: Upperparts brown; chin and center of throat white; sides of throat, breast, and flanks white mottled with brown; belly and under tail-coverts white.

Soft Parts: Bill black; iris dark brown; feet brown-black.

Measurements: Wing 78; tail 55; bill 9; tarsus 13.

Range: Palawan (once); a visitor from Asia.

GRAY-SPOTTED FLYCATCHER   PLATE 72

Muscicapa griseisticta (Swinhoe, 1861)

1861 *Hemichelidon griseisticta* Swinhoe, Ibis, p. 330, (Amoy, China)

Description: Upperparts gray-brown, primaries and tail darker; chin and upper throat white; sides of throat, breast, and flanks white heavily streaked with gray; belly and under tail-coverts white.

Soft Parts: Bill black; iris dark brown; feet black.

Measurements: Wing 86; tail 54; bill 10; tarsus 14.

Range: Found throughout the Philippines; a migrant from eastern Asia.

FERRUGINOUS FLYCATCHER   PLATE 72

Muscicapa cinereiceps (Sharpe, 1889)

1889 *Hemichelidon cinereiceps* Sharpe, Ibis, p. 194, (Kina Balu, Borneo)

Description: Top of head gray-brown; back and wing-coverts rusty brown; rump and outer rectrices chestnut, central rectrices brown; center of throat white; breast dark rufous; flank and under tail-coverts light rufous; center of belly white with a rufous wash.

Soft Parts: Bill black, base of lower mandible pale yellow; iris brown; feet gray.

Measurements: Wing 72; tail 52; bill 10; tarsus 13.

Range: Mindoro and Palawan; a visitor from China.

PLATE 71

A   JAPANESE BLUE FLYCATCHER
       (Ficedula cyanomelana), male—page 339

B   JAPANESE BLUE FLYCATCHER
       (Ficedula cyanomelana), female—page 339

C   BLUE-BREASTED FLYCATCHER
       (Cyornis herioti), male—page 339

D   BLUE-BREASTED FLYCATCHER
       (Cyornis herioti), female—page 339

E   GRAY-HEADED CANARY FLYCATCHER
       (Culicicapa ceylonensis)—page 347

F   HILL BLUE FLYCATCHER
       (Cyornis lemprieri), male—page 339

G   HILL BLUE FLYCATCHER
       (Cyornis lemprieri), female—page 339

H   MANGROVE BLUE FLYCATCHER
       (Cyornis rufigaster)—page 340

PLATE 71

PLATE 72

A   SOOTY FLYCATCHER
    (Muscicapa sibirica)—page 341

B   GRAY-SPOTTED FLYCATCHER
    (Muscicapa griseisticta)—page 341

C   FERRUGINOUS FLYCATCHER
    (Muscicapa cinereiceps)—page 341

D   BROWN FLYCATCHER
    (Muscicapa latirostris)—page 346

E   VERDITER FLYCATCHER
    (Muscicapa panayensis)—page 346

F   CITRINE CANARY FLYCATCHER
    (Culicicapa helianthea)—page 347

G   BLACK-NAPED BLUE MONARCH
    (Hypothymis azurea), male—page 348

H   BLACK-NAPED BLUE MONARCH
    (Hypothymis azurea), female—page 348

I   SHORT-CRESTED BLUE MONARCH
    (Hypothymis helenae)—page 348

J   CELESTIAL BLUE MONARCH
    (Hypothymis coelestis)—page 349

344

PLATE 72

BROWN FLYCATCHER   PLATE 72

Muscicapa latirostris randi Amadon and duPont, 1970

1970   *Muscicapa latirostris randi* Amadon and duPont, Nemouria, 1:10, (Dalton Pass, Nueva Vizcaya, Luzon)

Description: Upperparts grayish brown; upper wing-coverts have buffy edges; throat white with gray streaks; breast and upper belly gray; lower belly white.

Soft Parts: Bill, upper mandible dark brown, lower mandible dull yellow-brown; iris brown; feet black.

Measurements: Wing 65; tail 50; bill 10; tarsus 14.

Range: Luzon and Negros. (Endemic.)

VERDITER FLYCATCHER   PLATE 72

Muscicapa panayensis panayensis (Sharpe, 1877)

1877   *Eumyias panayensis* Sharpe, Trans. Linn. Soc. London, 1:326, (Panay)

Description: Upperparts verditer-blue; lores black; forehead and chin brighter blue; throat and breast lighter verditer-blue than back; belly whitish.

Soft Parts: Bill black; iris dark brown; feet dark brown.

Measurements: Wing 79; tail 68; bill 13; tarsus 16.

Range: Negros and Panay. (Endemic.)

Muscicapa panayensis nigrimentalis (Ogilvie-Grant, 1894)

1894   *Stoparola nigrimentalis* Ogilvie-Grant, Bull. Brit. Orn. Cl., 3:50, (Benguet, Luzon)

Description: Differs from *M. p. panayensis* by having the forehead and chin black, edges of primaries and underparts more silvery verditer-blue, and lower belly and under tail-coverts white.

Range: Luzon and Mindoro. (Endemic.)

Muscicapa panayensis nigriloris (Hartert, 1904)

1904   *Stoparola panayensis nigriloris* Hartert, Bull. Brit. Orn. Cl., 14:80, (Mt. Apo, Mindanao)

Description: Differs from *M. p. panayensis* by having the lower belly and under tail-coverts buffy.

Range: Mindanao. (Endemic.)

GRAY-HEADED CANARY FLYCATCHER PLATE 71

Culicicapa ceylonensis ceylonensis (Swainson, 1820)

1820 *Platyrhynchus ceylonensis* Swainson, Zool. Illustr., p. 1, (Ceylon)

Description: Top of head gray; back and rump olive-yellow; wings and tail brown with yellowish margins; chin and throat light gray; rest of underparts yellow.

Soft Parts: Bill brown; iris dark brown; feet light brown.

Measurements: Wing 66; tail 59; bill 13; tarsus 13.

Range: Palawan (once).

CITRINE CANARY FLYCATCHER PLATE 72

Culicicapa helianthea panayensis (Sharpe, 1877)

1877 *Xantholestes panayensis* Sharpe, Trans. Linn. Soc. London, 1:327, (Panay)

Description: Top of head olive; back, wing-coverts, and tail yellow-green; rump bright yellow; underparts bright yellow.

Soft Parts: Bill black; iris brown; feet yellowish brown.

Measurements: Wing 59; tail 48; bill 11; tarsus 8.

Range: Cebu, Leyte, Mindanao, Negros, Palawan, and Panay. (Endemic.)

Culicicapa helianthea mayri Deignan, 1947

1947 *Culicicapa helianthea mayri* Deignan, Proc. Biol. Soc. Wash., **60**:61, (Tataan, Tawi Tawi)

Description: Differs from *panayensis* by having the upperparts paler and the underparts greener.

Range: Bongao Island and Tawi Tawi. (Endemic.)

Culicicapa helianthea septentrionalis Parkes, 1960

1960 *Culicicapa helianthea septentrionalis* Parkes, Proc. Biol. Soc. Wash., **73**:218, (Mt. Santo Tomas, Benguet, Mountain Province, Luzon)

Description: Differs from *panayensis* by having the upperparts darker, the rump greenish yellow, and the underparts duller yellow.

Range: Northwestern Luzon. (Endemic.)

Culicicapa helianthea zimmeri Parkes, 1960

1960 *Culicicapa helianthea zimmeri* Parkes, Proc. Biol. Soc. Wash., **73**:218, (Mt. San Cristobal, Laguna Province, Luzon)

Description: Differs from *septentrionalis* by having the rump purer yellow and the underparts a richer golden yellow; also smaller (wing 55; tail 46).

Range: South-central Luzon. (Endemic.)

BLACK-NAPED BLUE MONARCH PLATE 72

Hypothymis azurea azurea (Boddaert, 1783)

1783 *Muscicapa azurea* Boddaert, Table Pl., enlum., p. 41, (Philippines = Manila)

1831 *Hypothymis occipitalis* Vigors, Proc. Zool. Soc. London, p. 97, (Manila)

1939 *Hypothymis azurea compilator* Peters, Bull. Mus. Comp. Zool., **86**:111, (15 km NE of Maluso, Basilan)

Description: Male—nasal tufts black; crown bright blue; nape black; rest of upperparts blue; chin and throat bright blue separated from the dull blue breast by a thin black line; belly pale gray with a blue wash. Female—nasal tufts black; top of head bright blue; back, wings, and tail olive-brown; chin and throat dull blue; breast gray-blue; belly white.

Soft Parts: Bill dark blue; iris brown; feet bluish.

Measurements: Wing 70; tail 75; bill 12; tarsus 16.

Range: Found throughout the Philippines, except Camiguin South. (Endemic.)

Hypothymis azurea catarmanensis Rand and Rabor, 1969

1969 *Hypothymis azurae* [sic] *catarmanensis* Rand and Rabor, Fieldiana: Zoology, **51**: 161, (Camiguin South)

Description: Male—differs from *azurea* by having the blues darker. Female—differs by having the back, wings, and tail blue and the throat and breast darker blue.

Range: Camiguin South. (Endemic.)

SHORT-CRESTED BLUE MONARCH PLATE 72

Hypothymis helenae helenae (Steere, 1890)

1890 *Cyanomyias Helenae* Steere, List Bds. Mamms. Steere Exped., p. 16, (Catbalogan, Samar)

1907 *Camiguinia personata* McGregor, Phil. Journ. Sci., **2**:346, (Camiguin Island)

Description: Male—forehead, lores, and chin black; head bright blue with a short crest; back and rump blue; wings and tail dark blue-black; throat and breast blue; belly and under tail-coverts white. Female—differs from male by lacking the black around the bill and by having grayer underparts.

Soft Parts: Bill bluish; iris brown; feet bluish.

Measurements: Wing 67; tail 63; bill 10; tarsus 14.

Range: Camiguin North, Luzon, Polillo, and Samar. (Endemic.)

Hypothymis helenae agusanae Rand, 1970

1970   *Hypothymis helenae agusanae* Rand, Nat. Hist. Bull. Siam Soc., **23**:362, (Balangbalang, Cabadbara, Mt. Hilong-hilong, Mindanao)

Description: Differs from *H. h. helenae* by having the blues brighter and paler, especially on the crown.

Range: Known only from the type locality.

CELESTIAL BLUE MONARCH   PLATE 72

Hypothymis coelestis Tweeddale, 1877

1877   *Hypothymis coelestis* Tweeddale, Ann. Mag. Nat. His., **20**:536, (Dinagat)

1970   *Hypothymis coelestis rabori* Rand, Nat. Hist. Bull. Siam Soc., **23**:363, (Besay, Bayawan, Negros)

Description: Forehead, crown, and long crest (40) bright cobalt-blue; rest of upperparts cobalt-blue; chin and throat blue; breast and belly gray with a bluish wash.

Soft Parts: Bill dark blue; iris white; feet dark blue.

Measurements: Wing 74; tail 76; bill 13; tarsus 17.

Range: Basilan, Dinagat, Luzon, Mindanao, Negros, Samar, and Sibuyan. (Endemic.)

RUFOUS PARADISE FLYCATCHER   PLATE 73

Terpsiphone cinnamomea unirufa Salomonsen, 1937

1843   *Tchitrea rufa* G. R. Gray, Ann. Mag. Nat. His., **11**:371, (Philippine Islands= Cataguan, Luzon)

1937   *Tersiphone unirufa* Salomonsen, Bull. Brit. Orn. Cl., **58**:15, new name for *Tchitrea rufa* G. R. Gray, 1843, preoccupied

1957   *Tersiphone unirufa ramosi* Manuel, Phil. Journ. Sci., **86**:4, (Polillo)

Description: Male—entire bird dark chestnut; tips to primaries dark brown; eye wattle bluish. Female—similar to male but lighter and duller.

Soft Parts: Bill blue-black; iris slate-blue; feet bluish.

Measurements: Wing ♂101, ♀84; tail ♂182, ♀81; bill 20; tarsus 18.

Range: Lubang, Luzon, Marinduque, Mindoro, Negros, Panay, Polillo, Romblon, Samar, Sibuyan, and Tablas. (Endemic.)

Terpsiphone cinnamomea cinnamomea (Sharpe, 1877)

1877   *Zeocephus cinnamomeus* Sharpe, Trans. Linn. Soc. London, **1**:328, (interior of Basilan)

Description: Differs from *unirufa* by having a shorter tail (♂120) and by being much paler.

Range: Basilan, Mindanao, and the Sulu Archipelago. (Endemic.)

349

BLACK PARADISE FLYCATCHER   PLATE 73

Terpsiphone atrocaudata periophthalmica (Ogilvie-Grant, 1895)

1895 *Callaeops periophthalmica* Ogilvie-Grant, Bull. Brit. Orn. Cl., 4:18, (Batan)

1907 *Terpsiphone nigra* McGregor, Phil. Journ. Sci., 2:340, (Batan)

Description: Male—entire bird glossy black except for the lower belly and under tail-coverts, which are white. Female—top of head black; back, wings, and tail dark rufous-brown; throat and breast gray-black; belly and under tail-coverts white.

Soft Parts: Bill dark brown; iris brown; wattle around eye blue; feet pale blue.

Measurements: Wing 87; tail ♂ 246, ♀ 103; bill 17; tarsus 15.

Range: Batan, Botel Tobago, and Mindoro. (Endemic.)

BLUE PARADISE FLYCATCHER   PLATE 73

Terpsiphone cyanescens (Sharpe, 1877)

1877 *Zeocephus cyanescens* Sharpe, Trans. Linn. Soc. London, 1:328, (Puerto Princesa, Palawan)

Description: Male—upperparts gray-blue, tail slightly more brownish; lores and chin black; underparts paler blue. Female—top of head blue; back, wings, and tail brown; lores and chin black; throat blue; breast gray-blue; belly and under tail-coverts whitish.

Soft Parts: Bill bluish; iris black; feet blue.

Measurements: Wing 95; tail ♂ 108, ♀ 99; bill 22; tarsus 18.

Range: Calamianes and Palawan. (Endemic.)

WHITE-BELLIED WHISTLER   PLATE 73

Pachycephala cinerea crissalis (Zimmer, 1918)

1918 *Hyloterpe crissalis* Zimmer, Phil. Journ. Sci., 13:230, (Mt. Banahao, Laguna Province, Luzon)

Description: Upperparts olive-brown; tail greenish olive; chin and throat gray-green with dark shaft streaks to the feathers of the chin and upper throat; breast grayish; belly and under tail-coverts white, washed with buff.

Soft Parts: Bill black; iris brown; feet pale gray.

Measurements: Wing 79; tail 69; bill 18; tarsus 22.

Range: Laguna Province, central Luzon. (Endemic.)

Pachycephala cinerea albiventris (Ogilvie-Grant, 1894)

1894   *Hyloterpe albiventris* Ogilvie-Grant, Bull. Brit. Orn. Cl., **3**:49, (mountains of northern Luzon = Benguet)

Description: Differs from *crissalis* by having the upperparts olive-green and the belly and under tail-coverts whitish.

Range: Northern Luzon. (Endemic.)

Pachycephala cinerea mindorensis (Bourns and Worcester, 1894)

1894   *Hyloterpe mindorensis* Bourns and Worcester, Occ. Papers Minn. Acad. Nat. Sci., **1**:22, (Mindoro)

Description: Differs from *albiventris* by having the throat and breast darker gray, the belly dirty white, and the under tail-coverts yellowish.

Range: Mindoro. (Endemic.)

Pachycephala cinerea winchelli (Bourns and Worcester, 1894)

1894   *Hyloterpe winchelli* Bourns and Worcester, Occ. Papers Minn. Acad. Nat. Sci., **1**: 21, (Panay, Masbate, Negros)

1894   *Hyloterpe major* Bourns and Worcester, Occ. Papers Minn. Acad. Nat. Sci., **1**:22, (Cebu, Tablas, Sibuyan)

Description: Differs from *crissalis* by having the upperparts brown; the chin and throat white washed with brown; and the breast, belly, and under tail-coverts white.

Range: Cebu, Masbate, Negros, Panay, Sibuyan, Tablas, and Ticao. (Endemic.)

Pachycephala cinerea plateni (Blasius, 1888)

1888   *Hyloterpe plateni* Blasius, Braunschweig. Anz., **52**:467, (Palawan)

1888   *Hyloterpe whiteheadi* Sharpe, Ibis, p. 198, (Palawan)

Description: Differs from *crissalis* by having the upperparts olive-gray; chin and throat paler and purer gray-white; breast, belly, and under tail-coverts white.

Range: Palawan. (Endemic.)

Pachycephala cinerea homeyeri (Blasius, 1890)

1890   *Hyloterpe Homeyeri* Blasius, Journ. f. Orn., **38**:143, (Jolo, Sulu)

Description: Differs from *winchelli* by having upperparts bright rufous-brown, chin and center of throat white, and sides of throat rufous-brown; similar in having breast, belly, and under tail-coverts pure white.

Range: Sulu Archipelago and islands north of Borneo.

PLATE 73

A   RUFOUS PARADISE FLYCATCHER
       (Terpsiphone cinnamomea), male—page 349

B   RUFOUS PARADISE FLYCATCHER
       (Terpsiphone cinnamoméa), female—page 349

C   BLACK PARADISE FLYCATCHER
       (Terpsiphone atrocaudata), male—page 350

D   BLACK PARADISE FLYCATCHER
       (Terpsiphone atrocaudata), female—page 350

E   BLUE PARADISE FLYCATCHER
       (Terpsiphone cyanescens)—page 350

F   WHITE-BELLIED WHISTLER
       (Pachycephala cinerea)—page 350

G   YELLOW-BELLIED WHISTLER
       (Pachycephala philippinensis)—page 354

PLATE 73

YELLOW-BELLIED WHISTLER   PLATE 73

Pachycephala philippinensis philippinensis (Walden, 1872)

1872 *Hyloterpe philippinensis* Walden, Ann. Mag. Nat. His., **10**:252, (Luzon)

Description: Upperparts olive-brown, top of head somewhat browner; chin and throat white with dark shaft streaks; breast band pale olive; rest of underparts yellow.

Soft Parts: Bill black; iris brown; feet bluish gray.

Measurements: Wing 83; tail 71; bill 17; tarsus 21.

Range: Luzon. (Endemic.)

Pachycephala philippinensis fallax (McGregor, 1904)

1904 *Hyloterpe fallax* McGregor, Bull. Phil. Mus., 4:27, (Calayan Island)

Description: Differs from *P. p. philippinensis* by having the top of the head browner, the rest of the upperparts darker olive-brown, and the flanks darker.

Range: Calayan Island. (Endemic.)

Pachycephala philippinensis illex (McGregor, 1904)

1904 *Hyloterpe illex* McGregor, Phil. Journ. Sci., **2**:348, (Camiguin North)

Description: Differs from *P. p. philippinensis* by having the breast and flanks yellower; also larger (wing 93; tail 75).

Range: Camiguin North. (Endemic.)

Pachycephala philippinensis siquijorensis Rand and Rabor, 1957

1957 *Pachycephala philippinensis siquijorensis* Rand and Rabor, Fieldiana: Zoology, 42:15, (Poo, Lazi, Siquijor)

Description: Differs from *apoensis* by having the underparts somewhat paler and the bill slightly larger (19).

Range: Siquijor. (Endemic.)

Pachycephala philippinensis apoensis (Mearns, 1905)

1905 *Hyloterpe apoensis* Mearns, Proc. Biol. Soc. Wash., **18**:86, (Mt. Apo, Mindanao)

Description: Differs from *P. p. philippinensis* by having the upperparts bright olive-green and the bill smaller (15).

Range: Dinagat, Leyte, Mindanao, and Samar. (Endemic.)

Pachycephala philippinensis boholensis Parkes, 1966

1966 *Pachycephala philippinensis boholensis* Parkes, Bull. Brit. Orn. Cl., **86**:170, (Cantaub, Sierra Bullones, Bohol)

Description: Differs from *apoensis* by having the outer margins of the primaries gray and the underparts paler yellow.
Range: Bohol. (Endemic.)

Pachycephala philippinensis basilanica (Mearns, 1909)

1909 *Hyloterpe apoensis basilanica* Mearns, Proc. U. S. Nat. Mus., **36**:442, (Basilan)
Description: Differs from *apoensis* by having the crown brownish, rest of upperparts paler, and the underparts a brighter yellow.
Range: Basilan. (Endemic.)

Family MOTACILLIDAE   PIPITS

FOREST WAGTAIL   PLATE 74

Dendronanthus indicus (Gmelin, 1789)

1789 *Motacilla indica* Gmelin, Syst. Nat., **1**:962, (India)
Description: Upperparts olive-brown; tail black and white; wings black with two white bars and a white patch in the primaries; superciliary, chin, and throat white; a black band on the breast; rest of underparts white.
Soft Parts: Bill brown; iris brown; feet brown.
Measurements: Wing 79; tail 72; bill 14; tarsus 22.
Range: Balabac and Calayan. (Only two records; a straggler from Siberia.)

YELLOW WAGTAIL   PLATE 74

Motacilla flava simillima Hartert, 1905

1905 *Motacilla flava simillima* Hartert, Vög. pal. Fauna, **1**:289, (Sulu Archipelago)
Description: Top of head and neck blue-gray; back and rump olive-green; wings dark brown with light margins; tail dark brown, outer rectrices white; superciliary and chin white; ear-coverts dark gray; underparts dark yellow and slightly darker on sides of breast.
Soft Parts: Bill black, base of lower mandible yellowish; iris brownish black; feet blackish gray.
Measurements: Wing 82; tail 73; bill 14; tarsus 29.
Range: Winters throughout the Philippines from Siberia.

PLATE 74

A GRAY WAGTAIL
      (*Motacilla cinerea*)—page 358

B FOREST WAGTAIL
      (*Dendronanthus indicus*)—page 355

C PIED WAGTAIL
      (*Motacilla alba*)—page 358

D YELLOW WAGTAIL
      (*Motacilla flava*)—page 355

E ORIENTAL TREE PIPIT
      (*Anthus hodgsoni*)—page 359

F PETCHORA PIPIT
      (*Anthus gustavi*)—page 359

G RED-THROATED PIPIT
      (*Anthus cervinus*)—page 359

H RICHARD'S PIPIT
      (*Anthus novaeseelandiae*)—page 358

PLATE 74

Motacilla flava taivana (Swinhoe, 1863)

1863   *Budytes taivanus* Swinhoe, Proc. Zool. Soc. London, p. 274, (Formosa)

Description: Differs from *simillima* by having the superciliary buffy yellow and the chin and throat with a yellowish wash.

Range: Luzon and Palawan; a migrant from Siberia.

GRAY WAGTAIL   PLATE 74

Motacilla cinerea robusta (Brehm, 1857)

1857   *Pallenura robusta* Brehm, Journ. f. Orn., **5**:32, (Japan)

Description: Upperparts gray; rump olive-yellow; tail black, outer rectrices white; superciliary white; throat black in spring, white in winter; breast, rump, and under tail-coverts yellow.

Soft Parts: Bill black; iris dark brown; feet dark brown.

Measurements: Wing 84; tail 97; bill 13; tarsus 21.

Range: Winters throughout the Philippines from Asia.

PIED WAGTAIL   PLATE 74

Motacilla alba ocularis Swinhoe, 1860

1860   *Motacilla ocularis* Swinhoe, Ibis, p. 55, (Amoy, China)

Description: Forehead and sides of face white, except for a black stripe through the eye; crown and hind neck black; back and rump gray; tail black, outer rectrices white; wings dark brown with light gray coverts and margins; chin and throat white; breast with a black band; rest of underparts gray-white.

Soft Parts: Bill black; iris brown; feet red-brown.

Measurements: Wing 89; tail 90; bill 14; tarsus 22.

Range: Balabac, Calayan, Lubang, Luzon, Negros, and Palawan; a migrant from Asia.

RICHARD'S PIPIT   PLATE 74

Anthus novaeseelandiae lugubris (Walden, 1875)

1875   *Corydalla lugubris* Walden, Trans. Zool. Soc. London, **9**:198, (Guimaras)

Description: Upperparts light buffy brown streaked with dark brown; tail brown, outer rectrices white; underparts buffy white; breast finely streaked with dark brown.

Soft Parts: Bill brown; iris dark brown; feet pinkish brown.

Measurements: Wing 82; tail 66; bill 16; tarsus 29.

Range: Found throughout the Philippines.

PETCHORA PIPIT

PLATE 74

Anthus gustavi gustavi Swinhoe, 1863

1863   *Anthus gustavi* Swinhoe, Proc. Zool. Soc. London, p. 90, (Amoy, China)

Description: Upperparts light brown streaked with brownish black; superciliary and face buff; chin and throat white; breast buffy streaked with black; belly and under tail-coverts white.

Soft Parts: Bill brown; iris dark brown; feet flesh color.

Measurements: Wing 84; tail 60; bill 13; tarsus 23.

Range: Winters in the Philippines from Asia.

ORIENTAL TREE PIPIT

PLATE 74

Anthus hodgsoni hodgsoni Richmond, 1907

1907   *Anthus hodgsoni* Richmond, in Blackwelder's Publ. Carnegie Inst. Wash., 1:493, (Bengal)

Description: Upperparts olive-brown; head and back streaked with black; lores, superciliary, chin, and throat buffy; breast and flanks dark buff streaked with dark brown; white.

Soft Parts: Bill light brown; iris dark brown; feet flesh color.

Measurements: Wing 85; tail 66; bill 16; tarsus 22.

Range: Winters in the Philippines from Asia.

Anthus hodgsoni yunnanensis Uchida and Kuroda, 1916

1916   *Anthus maculatus yunnanensis* Uchida and Kuroda, Annot. Zool. Japon, 9:134, (Mengtz, southern Yunnan)

Description: Differs from *A. h. hodgsoni* by almost completely lacking the streaking on the back.

Range: Winters in the Philippines from Asia.

RED-THROATED PIPIT

PLATE 74

Anthus cervinus (Pallas, 1811)

1811   *Motacilla cervina* Pallas, Zoo. Rosso-Asiat., 1:511, (Kolyma)

Description: Upperparts dark brown, feathers with buffy margins; tail brown, outer rectrices white; chin, throat, and superciliary reddish; breast and flanks buffy with dark brown streaks; belly buffy.

Soft Parts: Bill brown; iris dark brown; feet flesh color.
Measurements: Wing 88; tail 70; bill 15; tarsus 21.
Range: Winters in the Philippines from Asia.

Family ARTAMIDAE   WOOD-SWALLOWS

WHITE-BREASTED WOOD-SWALLOW   PLATE 75

Artamus leucorhynchus leucorhynchus (Linnaeus, 1771)

1771 *Lanius leucoryn(chus)* Linnaeus, Mantissa, p. 524, (Manila, Luzon)

Description: Upperparts slate-gray, except for the rump which is white; chin and throat slate-gray; rest of underparts white.
Soft Parts: Bill light blue; iris dark brown; feet black.
Measurements: Wing 133; tail 67; bill 21; tarsus 18.
Range: Found throughout the Philippines.

Family LANIIDAE   SHRIKES

TIGER SHRIKE   PLATE 75

Lanius tigrinus Drapiez, 1828

1828 *Lanius tigrinus* Drapiez, Dict. Hist. Nat., 13:523, (Java)

Description: Top of head, hind neck, and upper back gray; rest of upperparts red-brown with some black flecks; a black stripe through the eye from the lores to the ear-coverts; underparts gray-white.
Soft Parts: Bill blue-black; iris dark brown; feet plumbous.
Measurements: Wing 80; tail 77; bill 20; tarsus 22.
Range: Winters in the Philippines from Asia.

BROWN SHRIKE   PLATE 75

Lanius cristatus lucionensis Linnaeus, 1776

1776 *Lanius Lucionensis* Linnaeus, Syst. Nat., 1:135, (Luzon)

Description: Top of head gray; back and wing-coverts gray-brown; rump and tail dull rufous; superciliary white; lores and ear-coverts black; chin and throat white; breast, belly, and under tail-coverts pale rufous.
Soft Parts: Bill black; iris dark brown; feet black.
Measurements: Wing 89; tail 91; bill 20; tarsus 24.
Range: Winters in the Philippines from China.

Lanius cristatus cristatus Linnaeus, 1758

1758   *Lanius cristatus* Linnaeus, Syst. Nat., 1:93, (Bengal)

Description: Differs from *lucionensis* by having upperparts more rufous.

Range: Winters in northern Philippines; a migrant from eastern Asia.

Lanius cristatus superciliosus Latham, 1801

1801   *Lanius superciliosus* Latham, Ind. Orn., suppl., p. xx, (Java)

Description: Differs from *L. c. cristatus* by having the top of the head as well as the back rufous.

Range: Winters in northern Philippines; a migrant from eastern Asia.

SCHACH SHRIKE   PLATE 75

Lanius schach nasutus Scopoli, 1786

1786   *Lanius nasutus* Scopoli, Del. Flor. et Faun. Insubr., p. 85, (Panay)

Description: Top of head and hind neck black; back gray; rump pale rufous; wings and tail black, rectrices tipped with white; chin, throat, and breast white; flanks, belly, and under tail-coverts pale rufous.

Soft Parts: Bill black; iris brown; feet black.

Measurements: Wing 91; tail 125; bill 18; tarsus 27.

Range: Found throughout the Philippines, except the Sulu Archipelago. Basilan and Mindanao populations are intermediate toward *suluensis*.

Lanius schach suluensis (Mearns, 1905)

1905   *Cephalophoneus suluensis* Mearns, Proc. Biol. Soc. Wash., **18**:86, (Bual, Sulu Island)

Description: Differs from *nasutus* by having the upperparts paler, especially the back and rump.

Range: Sulu Archipelago. (Endemic.)

STRONG-BILLED SHRIKE   PLATE 75

Lanius validirostris validirostris Ogilvie-Grant, 1894

1894   *Lanius validirostris* Ogilvie-Grant, Bull. Brit. Orn. Cl., **3**:49, (northern Luzon)

Description: Upperparts gray; wings and tail brown-black; a black streak on the side of the head from the lores to the ear-coverts; all underparts gray-white, except flanks, which are rufous.

Soft Parts: Bill black; iris dark brown; feet brown-black.

Measurements: Wing 86; tail 94; bill 18; tarsus 26.

Range: Luzon. (Endemic.)

PLATE 75

A   SCHACH SHRIKE
       (Lanius schach)—page 361

B   BROWN SHRIKE
       (Lanius cristatus)—page 360

C   STRONG-BILLED SHRIKE
       (Lanius validirostris)—page 361

D   TIGER SHRIKE
       (Lanius tigrinus)—page 360

E   WHITE-BREASTED WOOD-SWALLOW
       (Artamus leucorhynchus)—page 360

PLATE 75

Lanius validirostris tertius Salomonsen, 1953

1953 *Lanius validirostris tertius* Salomonsen, Vid. Medd. Dansk nat. Foren., **115**:278, (Mt. Dulungan, Mindoro)

Description: Differs from *L. v. validirostris* by having the breast and belly washed with rufous; flanks and under tail-coverts darker rufous; also smaller.

Range: Mindoro. (Endemic.)

Lanius validirostris hachisuka Ripley, 1949

1949 *Lanius validirostris hachisuka* Ripley, Bull. Brit. Orn. Cl., **69**:121, (Apo Lake, Mt. Apo, Mindanao)

1958 *Lanius validirostris quartus* Rand and Rabor, Fieldiana: Zoology, **39**:85, (Duminagat, Mt. Malindang, Mindanao)

Description: Differs from *tertius* by having the rufous wash on the breast and belly and the rufous flanks darker.

Range: Mindanao. (Endemic.)

Family STURNIDAE   STARLINGS

LESSER GLOSSY STARLING   PLATE 76

Aplonis minor todayensis (Mearns, 1905)

1905 *Lamprocorax todayensis* Mearns, Proc. Biol. Soc. Wash., **18**:88, (Mt. Apo, Mindanao)

Description: All black with a purplish green gloss.

Soft Parts: Bill black; iris red; feet black.

Measurements: Wing 97; tail 69; bill 16; tarsus 18.

Range: Mindanao. (Endemic.)

PHILIPPINE GLOSSY STARLING   PLATE 76

Aplonis panayensis panayensis (Scopoli, 1783)

1783 *Muscicapa panayensis* Scopoli, Del. Flor. et Faun. Insubr., p. 96, (Philippines)

Description: Black with a green gloss. Immature—white below, streaked with black.

Soft Parts: Bill black; iris red; feet black.

Measurements: Wing 109; tail 79; bill 21; tarsus 23.

Range: Found throughout the Philippines. (Endemic.)

VIOLET-BACKED STARLING

PLATE 76

Sturnus philippensis (Forster, 1781)

1781 *Motacilla Philippensis* Forster, Ind. Zool., p. 41, (Philippines)

1783 *Motacilla violacea* Boddaert, Table Pl., enlum., p. 11, (Philippines)

Description: Male—top of head buffy white; back black glossed with violet; rump variable, black-buffy white to orange-buff; wings and tail black glossed with green; ear-coverts and half collar dark chestnut (the latter may be prominent or nearly absent); chin and throat white; sides of breast and belly white. Female—upperparts gray-brown; underparts whitish.

Soft Parts: Bill black; iris brown; feet dark green.

Measurements: Wing 105; tail 150; bill 18; tarsus 23.

Range: Winters in the Philippines from Japan.

SILKY STARLING

PLATE 76

Sturnus sericeus Gmelin, 1788

1788 *Sturnus sericeus* Gmelin, Syst. Nat., **1**:805, (China)

Description: Top of head buffy and hind neck buffy white; back and rump light gray; tail black with a green gloss; wings black with a green gloss and a white patch near shoulder; chin and throat white; breast gray; belly whitish.

Soft Parts: Bill red with a dark tip; iris whitish; feet orange.

Measurements: Wing 118; tail 60; bill 26; tarsus 29.

Range: Winters on Calayan; a straggler from China.

GRAY-BACKED STARLING

PLATE 76

Sturnus sinensis (Gmelin, 1788)

1788 *Oriolus sinensis* Gmelin, Syst. Nat., **1**:394, (China)

Description: Male—top of head buffy gray, rest of upperparts gray; wings black with a white shoulder patch; tail black with a terminal white band. Female—differs from male by being duller and having a gray shoulder patch.

Soft Parts: Bill gray; iris white; legs light brown.

Measurements: Wing 106; tail 64; bill 20; tarsus 24.

Range: Winters on Calayan and Luzon from southern China.

PLATE 76

A   VIOLET-BACKED STARLING
     (Sturnus philippensis)—page 365

B   GRAY-BACKED STARLING
     (Sturnus sinensis)—page 365

C   ASHY STARLING
     (Sturnus cineraceus)—page 368

D   SILKY STARLING
     (Sturnus sericeus)—page 365

E   PHILIPPINE GLOSSY STARLING
     (Aplonis panayensis)—page 364

F   LESSER GLOSSY STARLING
     (Aplonis minor)—page 364

PLATE 76

ASHY STARLING   PLATE 76

Sturnus cineraceus Temminck, 1835

1835 *Sturnus cineraceus* Temminck, Pl. Col., livr. 94, pl. 556, (Japan)

Description: Head black with a green gloss; forehead and ear-coverts streaked with white; back brownish gray; rump whitish; tail dark brown with a white tip; wings dark brown; chin and upper throat gray-green; breast and flanks gray; center of belly and under tail-coverts white.

Soft Parts: Bill orange with a dark tip; iris brown; feet yellowish.

Measurements: Wing 133; tail 70; bill 37; tarsus 32.

Range: Winters on Luzon from eastern Asia.

CRESTED MYNA   PLATE 77

Acridotheres cristatellus cristatellus (Linnaeus, 1766)

1766 *Gracula cristatella* Linnaeus, Syst. Nat., 1:165, (China)

Description: Upperparts blackish; tail black tipped with white; wings black, primaries white at base; underparts dull black; under tail-coverts tipped with white.

Soft Parts: Bill olive-yellow; iris yellow; feet yellowish.

Measurements: Wing 136; tail 84; bill 24; tarsus 39.

Range: Introduced around Manila and Luzon from China; spread to Negros.

MOUNT APO MYNA   PLATE 77

Basilornis miranda (Hartert, 1903)

1903 *Goodfellowia miranda* Hartert, Bull. Brit. Orn. Cl., 14:11, (Mindanao)

Description: Top of head, hind neck, and back glossy blue-black, a crest of decomposed feathers (length = 27); lower back and rump white; tail blue-black; wings brownish with blue-black coverts; underparts glossy blue-black.

Soft Parts: Bill greenish yellow; iris yellow-brown; bare skin around eye yellow; feet yellow-gray.

Measurements: Wing 124; tail 173; bill 25; tarsus 30.

Range: Mindanao. (Endemic.)

COLETO   PLATE 77

Sarcops calvus calvus (Linnaeus, 1766)

1766 *Gracula calva* Linnaeus, Syst. Nat., 1:164, (Luzon)

1949 *Sarcops calvus mindorensis* Gilliard, Am. Mus. Novit., 1429:4, (Mt. Dulangan, Mindoro)

Description: Forehead, stripe down center of crown, and nape black; back, rump, and tail-coverts silvery gray; wings and tail glossed with blue-green; underparts dull black; under tail-coverts mottled gray and black.

Soft Parts: Bill black; iris pink; bare skin around eye pinkish; feet black.

Measurements: Wing 127; tail 116; bill 28; tarsus 31.

Range: Catanduanes, Luzon, Marinduque, Mindoro, and Polillo. (Endemic.)

Sarcops calvus melanonotus Ogilvie-Grant, 1906

1906 *Sarcops melanonotus* Ogilvie-Grant, Bull. Brit. Orn. Cl., **16**:100, (Davao, Mindanao)

1952 *Sarcops calvus similis* Salomonsen, Vid. Medd. Dansk nat. Foren., **114**:361, (Balang-Bang, Tolong, Negros)

1952 *Sarcops calvus samarensis* Salomonsen, Vid. Medd. Dansk nat. Foren., **114**:361, (Oras, Samar)

1952 *Sarcops calvus minor* Salomonsen, Vid. Medd. Dansk nat. Foren., **114**:362, (Burungkot, Upi Municipality, Cotabato Province, Mindanao)

Description: Differs from *S. c. calvus* by having a wide black patch in the center of the back.

Range: Bohol, Cebu, Leyte, Mindanao, Negros, Panay, Samar, and Ticao. (Endemic.)

Sarcops calvus lowii Sharpe, 1877

1877 *Sarcops Lowii* Sharpe, Trans. Linn. Soc. London, **1**:344, (Sibutu, Sulu Islands)

Description: Differs from *melanonotus*, as does *S. c. calvus*, by lacking the black patch on the back; but also differs from both northern races by having the wings and underparts brownish black.

Range: Sulu Archipelago. (Endemic.)

TALKING   MYNA   **PLATE 77**

Gracula religiosa palawanensis (Sharpe, 1890)

1890 *Mainatus palawanensis* Sharpe, Cat. Bds. Brit. Mus., **13**:104, (Palawan)

Description: Top of head black; rest of upperparts black with a strong blue-green gloss; wings with a white patch in the primaries; underparts dull black.

Soft Parts: Bill orange; iris dark brown; eye wattles yellow; feet yellowish.

Measurements: Wing 159; tail 81; bill 29; tarsus 36.

Range: Balabac, Calamianes, and Palawan. (Endemic.)

PLATE 77

A   COLETO
       (Sarcops calvus)—page 368

B   MOUNT APO MYNA
       (Basilornis miranda)—page 368

C   TALKING MYNA
       (Gracula religiosa)—page 369

D   CRESTED MYNA
       (Acridotheres cristatellus)—page 368

PLATE 77

Family NECTARINIIDAE   SUNBIRDS

PLAIN-THROATED SUNBIRD   **PLATE** 78

Anthreptes malacensis paraguae Riley, 1920

1920 *Anthreptes malacensis paraguae* Riley, Proc. Biol. Soc. Wash., **33**:55, (Puerto Princesa, Palawan)

Description: Male—top of head and upper back metallic purplish green; lower back and rump metallic purple; tail dark brown; wings brown, edgings greenish or faintly orange, bend metallic purple, and ends of scapulars reddish; lores and patch behind the eye greenish brown, sometimes with orange tinge; chin and throat dull reddish bordered with a metallic purplish stripe; breast and belly yellowish. Female—upperparts dull olive-gray; underparts yellowish.

Soft Parts: Bill black; iris brick-red; feet olive-brown.

Measurements: Wing 65; tail 49; bill 18; tarsus 16.

Range: Palawan. (Endemic.)

Anthreptes malacensis chlorigaster Sharpe, 1877

1877 *Anthreptes chlorigaster* Sharpe, Trans. Linn. Soc. London, **1**:342, (Negros)

1926 *Anthreptes malacensis basilanicus* Hachisuka, Bull. Brit. Orn. Cl., **47**:68, (Basilan)

Description: Differs from *griseigularis* by having the chin and throat more reddish brown and the breast and belly more yellowish as in *paraguae*; red of wing edgings very dark.

Range: Cebu, Lubang, Masbate, Negros, Panay, Romblon, Sibuyan, Tablas, and Ticao. (Endemic.)

Anthreptes malacensis heliolusius Oberholser, 1923

1923 *Anthreptes malacensis heliolusius* Oberholser, Journ. Wash. Acad. Sci., **13**:228, (Basilan)

Description: Differs from *chlorigaster* by having olive-brown cheeks, not reddish; red of wing-coverts and edgings paler; underparts slightly brighter.

Range: Basilan and western Mindanao. (Endemic.)

Anthreptes malacensis wiglesworthi Hartert, 1902

1902 *Anthreptes malacensis wiglesworthi* Hartert, Nov. Zool., **9**:209, (Sulu Island)

Description: Differs from *heliolusius* by having underparts an even brighter yellow, cheeks redder, and edges of remiges paler and brighter.

Range: Sulu Archipelago, except Sibutu. (Endemic.)

Anthreptes malacensis iris Parkes, 1971

1971 *Anthreptes malacensis iris* Parkes, Nemouria, 4:44, (Sibutu)

Description: Crown and dorsum steel-blue. Male—differs from *wiglesworthi* by having the underparts brighter yellow; flanks and under tail-coverts grayer. Female—differs by lacking the reddish wash of the wing-coverts and edgings.

Range: Sibutu, intergrading with *wiglesworthi* on Bongao.

Anthreptes malacensis cagayanensis Mearns, 1905

1905 *Anthreptes cagayanensis* Mearns, Proc. Biol. Soc. Wash., **18**:6, (Cagayan Sulu)

Description: Differs from *wiglesworthi* by being much brighter yellow below and by having olive, not red, edges of wing feathers.

Range: Cagayan Sulu. (Endemic.)

Anthreptes malacensis griseigularis (Tweeddale, 1877)

1877 *Anthothreptus griseigularis* Tweeddale, Proc. Zool. Soc. London, p. 830, (Suriago, Mindanao)

Description: Differs from *paraguae* by having the top of the head and upper back metallic green, the sides of the face redder, the chin and throat gray, and the rest of the underparts dull olive-green.

Range: Leyte, northeastern Mindanao, and Samar. (Endemic.)

Anthreptes malacensis birgitae Salomonsen, 1953

1953 *Anthreptes malacensis birgitae* Salomonsen, Vid. Medd. Dansk nat. Foren., **115**: 251, (Barit, Abra Province, Luzon)

Description: Differs from *griseigularis* by having a much longer bill (19) and underparts darker and duller.

Range: Luzon and Mindoro. (Endemic.)

VAN HASSELT'S SUNBIRD   PLATE 78

Nectarinia sperata sperata (Linnaeus, 1766)

1766 *Certhia sperata* Linnaeus, Syst. Nat., **1**:186, (Manila, Luzon)

1952 *Cinnyris sperata manueli* Salomonsen, Vid. Medd. Dansk nat. Foren., **114**:356, (Karlagan, Polillo)

1952 *Cinnyris sperata minima* Salomonsen, Vid. Medd. Dansk nat. Foren., **114**:356, (Limot, Mati Municipality, Davao Province, Mindanao)

1953 *Cinnyris sperata trochilus* Salomonsen, Vid. Medd. Dansk nat. Foren., **115**:256, (Talacogon, Agusan Province, Mindanao)

Description: Male—top of head metallic coppery green; mantle maroon; lower back, rump, and tail-coverts metallic green; tail black; wings black, primaries and secondaries edged with orange-red; chin and throat metallic purple; breast scarlet; belly and under tail-coverts yellowish olive. Female—olive-green, brighter below; edging to wings brownish.

Soft Parts: Bill black; iris dark brown; feet black.

Measurements: Wing 51; tail 32; bill 18; tarsus 13.

Range: Central Luzon, south to Mindanao; also Palawan. (Endemic.)

Nectarinia sperata henkei (A. B. Meyer, 1884)

1884   *Cinnyris henkei* A. B. Meyer, Zeitschr. ges. Orn., **1**:207, (no locality=northern Luzon)

1894   *Cinnyris whiteheadi* Ogilvie-Grant, Bull. Brit. Orn. Cl., **3**:50, (mountains of northern Luzon=Benguet)

Description: Male—differs from *N. s. sperata* by having the mantle black.

Range: Babuyan Islands and northern Luzon. (Endemic.)

Nectarinia sperata marinduquensis duPont, 1971

1971   *Nectarinia sperata marinduquensis* duPont, Nemouria, 3:3, (Boac, Marinduque)

Description: Female—differs from *N. s. sperata* by having the lower back, rump, and upper tail-coverts dark red; outer margins to primaries and secondaries burnt orange. Male—similar to those of *N. s. sperata*.

Range: Marinduque. (Endemic.)

Nectarinia sperata juliae (Tweeddale, 1877)

1877   *Nectarophila juliae* Tweeddale, Proc. Zool. Soc. London, p. 547, (Malanipa Island)

Description: Male—differs from *N. s. sperata* by having the breast bright yellow.

Range: Basilan, Malanipa, western Mindanao, and Sulu Archipelago. (Endemic.)

Nectarinia sperata theresae Gilliard, 1950

1950   *Nectarinia sperata theresae* Gilliard, Bull. Am. Mus. Nat. Hist., **94**:500, (Lamao, Bataan Province, Luzon)

Description: A hybrid between *N. s. sperata* × *henkei*. This hybrid is easily recognized by the intergradation of the maroon and black on the mantle.

Range: Bataan Province and central Luzon.

Nectarinia sperata davaoensis Delacour, 1945

1945   *Nectarinia sperata davaoensis* Delacour, Zoologica, **30**:115, (Martina, Davao, Mindanao)

Description: A hybrid between *N. s. sperata* × *juliae*. This hybrid is easily recognized by its orange-vermilion breast. Some specimens within the same population tend to be more like *sperata* and others like *juliae*.

Range: A band from Davao to Gingoog City, Mindanao. (Endemic.)

MACKLOT'S SUNBIRD PLATE 78

Nectarinia calcostetha Jardine, 1843

1843 *Nectarinia calcostetha* Jardine, Pl. Col., livr. 23, pl. 138, (Java)

Description: Male—top of head metallic green; hind neck and upper back black; lower back, rump, and wing-coverts metallic green; wings and tail black; chin and throat metallic coppery red bordered with metallic purplish blue; breast metallic purplish blue; pectoral tufts yellow; belly and under tail-coverts black. Female—top of head gray-brown; rest of upperparts olive-yellow; underparts gray washed with olive-green.

Soft Parts: Bill black; iris black; feet black.

Measurements: Wing 60; tail 52; bill 20; tarsus 14.

Range: Balabac and Palawan.

OLIVE-BACKED SUNBIRD PLATE 78

Nectarinia jugularis jugularis (Linnaeus, 1766)

1766 *Certhia jugularis* Linnaeus, Syst. Nat., **1**:185, (Philippines)

1905 *Cyrtostomus dinagatensis* Mearns, Proc. Biol. Soc. Wash., **18**:5, (Dinagat)

1908 *Cyrtostomus jugularis mindanensis* Mearns, Proc. U. S. Nat. Mus., **36**:443, (Zamboanga, Mindanao)

1941 *Cinnyris picta* Hachisuka, Proc. Biol. Soc. Wash., **54**:52, (Atong-Atong Plantation, Basilan); type a composite specimen

Description: Male—upperparts olive-green; tail black tipped with white; throat metallic blue-black; breast and belly dark yellow, sometimes with brown band bordering throat patch. Female—similar to male but the throat is yellow.

Soft Parts: Bill black; iris dark brown; feet black.

Measurements: Wing 55; tail 32; bill 20; tarsus 14.

Range: Central Luzon to Mindanao and Basilan. (Endemic.)

Nectarinia jugularis obscurior (Ogilvie-Grant, 1894)

1894 *Cinnyris obscurior* Ogilvie-Grant, Bull. Brit. Orn. Cl., **3**:50, (northern Luzon = Benguet)

Description: Differs from *N. j. jugularis* by having the underparts paler yellow. Most males have a brown band between the throat and breast. Bill slightly narrower at base (♂3.5–4.0 vs. 4.3–4.4).

Range: Northern Luzon.

PLATE 78

A   VAN HASSELT'S SUNBIRD
     (Nectarinia sperata), female—page 373

B   VAN HASSELT'S SUNBIRD
     (Nectarinia sperata), male—page 373

C   OLIVE-BACKED SUNBIRD
     (Nectarinia jugularis), male—page 375

D   OLIVE-BACKED SUNBIRD
     (Nectarinia jugularis), female—page 375

E   MACKLOT'S SUNBIRD
     (Nectarinia calcostetha), male—page 375

F   MACKLOT'S SUNBIRD
     (Nectarinia calcostetha), female—page 375

G   PLAIN-THROATED SUNBIRD
     (Anthreptes malacensis), male—page 372

H   PLAIN-THROATED SUNBIRD
     (Anthreptes malacensis), female—page 372

PLATE 78

Nectarinia jugularis aurora (Tweeddale, 1878)

1878   *Cyrtostomus aurora* Tweeddale, Proc. Zool. Soc. London, p. 620, (Puerto Princesa, Palawan)

Description: Male—differs from *N. j. jugularis* by having a bright orange spot on the breast; however, it may cover the entire breast or appear to be nonexistent, as this is a very variable character.

Range: Cagayan, Calamiane and Cuyon Islands, and Palawan. (Endemic.)

Nectarinia jugularis woodi (Mearns, 1909)

1909   *Cyrtostomus jugularis woodi* Mearns, Proc. U. S. Nat. Mus., **36**:444, (one of "Three Islands" south of Sibutu)

Description: Male—differs from *N. j. jugularis* by having center of the throat metallic purplish blue.

Range: Sulu Archipelago.

HACHISUKA'S SUNBIRD   PLATE 79

Aethopyga primigenius primigenius (Hachisuka, 1941)

1941   *Philippinia primigenius* Hachisuka, Bull. Biogeogr. Soc. Japan, **11**:6, (Mt. Apo, Mindanao)

Description: Top of head and neck dark gray; back olive-green; rump bright yellow; tail and wings dark olive-brown, rectrices tipped with white; chin and throat dark gray; breast and center of belly white; flanks and under tail-coverts yellow.

Soft Parts: Bill black; iris brick-red; feet black.

Measurements: Wing 51; tail 37; bill 20; tarsus 15.

Range: Mt. Apo, Mt. Katanglad, and Mt. McKinley, Mindanao. (Endemic.)

Aethopyga primigenius diuatae Salomonsen, 1953

1953   *Aethopyga primigenius diuatae* Salomonsen, Vid. Medd. Dansk nat. Foren., **115**:275, (Mt. Hilong-Hilong, Diuata Mountains, northeast Mindanao)

Description: Differs from *A. p. primigenius* by having the upperparts somewhat paler; throat darker with a central pale gray-white streak ending with a yellow spot on the breast; belly richer gray-white.

Range: Diuata Mountains, northeast Mindanao. (Endemic.)

APO SUNBIRD   PLATE 79

Aethopyga boltoni malindangensis Rand and Rabor, 1957

1957   *Aethopyga boltoni malindangensis* Rand and Rabor, Fieldiana: Zoology, **42**:17, (Mt. Malindang, Mindanao)

Description: Head, back, and wings dark olive-green, forehead with a metallic green gloss; rump light yellow; tail black with a green gloss, all but two central rectrices tipped with white; chin and throat light yellow with dark gray sides; breast orange-yellow with some bright orange tufts on the sides; belly olive-yellow.

Soft Parts: Bill black; iris red; feet black.

Measurements: Wing 56; tail 53; bill 22; tarsus 17.

Range: Central and western Mindanao. (Endemic.)

Aethopyga boltoni boltoni Mearns, 1905

1905   *Aethopyga boltoni* Mearns, Proc. Biol. Soc. Wash., **18**:4, (Mt. Apo, Mindanao)

Description: Differs from *malindangensis* by having the top of the head duller; underparts also duller, especially the breast.

Range: Mt. Apo and Mt. McKinley, eastern Mindanao. (Endemic.)

FLAMING SUNBIRD   PLATE 79

Aethopyga flagrans flagrans Oustalet, 1876

1876   *Aethopyga flagrans* Oustalet, Journ. Institut., p. 108, (Lagune, Luzon)

1895   *Cinnyris excellens* Ogilvie-Grant, Bull. Brit. Orn. Cl., 4:18, (Albay Province, Luzon)

Description: Male—forehead and forecrown metallic blue-green; hind crown, back, and wing-coverts bright olive-yellow washed with orange; upper tail-coverts metallic blue-green; tail black with metallic green edges; chin dark metallic purple; throat and breast dull black with a bright reddish orange stripe in the middle extending to the central part of the belly; rest of belly and flanks olive-yellow; under tail-coverts whitish. Female—upperparts olive-green; underparts grayer with a yellowish patch in the breast.

Soft Parts: Bill black; iris brown; feet black.

Measurements: Wing 49; tail 29; bill 18; tarsus 14.

Range: Catanduanes and northwestern and southern Luzon. (Endemic.)

Aethopyga flagrans decolor Parkes, 1963

1963   *Aethopyga flagrans decolor* Parkes, Bull. Brit. Orn. Cl., **83**:8, (Cape Engano, northeastern Luzon)

Description: Differs from *A. f. flagrans* by having the upperparts dull olive-yellow and the breast stripe and patch on the belly less red.

Range: Northeastern Luzon. (Endemic.)

Aethopyga flagrans guimarasensis (Steere, 1890)

1890   *Cinnyris guimarasensis* Steere, List Bds. Mamms. Steere Expd., p. 22, (Guimaras)

Description: Differs from *A. f. flagrans* by having the mantle blood-red.

Range: Guimaras and Panay. (Endemic.)

PLATE 79

A   MOUNTAIN SUNBIRD
      (Aethopyga pulcherrima), male—page 382

B   MOUNTAIN SUNBIRD
      (Aethopyga pulcherrima), female—page 382

C   FLAMING SUNBIRD
      (Aethopyga flagrans), female—page 379

D   FLAMING SUNBIRD
      (Aethopyga flagrans), male—page 379

E   HACHISUKA'S SUNBIRD
      (Aethopyga primigenius)—page 378

F   APO SUNBIRD
      (Aethopyga boltoni)—page 378

A

B

C

D

E

F

PLATE 79

Aethopyga flagrans daphoenonota Parkes, 1963

1963 *Aethopyga flagrans daphoenonota* Parkes, Bull. Brit. Orn. Cl., **83**:8, (Luzuriaga, Cuernos de Negros, Negros)

Description: Male—differs from *guimarasensis* by having the blood-red mantle more extensive and the orange of the underparts darker; wing-coverts and edgings orange, not greenish. Female—has orange edgings and is greener, less gray above.

Range: Negros. (Endemic.)

MOUNTAIN SUNBIRD   PLATE 79

Aethopyga pulcherrima pulcherrima Sharpe, 1876

1876 *Aethopyga pulcherrima* Sharpe, Nature, **14**:297, (Basilan)

1878 *Aethopyga dubia* Tweeddale, Proc. Zool. Soc. London, p. 112, (Dinagat)

Description: Male—forehead and spot behind the eye metallic purplish green; crown and back olive-green; rump bright yellow; upper tail-coverts and wing-coverts metallic green; tail black glossed with metallic green; primaries and secondaries olive-green; chin and throat bright yellow; breast yellowish with traces of a red-orange patch; belly grayish yellow. Female—differs from male by having upperparts olive-green, except rump; underparts dull olive-gray.

Soft Parts: Bill black; iris red-brown; feet black.

Measurements: Wing 48; tail 22; bill 19; tarsus 14.

Range: Basilan, Dinagat, Leyte, Mindanao, and Samar. (Endemic.)

Aethopyga pulcherrima jefferyi (Ogilvie-Grant, 1894)

1894 *Eudrepanis jefferyi* Ogilvie-Grant, Bull. Brit. Orn. Cl., **3**:50, (northern Luzon)

Description: Male—differs from *A. p. pulcherrima* by having the forehead dark metallic blue, the lower back bright yellow like the rump, and the metallic green of the wing-coverts extending to edges of primaries and secondaries.

Range: Luzon. (Endemic.)

Aethopyga pulcherrima decorosa (McGregor, 1907)

1907 *Eudrepanis decorosa* McGregor, Phil. Journ. Sci., **2**:330, (Guindulman, Bohol)

Description: Male—differs from *jefferyi* by having the primaries and secondaries edged with metallic purplish blue, the rump paler yellow, and the red breast spot obsolete.

Range: Bohol. (Endemic.)

LOVELY SUNBIRD   PLATE 80

Aethopyga shelleyi shelleyi Sharpe, 1876

1876 *Aethopyga shelleyi* Sharpe, Nature, **14**:297, (Palawan)

Description: Male—crown metallic purplish green; hind neck and upper back dark red; lower back and rump bright yellow; upper tail-coverts and tail metallic blue-green; sides of head dark red; chin and throat yellow with a red margin followed by peacock blue-green malar stripes; breast yellow streaked with red; belly pale gray. Female—upperparts olive-green; underparts grayish yellow.

Soft Parts: Bill black; iris dark brown; feet black.

Measurements: Wing 46; tail 45; bill 16; tarsus 14.

Range: Balabac, Calamianes, and Palawan. (Endemic.)

Aethopyga shelleyi flavipectus Ogilvie-Grant, 1894

1894 *Aethopyga flavipectus* Ogilvie-Grant, Bull. Brit. Orn. Cl., **3**:49, (northern Luzon)

1894 *Aethopyga minuta* Bourns and Worcester, Occ. Papers Minn. Acad. Nat. Sci., 1:18, (Mindoro)

Description: Male—differs from *A. s. shelleyi* by having the red on the breast nonexistent or only slightly traceable.

Range: Luzon, Mindoro, and Polillo. (Endemic.)

Aethopyga shelleyi rubrinota McGregor, 1905

1905 *Aethopyga rubrinota* McGregor, Bur. Govt. Lab., Manila, 25:30, (Port Tilig, Lubang)

Description: Male—differs from *flavipectus* by having the breast lighter yellow.

Range: Lubang. (Endemic.)

Aethopyga shelleyi bella Tweeddale, 1877

1877 *Aethopyga bella* Tweeddale, Ann. Mag. Nat. His., **20**:537, (Surigao, northern Mindanao)

Description: Male—differs from *A. s. shelleyi* by having fewer red streaks on the breast; also, somewhat smaller (wing 43). Female—rump yellow.

Range: Leyte, Mindanao, and Samar. (Endemic.)

Aethopyga shelleyi bonita Bourns and Worcester, 1894

1894 *Aethopyga bonita* Bourns and Worcester, Occ. Papers Minn. Acad. Nat. Sci., 1:17, (Negros, Cebu, Masbate)

Description: Male—differs from *bella* by having the yellow of the lower back and rump darker and the breast very heavily streaked with red.

Range: Cebu, Masbate, Negros, Panay, and Ticao. (Endemic.)

Aethopyga shelleyi arolasi Bourns and Worcester, 1894

1894 *Aethopyga arolasi* Bourns and Worcester, Occ. Papers Minn. Acad. Nat. Sci., 1:17, (Tawi Tawi and Sulu)

Description: Male—differs from *bella* by having heavier orange-red streaking on the breast; also, slightly larger; abdomen and under tail-coverts yellower. Female—has yellow rump reduced.

Range: Sulu Archipelago. (Endemic.)

YELLOW-BACKED SUNBIRD   PLATE 80

Aethopyga siparaja magnifica Sharpe, 1876

1876   *Aethopyga magnifica* Sharpe, Nature, **14**:297, (Negros)

Description: Male—forehead black with a metallic purplish gloss; crown and back dark red; rump bright orange-yellow; tail black with a purplish gloss; wings black; chin, throat, and breast bright red; jugular stripes metallic purple; belly and under tail-coverts black. Female—head, back, and rump dark olive-green; tail black with some red on margins; wings dark brown with rufous edges; underparts gray-green.

Soft Parts: Bill brown; iris brown; feet dark brown.

Measurements: Wing 55; tail 49; bill 21; tarsus 15.

Range: Cebu, Negros, Panay, Sibuyan, and Tablas. (Endemic.)

LITTLE SPIDER HUNTER   PLATE 80

Arachnothera longirostra dilutor Sharpe, 1876

1876   *Arachnothera dilutor* Sharpe, Nature, **14**:298, (Palawan)

Description: Crown olive-brown; rest of upperparts dull olive-green; chin and throat gray; breast and belly pale grayish green; pectoral tufts dull orange-yellow.

Soft Parts: Bill black; iris red-brown; feet blue-black.

Measurements: Wing 65; tail 47; bill 34; tarsus 17.

Range: Palawan. (Endemic.)

Arachnothera longirostra flammifera Tweeddale, 1878

1878   *Arachnothera flammifera* Tweeddale, Proc. Zool. Soc. London, p. 343, (Leyte)

Description: Differs from *dilutor* by having the upperparts with a faint orange-green wash; flanks, belly, and under tail-coverts yellow; pectoral tufts bright orange.

Range: Bohol, Leyte, Mindanao, and Samar. (Endemic.)

Arachnothera longirostra randi Salomonsen, 1953

1953   *Arachnothera longirostris randi* Salomonsen, Vid. Medd. Dansk nat. Foren., **115**:271, (Basilan)

Description: Differs from *flammifera* by having a much longer bill (34).

Range: Basilan. (Endemic.)

NAKED-FACED SPIDER HUNTER   PLATE 80

Arachnothera clarae luzonensis Alcasid and Gonzales, 1968

1968 *Arachnothera clarae luzonensis* Alcasid and Gonzales, Bull. Brit. Orn. Cl., **88**:129, (Pakil, Laguna, Luzon)

Description: Upperparts olive-green; edges of primaries and secondaries burnt orange; chin, throat, and breast gray; belly, flanks, thighs, and under tail-coverts pale gray-brown.

Soft Parts: Bill black; iris black; feet light brown; naked skin on face pinkish.

Measurements: Wing 85; tail 42; bill 35; tarsus 19.

Range: Known only from Laguna Province, central Luzon. (Endemic.)

Arachnothera clarae philippinensis (Steere, 1890)

1890 *Philemon philippinensis* Steere, List Bds. Mamms. Steere Expd., p. 21, (Samar)

Description: Differs from *luzonensis* by having the forehead naked and the underparts greener.

Range: Leyte and Samar. (Endemic.)

Arachnothera clarae malindangensis Rand and Rabor, 1957

1957 *Arachnothera clarae malindangensis* Rand and Rabor, Fieldiana: Zoology, **42**:17, (Masawan, Mt. Malindang, Mindanao)

Description: Differs from *luzonensis* by having the upperparts lighter olive-green, edges to primaries and secondaries golden, and underparts olive-gray.

Range: Central and western Mindanao. (Endemic.)

Arachnothera clarae clarae Blasius, 1890

1890 *Arachnothera clarae* Blasius, Braunschweig. Anz., 87:877, (Davao, Mindanao)

Description: Differs from *malindangensis* by having the underparts paler olive-gray.

Range: Eastern Mindanao. (Endemic.)

Family DICAEIDAE   FLOWERPECKERS

OLIVE-BACKED FLOWERPECKER   PLATE 81

Prionochilus olivaceus parsonsi McGregor, 1927

1927 *Prionochilus parsonsi* McGregor, Phil. Journ. Sci., **32**:520, (Malinao, Luzon)

Description: Upperparts golden olive; tail and primaries blackish brown; lores and sides of throat and breast black; center of underparts white.

385

Soft Parts: Bill black; iris brick-red; feet black.

Measurements: Wing 55; tail 28; bill 11; tarsus 14.

Range: Sierra Madre, eastern Luzon. (Endemic.)

Prionochilus olivaceus olivaceus Tweeddale, 1877

1877 *Prionochilus olivaceus* Tweeddale, Ann. Mag. Nat. His., **20**:536, (Dinagat)

Description: Differs from *parsonsi* by having the sides of the face, throat, and breast pale olive-gray.

Range: Basilan, Dinagat, and Mindanao. (Endemic.)

Prionochilus olivaceus samarensis Steere, 1890

1890 *Prionochilus Samarensis* Steere, List Bds. Mamms. Steere Expd., p. 22, (Samar and Leyte=Samar)

Description: Differs from *P. o. olivaceus* by usually lacking the white loral spot; sides of breast browner, tending to streak at posterior end.

Range: Bohol, Leyte, and Samar. (Endemic.)

PALAWAN YELLOW-RUMPED FLOWERPECKER   PLATE 81

Prionochilus plateni Blasius, 1888

1888 *Prionochilus plateni* Blasius, Braunschweig. Anz., **37**:335, (Palawan)

1888 *Prionochilus johannae* Sharpe, Ibis, p. 201, (Palawan)

1948 *Anaimos plateni culionensis* Rand, Fieldiana: Zoology, **31**:205, (San Pedro, Culion)

Description: Male—upperparts blue-black, except for red patch in center of crown and yellow rump; chin and malar stripe white; throat, breast, and belly yellow with a red spot in the middle of the breast. Female—upperparts olive-green; center of crown and rump yellowish; chin and throat whitish; rest of underparts yellowish.

Soft Parts: Bill black, base of lower mandible gray; iris dark brown; feet black.

Measurements: Wing 58; tail 29; bill 12; tarsus 13.

Range: Balabac, Culion, and Palawan. (Endemic.)

STRIPED FLOWERPECKER   PLATE 81

Dicaeum aeruginosum aeruginosum (Bourns and Worcester, 1894)

1894 *Prionochilus aeruginosum* Bourns and Worcester, Occ. Papers Minn. Acad. Nat. Sci., 1:20, (Cebu and Mindanao=Cebu)

Description: Upperparts brown; underparts white streaked with brown, heaviest on breast.

Soft Parts: Bill brown; iris brown; feet dark gray.

Measurements: Wing 65; tail 40; bill 9; tarsus 13.

Range: Cebu, Mindanao, Mindoro, and Negros. Mindoro specimens intermediate toward *striatissimum*. (Endemic.)

Dicaeum aeruginosum striatissimum Parkes, 1962

1962   *Dicaeum aeruginosum striatissimum* Parkes, Postilla, 67:4, (Solsona, Ilocos Norte Province, Luzon)

Description: Differs from *D. a. aeruginosum* by having the upperparts darker and the underparts more heavily streaked.

Range: Luzon and Sibuyan. (Endemic.)

Dicaeum aeruginosum affine (Zimmer, 1918)

1918   *Acmonorhynchus affinis* Zimmer, Phil. Journ. Sci., **13**:348, (Brooke's Point, Palawan)

1936   *Piprisoma diversum* Riley, Proc. Biol. Soc. Wash., **49**:113, (Puerto Princesa, Palawan)

Description: Differs from *D. a. aeruginosum* by having the upperparts more olive-green and the underparts paler because of narrower streaks.

Range: Palawan. (Endemic.)

GRAY-BREASTED FLOWERPECKER   PLATE 81

Dicaeum proprium Ripley and Rabor, 1966

1966   *Dicaeum proprium* Ripley and Rabor, Proc. Biol. Soc. Wash., **79**:305, (Mt. Mayo, Davao Province, Mindanao)

Description: Male—upperparts blue-black with a light, glossy, greenish wash; primaries dark brown; white tufts under wings; chin and malar stripe gray-white separated by a blue-black jugular stripe; throat, center of breast, and belly taupe; flanks darker; under tail-coverts gray-white.

Soft Parts: Unknown.

Measurements: Wing 62; tail 29; bill 10; tarsus 12.

Range: Known only from the type locality.

OLIVE-CAPPED FLOWERPECKER   PLATE 81

Dicaeum nigrilore Hartert, 1904

1904   *Dicaeum nigrilore* Hartert, Bull. Brit. Orn. Cl., **15**:8, (Mt. Apo, Mindanao)

1941   *Dicaeum isag* Hachisuka, Bull. Biogeogr. Soc. Jap., **11**:1, (Mt. Apo, Mindanao)

1953   *Dicaeum nigrilore diuatae* Salomonsen, Vid. Medd. Dansk nat. Foren., **115**:274, (Diuata Mountains, Mindanao)

Description: Top of head light olive; back brownish; rump olive; tail and wings dark brown; lores and patch under eye black; chin white; throat, breast, and belly gray; flanks and under tail-coverts yellow.

Soft Parts: Bill black; iris brown; feet gray.

Measurements: Wing 55; tail 29; bill 16; tarsus 15.

Range: Mindanao. (Endemic.)

YELLOW-CROWNED FLOWERPECKER   PLATE 81

Dicaeum anthonyi anthonyi (McGregor, 1914)

1914   *Prionochilus anthonyi* McGregor, Phil. Journ. Sci., **9**:531, (Mt. Polis, Luzon)

Description: Male—forehead and lores black; crown orange-yellow; rest of upperparts black with a blue gloss; chin and throat white; breast and belly yellowish; under tail-coverts orange-yellow. Female—upperparts dull olive; underparts grayish white.

Soft Parts: Bill black; iris brown; feet black.

Measurements: Wing 57; tail 31; bill 12; tarsus 16.

Range: Mt. Polis and Mt. Tabuan, Luzon. (Endemic.)

Dicaeum anthonyi kampalili Manuel and Gilliard, 1953

1952   *Dicaeum rubricapilla* Manuel and Gilliard, Am. Mus. Novit., 1545:5, (Mt. Kampalili, Mindanao)

1953   *Dicaeum kampalili* Manuel and Gilliard, Auk, **70**:90, new name for *Dicaeum rubricapilla* Manuel and Gilliard, 1952

Description: Male—differs from *D. a. anthonyi* by having the crown redder and the underparts grayer; also smaller (wing 55; tail 25).

Range: Mindanao, except Zamboanga Peninsula. (Endemic.)

Dicaeum anthonyi masawan Rand and Rabor, 1957

1957   *Dicaeum anthonyi masawan* Rand and Rabor, Fieldiana: Zoology, **42**:16, (Masawan, Mt. Malindang, Mindanao)

Description: Male—differs from *kampalili* by having the breast and flanks washed with yellow and the belly much yellower.

Range: Zamboanga Peninsula, Mindanao. (Endemic.)

BICOLORED FLOWERPECKER

PLATE 81

Dicaeum bicolor inexpectatum (Hartert, 1895)

1895 *Prionochilus inexpectatus* Hartert, Nov. Zool., **2**:64, (Mindoro)

Description: Male—upperparts black glossed with blue; underparts gray with a whitish streak down the middle. Female—upperparts olive, browner on crown; underparts gray with an olive wash and a lighter streak down the middle.

Soft Parts: Bill black; iris red; feet black.

Measurements: Wing 52; tail 24; bill 9; tarsus 12.

Range: Catanduanes, Luzon, and Mindoro. (Endemic.)

Dicaeum bicolor viridissimum Parkes, 1971

1971 *Dicaeum bicolor viridissimum* Parkes, Nemouria 4:51, (Canlaon Volcano, Negros)

Description: Male—differs from *inexpectatum* in having iridescence of upperparts, especially rump, green rather than blue. Female—less purely gray on underparts and more washed with olive-green; green of upperparts extends farther forward to head.

Range: Negros.

Dicaeum bicolor bicolor (Bourns and Worcester, 1894)

1894 *Prionochilus bicolor* Bourns and Worcester, Occ. Papers Minn. Acad. Nat. Sci., 1: 20, (Ayala, Mindanao)

Description: Male—differs from *inexpectatum* in being whiter below, with almost no gray on flanks; dorsal iridescence more purple. Female—more different: much darker green above and quite glossy; underparts like female *viridissimum*.

Range: Bohol, Leyte, Mindanao, and Samar. (Endemic.)

FOUR-COLORED FLOWERPECKER

PLATE 81

Dicaeum quadricolor (Tweeddale, 1877)

1877 *Prionochilus quadricolor* Tweeddale, Proc. Zool. Soc. London, p. 762, (Cebu)

Description: Male—top of head and hind neck black; back feathers black with bright orange-red ends; lower back and rump greenish yellow; tail and wings black; underparts grayish white. Female—upperparts olive-brown.

Soft Parts: Bill black; iris brown; feet black.

Measurements: Wing 54; tail 30; bill 10; tarsus 13.

Range: Cebu. (Extinct.)

PLATE 80

A   LOVELY SUNBIRD
        (Aethopyga shelleyi), female—page 382

B   LOVELY SUNBIRD
        (Aethopyga shelleyi), male—page 382

C   YELLOW-BACKED SUNBIRD
        (Aethopyga siparaja), female—page 384

D   YELLOW-BACKED SUNBIRD
        (Aethopyga siparaja), male—page 384

E   NAKED-FACED SPIDER HUNTER
        (Arachnothera clarae)—page 385

F   LITTLE SPIDER HUNTER
        (Arachnothera longirostra), male—page 384

G   LITTLE SPIDER HUNTER
        (Arachnothera longirostra), female—page 384

PLATE 80

PLATE 81

A   PALAWAN YELLOW-RUMPED FLOWERPECKER
    (*Prionochilus plateni*), male—page 386

B   PALAWAN YELLOW-RUMPED FLOWERPECKER
    (*Prionochilus plateni*), female—page 386

C   GRAY-BREASTED FLOWERPECKER
    (*Dicaeum proprium*)—page 387

D   OLIVE-CAPPED FLOWERPECKER
    (*Dicaeum nigrilore*)—page 387

E   BICOLORED FLOWERPECKER
    (*Dicaeum bicolor*)—page 389

F   STRIPED FLOWERPECKER
    (*Dicaeum aeruginosum*)—page 386

G   FOUR-COLORED FLOWERPECKER
    (*Dicaeum quadricolor*)—page 389

H   OLIVE-BACKED FLOWERPECKER
    (*Prionochilus olivaceus*)—page 385

I   YELLOW-CROWNED FLOWERPECKER
    (*Dicaeum anthonyi*), female—page 388

J   YELLOW-CROWNED FLOWERPECKER
    (*Dicaeum anthonyi*), male—page 388

PLATE 81

PHILIPPINE FLOWERPECKER   PLATE 82

Dicaeum australe australe (Hermann, 1783)

1783   *Pipra australe* Hermann, Tab. Aff. Anim., p. 223, (New Guinea = Luzon)

1789   *Pipra papuensis* Gmelin, Syst. Nat., 1:1004, (New Guinea = Philippines)

1894   *Dicaeum flaviventer* Meyer, Journ. f. Orn., 42:91, (Cebu)

Description: Upperparts black with a bluish gloss; chin and throat white; breast and belly gray with a scarlet stripe in the middle.

Soft Parts: Bill black; iris brown; feet black.

Measurements: Wing 56; tail 28; bill 11; tarsus 9.

Range: Basilan, Bohol, Camiguin North, Cebu, Dinagat, Leyte, Lubang, Luzon, Marinduque, Masbate, Mindanao, Samar, Ticao, and Verde. (Endemic.)

Dicaeum australe haematostictum Sharpe, 1876

1876   *Dicaeum haematostictum* Sharpe, Nature, 14:298, (Guimaras)

1926   *Dicaeum haematostictum whiteheadi* Hachisuka, Bull. Brit. Orn. Cl., 47:55, (Mt. Canloan, Negros)

Description: Differs from *D. a. australe* by having a black collar on the upper breast and by having the scarlet stripe much wider.

Range: Guimaras, Negros, and Panay. (Endemic.)

MINDORO FLOWERPECKER   PLATE 82

Dicaeum retrocinctum Gould, 1872

1872   *Dicaeum retrocinctum* Gould, Ann. Mag. Nat. His., 10:114, (Mindoro)

Description: Upperparts blue-black with a scarlet collar on the hind neck; chin and throat black with a red goatee; sides of throat, breast, and belly gray-white; in the center of the breast and belly is a scarlet stripe with black margins.

Soft Parts: Bill black; iris dark red-brown; feet black.

Measurements: Wing 52; tail 25; bill 13; tarsus 15.

Range: Mindoro. (Endemic.)

ORANGE-BREASTED FLOWERPECKER   PLATE 82

Dicaeum trigonostigma xanthopygium Tweeddale, 1877

1877   *Dicaeum xanthopygium* Tweeddale, Ann. Mag. Nat. His., 20:95, (Monte Alban, Luzon)

Description: Male—top of head and upperparts dark blue; a bright red-orange patch in middle of the back; rump yellow; tail blue-black; lores and sides of head black; underparts yellow with an orange wash. Female—upperparts dark olive-green; rump yellowish; underparts olive; yellow in center of breast and belly.
Soft Parts: Bill blackish; iris light brown; feet blackish.
Measurements: Wing 53; tail 25; bill 12; tarsus 12.
Range: Luzon, Marinduque, Mindoro, and Polillo. (Endemic.)

Dicaeum trigonostigma sibuyanicum Bourns and Worcester, 1894

1894 *Dicaeum sibuyanica* Bourns and Worcester, Occ. Papers Minn. Acad. Nat. Sci., 1: 18, (Sibuyan)

Description: Male—differs from *xanthopygium* by having the rump very dark olive-green and the chin and throat gray.
Range: Sibuyan. (Endemic.)

Dicaeum trigonostigma intermedia Bourns and Worcester, 1894

1894 *Dicaeum intermedia* Bourns and Worcester, Occ. Papers Minn. Acad. Nat. Sci., 1: 19, (Romblon and Tablas)

Description: Male—differs from *sibuyanicum* by having the chin and throat much paler gray, washed with pale yellow; olive-green patch on rump reduced or absent. Female—duller below.
Range: Romblon and Tablas. (Endemic.)

Dicaeum trigonostigma dorsale Sharpe, 1876

1876 *Dicaeum dorsale* Sharpe, Nature, **14**:298, ("Palawan"; error = Panay)
Description: Male—differs from *xanthopygium* by having the rump dark blue and the breast and belly more orange.
Range: Masbate, Negros, and Panay. (Endemic.)

Dicaeum trigonostigma pallidius Bourns and Worcester, 1894

1894 *Dicaeum pallidior* Bourns and Worcester, Occ. Papers Minn. Acad. Nat. Sci., 1: 18, (Cebu)

Description: Male—differs from *dorsale* by having the upperparts lighter blue and the underparts uniform yellow with only a trace of orange on the breast.
Range: Cebu. (Extinct.)

Dicaeum trigonostigma cinereigulare Tweeddale, 1877

1877 *Dicaeum cinereigulare* Tweeddale, Proc. Zool. Soc. London, p. 829, (Butuan, Mindanao)

Description: Male—differs from *dorsale* by having a grayish band across the center of the throat and the breast and belly darker orange.

Range: Bohol, Leyte, Mindanao, and Samar. (Endemic.)

Dicaeum trigonostigma besti Steere, 1890

1890   *Dicaeum besti* Steere, List Bds. Mamms. Steere Expd., p. 22, (Siquijor)

Description: Male—differs from *cinereigulare* by having less yellow on throat. Also larger (wing 52 vs. 49; bill 11 vs. 9).

Range: Siquijor. (Endemic.)

Dicaeum trigonostigma isidroi Rand and Rabor, 1969

1969   *Dicaeum trigonostigma isidroi* Rand and Rabor, Fieldiana: Zoology, **51**:163, (Camiguin South)

Description: Differs from *cinereigulare* by having the throat paler yellow and the sides of the throat purer gray-white, lacking yellow wash. Also larger (wing 56 vs. 51).

Range: Camiguin South. (Endemic.)

Dicaeum trigonostigma assimile Bourns and Worcester, 1894

1894   *Dicaeum assimilis* Bourns and Worcester, Occ. Papers Minn. Acad. Nat. Sci., 1: 19, (Sulu, Tawi Tawi)

1941   *Dicaeum dorsale hanadori* Hachisuka, Tori, **11**:87, (Siasi)

Description: Male—differs from *cinereigulare* by having the rump yellow, the chin and throat dark gray, and the breast and belly paler orange.

Range: Jolo, Siasi, Sulu, and Tawi Tawi. (Endemic.)

Dicaeum trigonostigma sibutuense Sharpe, 1893

1893   *Dicaeum sibutuense* Sharpe, Bull. Brit. Orn. Cl., **3**:10, (Sibutu)

Description: Male—differs from *assimile* by having the rump dark olive-green.

Range: Sibutu. (Endemic.)

WHITE-BELLIED FLOWERPECKER   PLATE 82

Dicaeum hypoleucum obscurum Ogilvie-Grant, 1894

1894   *Dicaeum obscurum* Ogilvie-Grant, Bull. Brit. Orn. Cl., **3**:50, (mountains of northern Luzon = Benguet)

1962   *Dicaeum hypoleucum lagunae* Parkes, Postilla, 67:5, (Pangil, Laguna Province, Luzon)

Description: Upperparts olive-brown; tail and primaries dark brown; underparts grayish olive.

Soft Parts: Bill black; iris brown; feet brownish.

Measurements: Wing 55; tail 27; bill 12; tarsus 14.

Range: Northwestern and central Luzon. (Endemic.)

Dicaeum hypoleucum cagayanensis Rand and Rabor, 1967

1967 *Dicaeum hypoleucum cagayanensis* Rand and Rabor, Fieldiana: Zoology, 51:89, (Mt. Cagua, Gonzaga, Cagayan Prov., Luzon)

Description: Differs from *obscurum* by having the underparts paler and washed with yellow.

Range: Northeastern Luzon. (Endemic.)

Dicaeum hypoleucum pontifex Mayr, 1946

1877 *Dicaeum Everetti* Tweeddale, Ann. Mag. Nat. His., 4:537, (Dinagat); not *Prionochilus everetti* Sharpe, 1877

1878 *Dicaeum modestum* Tweeddale, Proc. Zool. Soc. London, p. 380, (Panaon); not *Prionochilus modestus* Hume, 1875

1946 *Dicaeum hypoleucum pontifex* Mayr, Zoologica, 31:8, new name for *Dicaeum Everetti* Tweeddale, 1877, preoccupied

Description: Differs from *obscurum* by having the underparts gray-white.

Range: Bohol, Dinagat, Leyte, Mindanao (except Zamboanga Peninsula), Panaon, and Samar. (Endemic.)

Dicaeum hypoleucum hypoleucum Sharpe, 1876

1876 *Dicaeum hypoleucum* Sharpe, Nature, 14:298, (Basilan)

1877 *Dicaeum mindanense* Tweeddale, Proc. Zool. Soc. London, p. 547, (Pasananca, Mindanao)

Description: Male—differs from *pontifex* by having upperparts blackish and underparts lighter. Female—more olivaceous.

Range: Basilan, Bongao, Jolo, Zamboanga Peninsula of Mindanao, and Siasi. (Endemic.)

PYGMY FLOWERPECKER   PLATE 82

Dicaeum pygmaeum pygmaeum (Kittlitz, 1833)

1833 *Nectarinia pygmea* (in text; *pygmaea* on plate) Kittlitz, Mem. Acad. Imp. Sci., St. Petersb., 2:2, (Luzon = Manila)

Description: Male—top of head, back, wings, and tail olive-black with a blue-green gloss; rump dull olive-yellow; face and sides of throat gray; chin and center of throat white; rest of underparts buffy. Female—similar to male but much duller.

Soft Parts: Bill black; iris dark brown; feet brown-black.

Measurements: Wing 47; tail 25; bill 10; tarsus 11.

Range: Southern and central Luzon, south to Mindanao (except western peninsula). (Endemic.)

Dicaeum pygmaeum salomonseni Parkes, 1962

1962 *Dicaeum pygmaeum salomonseni* Parkes, Postilla, 67:6, (Mt. Sicapo-o [Mt. Simminublan], Ilocos Norte Province, Luzon)

Description: Male—differs from *D. p. pygmaeum* by having the back blacker, lacking the green gloss; face and flanks grayer. Female—differs by being grayer.

Range: Northern Luzon. (Endemic.)

Dicaeum pygmaeum davao Mearns, 1905

1905 *Dicaeum davao* Mearns, Proc. Biol. Soc. Wash., **18**:87, (Cotabato, Mindanao)

Description: Differs from *D. p. pygmaeum* by having the face, sides of throat, and flanks darker; belly and under tail-coverts more yellowish.

Range: Western peninsula of Mindanao. (Endemic.)

Dicaeum pygmaeum palawanorum Hachisuka, 1926

1926 *Dicaeum pygmaeum palawanorum* Hachisuka, Bull. Brit. Orn. Cl., **47**:55, (Iwahig, Palawan)

Description: Differs from *D. p. pygmaeum* by having the upperparts slightly lighter, except the rump, which is duller olive-yellow; underparts lighter; also larger (wing 50).

Range: Balabac, Calamianes, and Palawan. (Endemic.)

FIRE-THROATED FLOWERPECKER   PLATE 82

Dicaeum ignipectus luzoniense Ogilvie-Grant, 1894

1894 *Dicaeum luzoniense* Ogilvie-Grant, Bull. Brit. Orn. Cl., 3:50, (mountains of northern Luzon = Benguet)

Description: Male—upperparts dark glossy green; sides of head and neck dull black; chin whitish; throat and upper breast scarlet; breast whitish; flanks olive; under tail-coverts orange-yellow. Female—upperparts similar to male but lighter, especially the rump; underparts gray-white, except the flanks and under tail-coverts, which are similar to those of the male.

Soft Parts: Bill black; iris brown; feet black.
Measurements: Wing 54; tail 32; bill 9; tarsus 12.
Range: Northern Luzon. (Endemic.)

Dicaeum ignipectus bonga Hartert, 1904

1904   *Dicaeum bonga* Hartert, Bull. Brit. Orn. Cl., **14**:80, (Samar)

Description: Differs from *luzoniense* by being smaller (wing 47).
Range: Samar. (Endemic.)

Dicaeum ignipectus apo Hartert, 1904

1904   *Dicaeum apo* Hartert, Bull. Brit. Orn. Cl., **14**:79, (Mt. Apo, Mindanao)

Description: Differs from *luzoniense* by having the sides of the head glossy green, the flanks darker olive-green, and the under tail-coverts lighter yellow.
Range: Mindanao and Negros. (Endemic.)

Family ZOSTEROPIDAE   WHITE-EYES

PHILIPPINE   WHITE-EYE   PLATE 83

Zosterops meyeni meyeni Bonaparte, 1850

1832?   *D(icaeum) flavum* Kittlitz, Kupfert. Naturg. Vögel, (2), p. 15, (Luzon)

1850   *Zosterops meyeni* Bonaparte, Consp. Av., **1**:398, new name for *D. flavum* Kittlitz, 1832

Description: Upperparts light olive-green; forehead, chin, throat, and under tail-coverts light yellow; eye-ring white with a very small dark spot in front of the eye; breast and belly dirty white.
Soft Parts: Bill gray; iris brown; feet gray-black.
Measurements: Wing 53; tail 38; bill 11; tarsus 14.
Range: Banton, Calayan, Lubang, Luzon, and Verde. (Endemic.)

Zosterops meyeni batanis McGregor, 1907

1907   *Zosterops batanis* McGregor, Phil. Journ. Sci., **2**:343, (Batan Island)

Description: Differs from *Z. m. meyeni* by having upperparts brighter olive-green, especially the crown and rump; belly with a light yellow wash; also larger (wing 57; tail 40; long bill) and black loral spot more distinct.
Range: Batan Island and small islands to the north. (Endemic.)

PLATE 82

A   PHILIPPINE FLOWERPECKER
     (*Dicaeum australe*), female—page 394

B   PHILIPPINE FLOWERPECKER
     (*Dicaeum australe*), male—page 394

C   ORANGE-BREASTED FLOWERPECKER
     (*Dicaeum trigonostigma*), male—page 394

D   ORANGE-BREASTED FLOWERPECKER
     (*Dicaeum trigonostigma*), female—page 394

E   WHITE-BELLIED FLOWERPECKER
     (*Dicaeum hypoleucum*)—page 396

F   MINDORO FLOWERPECKER
     (*Dicaeum retrocinctum*)—page 394

G   FIRE-THROATED FLOWERPECKER
     (*Dicaeum ignipectus*), male—page 398

H   FIRE-THROATED FLOWERPECKER
     (*Dicaeum ignipectus*), female—page 398

I   PYGMY FLOWERPECKER
     (*Dicaeum pygmaeum*)—page 397

PLATE 82

PLATE 83

A   PHILIPPINE WHITE-EYE
        (Zosterops meyeni)—page 399

B   MOUNTAIN WHITE-EYE
        (Zosterops montana)—page 404

C   EVERETT'S WHITE-EYE
        (Zosterops everetti)—page 405

D   YELLOW WHITE-EYE
        (Zosterops nigrorum)—page 406

E   CINNAMON WHITE-EYE
        (Hypocryptadius cinnamomeus)—page 408

F   GOODFELLOW'S WHITE-EYE
        (Lophozosterops goodfellowi)—page 408

PLATE 83

MOUNTAIN WHITE-EYE   PLATE 83

Zosterops montana whiteheadi Hartert, 1903

1903 *Zosterops whiteheadi* Hartert, Bull. Brit. Orn. Cl., **14**:13, (Lepanto, Luzon)

Description: Upperparts olive-green; eye-ring white with a black spot by the lores that breaks through the eye-ring; lores and forehead light yellow-green; chin and throat yellow; center of breast and belly whitish; flanks light gray-brown; under tail-coverts yellow.
Soft Parts: Bill black; iris gray; feet black.
Measurements: Wing 50; tail 39; bill 11; tarsus 14.
Range: Luzon. (Endemic.)

Zosterops montana halconensis Mearns, 1907

1907 *Zosterops halconensis* Mearns, Phil. Journ. Sci., **2**:360, (Mt. Halcon, Mindoro)

Description: Differs from *Z. m. whiteheadi* by having the upperparts darker olive-green and the throat and under tail-coverts deeper yellow; also, much larger (wing 58; tail 42; bill 14; tarsus 16).
Range: Mindoro. (Endemic.)

Zosterops montana gilli duPont, 1971

1971 *Zosterops montana gilli* duPont, Nemouria, **3**:5, (Matabang Bundok, Kilo-Kilo, Sta. Cruz, Marinduque)

Description: Differs from *halconensis* by having the upperparts brighter yellowish olive-green; yellow of chin, throat, and under tail-coverts brighter and more extensive.
Range: Marinduque.

Zosterops montana parkesi duPont, 1971

1971 *Zosterops montana parkesi* duPont, Nemouria, **3**:4, (Mt. Mantalingajan, Palawan)

Description: Differs from *whiteheadi* by having upperparts much yellower green, forehead and face golden green, eye-ring bolder, chin and throat richer yellow and more extensive, flanks same whitish color of breast and belly, and under tail-coverts richer yellow; also, much larger (wing 55; tail 40).
Range: Palawan. (Endemic.)

Zosterops montana pectoralis Mayr, 1945

1945 *Zosterops montana pectoralis* Mayr, Zoologica, **30**:116, (Canloan Volcano, Negros)

1956 *Zosterops montana finitima* Ripley and Rabor, Condor, **58**:290, (Luzuriaga, Mt. Cuernos de Negros, Negros)

404

Description: Differs from *whiteheadi* by having the upperparts paler olive-green and the yellow of the underparts lighter and more extensive, often forming a streak down the belly; also larger (wing 58).

Range: Negros. (Endemic.)

Zosterops montana diuatae Salomonsen, 1953

1953　*Zosterops montana diuatae* Salomonsen, Vid. Medd. Dansk nat. Foren., **115**:280, (Mt. Hilong-Hilong, Diuata Mts., Mindanao)

Description: Differs from *whiteheadi* by having upperparts paler olive-green; forehead, throat, and under tail-coverts lighter yellow; flanks gray; also larger (wing 57).

Range: Mountains of northern Mindanao from Mt. Malindang to the Diuata Mts. (Endemic.)

Zosterops montana vulcani Hartert, 1903

1903　*Zosterops whiteheadi vulcani* Hartert, Bull. Brit. Orn. Cl., **14**:14, (Mt. Apo, Mindanao)

Description: Differs from *diuatae* by having the flanks much browner and the yellow of the throat and under tail-coverts paler.

Range: Mt. Apo and Mt. Katanglad, Mindanao. (Endemic.)

EVERETT'S WHITE-EYE　　　　　　　　　PLATE 83

Zosterops everetti basilanica Steere, 1890

1890　*Zosterops Basilanica* Steere, List Bds. Mamms. Steere Expd., p. 21, (Basilan, Samar, Leyte = Basilan)

1922　*Zosterops forbesi* Bangs, Bull. Mus. Comp. Zool., **65**:83, (Camiguin South)

Description: Upperparts olive-green; eye-ring white broken by a black dot in front of the eye; chin and throat yellow-green; stripe in center of breast, belly, and under tail-coverts yellow; sides of breast and flanks dark gray.

Soft Parts: Bill black; iris brown; feet lead color.

Measurements: Wing 55; tail 38; bill 12; tarsus 14.

Range: Basilan, Camiguin South, Dinagat, and Mindanao. (Endemic.)

Zosterops everetti boholensis McGregor, 1908

1907　*Zosterops laeta* McGregor, Phil. Journ. Sci., **2**:329, (Bohol)

1908　*Zosterops boholensis* McGregor, Phil. Journ. Sci., **3**:283, new name for *Zosterops laeta* McGregor, 1907

Description: Differs from *basilanica* by having the upperparts richer olive-green, the yellow of underparts more golden, and the gray of the sides of the breast and flanks lighter.
Range: Bohol, Leyte, and Samar. (Endemic.)

Zosterops everetti everetti Tweeddale, 1878

1878   *Zosterops everetti* Tweeddale, Proc. Zool. Soc. London, p. 762, (Cebu)
Description: Differs from *boholensis* by having the upperparts slightly darker and a dark line under the eye.
Range: Cebu. (Extinct.)

Zosterops everetti siquijorensis Bourns and Worcester, 1894

1894   *Zosterops siquijorensis* Bourns and Worcester, Occ. Papers Minn. Acad. Nat. Sci., 1:21, (Siquijor)
Description: Differs from *boholensis* by having the upperparts lighter, the yellow of underparts brighter, and the gray of the sides of the breast and flanks paler.
Range: Negros and Siquijor. (Endemic.)

Zosterops everetti mandibularis Stresemann, 1931

1931   *Zosterops everetti mandibularis* Stresemann, Mitt. Zool. Mus. Berlin, **17**:221, (Maimbun, Sulu)
Description: Differs from *basilanica* by having the upperparts lighter olive-green; the chin and throat yellower; the sides of the breast and flanks paler gray; and the yellow stripe down the center of the breast, belly, and under tail-coverts brighter yellow.
Range: Sulu Archipelago. (Endemic.)

YELLOW   WHITE-EYE   PLATE 83

Zosterops nigrorum luzonica Ogilvie-Grant, 1895

1895   *Zosterops luzonica* Ogilvie-Grant, Bull. Brit. Orn. Cl., 4:22, (Mt. Mayon, Luzon)
Description: Forehead and lores olive-yellow; rest of upperparts olive-green; eye-ring white; underparts dark yellow; sides of breast and flanks olivish.
Soft Parts: Bill black; iris brown; feet lead color.
Measurements: Wing 52; tail 36; bill 12; tarsus 15.
Range: Central and southern Luzon. (Endemic.)

Zosterops nigrorum aureiloris Ogilvie-Grant, 1895

1895 *Zosterops aureiloris* Ogilvie-Grant, Bull. Brit. Orn. Cl., 4:40, (Lepanto, northern Luzon)

1969 *Zosterops nigrorum sierramadrensis* Rand and Rabor, Fieldiana: Zoology, 51:165, (Mt. Cagua, Cagayan Prov., Luzon)

Description: Differs from *luzonica* by having the yellow of the forehead more extensive and brighter than the throat; rest of upperparts brighter green and the yellow of the underparts brighter. Rump yellower than back.

Range: Northern Luzon. (Endemic.)

Zosterops nigrorum meyleri McGregor, 1907

1907 *Zosterops meyleri* McGregor, Phil. Journ. Sci., 2:348, (Camiguin North)

Description: Differs from *aureiloris* by having a broader white eye-ring; also larger (wing 54 vs. 52).

Range: Camiguin North. (Endemic.)

Zosterops nigrorum mindorensis Parkes, 1971

1971 *Zosterops nigrorum mindorensis* Parkes, Nemouria, 4:60, (northern slopes of Mt. Halcon, Mindoro)

Description: Richest, deepest yellow of races of *Z. nigrorum,* both above and below; blackish color under the eye slightly more extensive and white eye-ring slightly broader than in Luzon races.

Range: Mindoro. (Endemic.)

Zosterops nigrorum nigrorum Tweeddale, 1878

1878 *Zosterops nigrorum* Tweeddale, Proc. Zool. Soc. London, p. 286, (Valencia, Negros)

Description: Differs from *luzonica* by having the upperparts duller olive, a black spot in the front of the eye-ring, and the throat and under tail-coverts richer yellow.

Range: Caluya, Cresta de Gallo, Masbate, Negros, Panay, and Ticao. (Endemic.)

Zosterops nigrorum richmondi McGregor, 1904

1904 *Zosterops flavissima* McGregor, Bull. Phil. Mus., 4:26, (Cagayancillo Island)

1904 *Zosterops richmondi* McGregor, Proc. Biol. Soc. Wash., **17**:165, new name for *Zosterops flavissima* McGregor, 1904; not *Zosterops flavissima* Hartert, 1903

Description: Differs from *Z. n. nigrorum* by being lighter, especially the underparts, which are brighter yellow; also larger (wing 57 vs. 54).

Range: Cagayan Island, Sulu Sea. (Endemic.)

Zosterops nigrorum catarmanensis Rand and Rabor, 1969

1969   *Zosterops nigrorum catarmanensis* Rand and Rabor, Fieldiana: Zoology, **51**:13, (Camiguin South)

Description: Differs from *richmondi* by being paler, especially the underparts, which are lighter yellow.

Range: Camiguin South. (Endemic.)

GOODFELLOW'S WHITE-EYE   PLATE 83

Lophozosterops goodfellowi goodfellowi (Hartert, 1903)

1903   *Zosterops goodfellowi* Hartert, Bull. Brit. Orn. Cl., **14**:13, (Mt. Apo, Mindanao)

Description: Forehead and sides of face gray-brown; lores blackish; upperparts olive-green; chin and throat dirty white; breast and flanks olive-green; belly yellowish.

Soft Parts: Bill black; iris red-brown; feet olive.

Measurements: Wing 72; tail 47; bill 14; tarsus 19.

Range: Central Mindanao around Mt. Apo. (Endemic.)

Lophozosterops goodfellowi malindangensis (Mearns, 1909)

1909   *Zosterops goodfellowi malindangensis* Mearns, Proc. U. S. Nat. Mus., **36**:443, (Mt. Malindang, Mindanao)

1969   *Lophozosterops goodfellowi gracilis* Mees, Zool. Verhandelingen, 102:195, (Mt. Hilong-Hilong, northeast Mindanao)

Description: Differs from *L. g. goodfellowi* by having the forehead grayer and the underparts washed with brown.

Range: Northern Mindanao. (Endemic.)

INCERTAE SEDIS

CINNAMON WHITE-EYE   PLATE 83

Hypocryptadius cinnamomeus Hartert, 1903

1903   *Hypocryptadius cinnamomeus* Hartert, Bull. Brit. Orn. Cl., **14**:13, (Mt. Apo and Katanglad, Mindanao)

1957   *Hypocryptadius cinnamomeus malindangensis* Rand and Rabor, Fieldiana: Zoology, **42**:18, (Mt. Malindang, Mindanao)

1962   *Hypocryptadius cinnamomeus pallidigula* deSchauensee and duPont, Proc. Acad. Nat. Sci. Phila., **114**:171, (Daggayan, Misamis Oriental, Mindanao)

408

Description: Upperparts cinnamon-rufous; tail and primaries darker; chin, throat, and breast buff with a cinnamon wash; belly gray-white.

Soft Parts: Bill black; iris unknown; feet black.

Measurements: Wing 89; tail 55; bill 16; tarsus 19.

Range: Mindanao. (Endemic.)

Family PLOCEIDAE   WEAVERBIRDS

TREE SPARROW   PLATE 84

Passer montanus saturatus Stejneger, 1885

1885 *Passer saturatus* Stejneger, Proc. U. S. Nat. Mus., **8**:19, (Riukius = Okinawa)

1941 *Passer montanus manillensis* Hachisuka, Tori, **11**:88, (Manila, Luzon)

Description: Crown and hind neck chestnut; upper back and wing-coverts olive-buff streaked with brown-black; lower back and rump olive-brown; tail brown; wings dark brown; chin, center of throat, and ear-coverts black; rest of underparts gray-white.

Soft Parts: Bill black; iris dark brown; feet light brown.

Measurements: Wing 71; tail 54; bill 13; tarsus 18.

Range: Introduced around Manila, Luzon, from Japan or Formosa.

Passer montanus malaccensis Dubois, 1885

1885 *Passer montanus malaccensis* Dubois, Fauna Ill. Vert. Belg. Ois., **1**:572, (Malacca)

Description: Differs from *saturatus* by having the upperparts more rufous, especially the back, rump, and wings.

Range: Introduced around Cebu City, Cebu, from the Malay Peninsula. Birds reported from Negros may be assigned here.

Family ESTRILDIDAE   GRASS FINCHES, MANNIKINS, WAXBILLS

RED AVADAVAT   PLATE 84

Amandava amandava (Linnaeus, 1758)

1758 *Fringilla amandava* Linnáeus, Syst. Nat., **1**:180, (Calcutta)

Description: Male—top of head mottled olive and dark red; back olive-brown; upper tail-coverts dark red; tail black; wing-coverts dark brown with white spots; underparts bright red with fine white spots on sides of breast and flanks. Female—upperparts olive-brown; chin and throat whitish; rest of underparts buffy.

Soft Parts: Bill bright red; iris orange-red; feet pale brown.

Measurements: Wing 47; tail 34; bill 10; tarsus 13.

Range: Introduced around Manila, Luzon, from southeastern Asia.

GREEN-TAILED PARROT-FINCH   PLATE 84

Erythrura hyperythra brunneiventris (Grant, 1894)

1894 *Chlorura brunneiventris* Grant, Bull. Brit. Orn. Cl., 3:50, (northern Luzon)

Description: Forehead black followed by a blue band on the forecrown; rest of upperparts bright green; underparts dark cinnamon-rufous; sides of breast green.

Soft Parts: Bill black; iris dark brown; feet pinkish.

Measurements: Wing 61; tail 39; bill 10; tarsus 14.

Range: Northern Luzon and Mindoro. (Endemic.)

GREEN-FACED PARROT-FINCH   PLATE 84

Erythrura viridifacies Hachisuka and Delacour, 1937

1937 *Erythrura viridifacies* Hachisuka and Delacour, Bull. Brit. Orn. Cl., 57:66, (Manila, Luzon)

Description: Upperparts dark green; upper tail-coverts and tail dark red; underparts green.

Soft Parts: Bill black; iris unknown; feet unknown.

Measurements: Wing 58; tail 46; bill 12; tarsus 19.

Range: Luzon and Negros. (Endemic.)

MINDANAO PARROT-FINCH   PLATE 84

Erythrura coloria Ripley and Rabor, 1961

1961 *Erythrura coloria* Ripley and Rabor, Postilla, 50:18, (Mt. Katanglad, Mindanao)

Description: Forehead dark blue; crown, back, rump, and wings dark green; upper tail-coverts and tail red; cheeks dark blue followed by a bright red patch; chin with a few blue feathers; rest of underparts dark green.

Soft Parts: Bill black; iris brown; feet dark brown.

Measurements: Wing 53; tail 38; bill 11; tarsus 17.

Range: Central Mindanao. (Endemic.)

NUTMEG MANNIKIN

PLATE 84

Lonchura punctulata cabanisi (Sharpe, 1890)

1872 *Oxycerca (Uroloncha) jagori* Cabanis, Journ. f. Orn., **20**:317, (Luzon)

1890 *Munia cabanisi* Sharpe, Cat. Bds. Brit. Mus., **13**:353, new name for *Oxycerca (Uroloncha) jagori* Cabanis, 1872

Description: Upperparts brown with pale shaft streaks; tail more olive-yellow; chin and upper throat dark brown; rest of underparts mottled brown and white.

Soft Parts: Bill horn-blue; iris brown; feet bluish.

Measurements: Wing 51; tail 39; bill 11; feet 14.

Range: Luzon, Mindoro, and Panay. (Endemic.)

WHITE-BREASTED MANNIKIN

PLATE 84

Lonchura leucogastra everetti (Tweeddale, 1877)

1877 *Orycerca everetti* Tweeddale, Ann. Mag. Nat. His., **20**:96, (Monte Alban, Luzon)

Description: Upperparts dark brown; shaft streaks white on back and wing-coverts; chin, throat, breast, flanks, and under tail-coverts brown; belly white.

Soft Parts: Bill black; iris dark red-brown; feet dark bluish.

Measurements: Wing 53; tail 41; bill 12; tarsus 13.

Range: Catanduanes, Luzon, Mindoro, and Polillo. (Endemic.)

Lonchura leucogastra manueli Parkes, 1958

1958 *Lonchura leucogastra manueli* Parkes, Proc. U. S. Nat. Mus., **108**:280, (Isabella, Basilan)

Description: Differs from *everetti* by having the browns richer and darker and the bill slightly larger.

Range: South of Luzon to Tawi Tawi. (Endemic.)

Lonchura leucogastra palawana Ripley and Rabor, 1962

1962 *Lonchura leucogastra palawana* Ripley and Rabor, Postilla, 73:11, (Macagua, Brooke's Point, Palawan)

Description: Differs from *everetti* by having the dark browns very dark brown-black and the bill smaller and more slender.

Range: Calamianes, Palawan, and Sulu Archipelago. (Endemic.)

PLATE 84

A   TREE SPARROW
    (*Passer montanus*)—page 409

B   RED AVADAVAT
    (*Amandava amandava*)—page 409

C   GREEN-TAILED PARROT-FINCH
    (*Erythrura hyperythra*)—page 410

D   GREEN-FACED PARROT-FINCH
    (*Erythrura viridifacies*)—page 410

E   MINDANAO PARROT-FINCH
    (*Erythrura coloria*)—page 410

F   NUTMEG MANNIKIN
    (*Lonchura punctulata*)—page 411

G   WHITE-BREASTED MANNIKIN
    (*Lonchura leucogastra*)—page 411

H   CHESTNUT MANNIKIN
    (*Lonchura malacca*)—page 414

I   DUSKY MANNIKIN
    (*Lonchura fuscans*)—page 414

J   JAVA SPARROW
    (*Padda oryzivora*)—page 414

PLATE 84

CHESTNUT MANNIKIN PLATE 84

Lonchura malacca jagori (Martens, 1866)

1834 *Fringilla minuta* Meyen, Nov. Acad. Leo. Car. Nat. Cur., **16**:86, (Philippines)

1866 *Munia (Dermophrys) Jagori* "Cabania" Martens, Journ. f. Orn., **14**:14, (Manila, Luzon)

1953 *Lonchura malacca gregalis* Salomonsen, Vid. Medd. Dansk nat. Foren., **115**:265, (Opol, Misamis, Mindanao)

Description: Head, neck, chin, throat, and upper breast black; back, wings, and tail chestnut; rump dark reddish chestnut; flanks dark chestnut; center of belly and under tail-coverts black. Birds from the north have a proportionately higher percentage of browner heads.

Soft Parts: Bill bluish brown; iris dark brown; feet bluish.

Measurements: Wing 54; tail 36; bill 12; tarsus 15.

Range: Central Luzon, south to the Celebes.

Lonchura malacca formosana (Swinhoe, 1865)

1865 *Munia formosana* Swinhoe, Ibis, p. 365, (Formosa)

Description: Differs from *jagori* by having the top of the head gray-brown and the chestnut parts paler.

Range: Northern Luzon.

DUSKY MANNIKIN PLATE 84

Lonchura fuscans (Cassin, 1852)

1852 *Spermestes fuscans* Cassin, Proc. Acad. Nat. Sci. Phila., **6**:185, (Borneo)

Description: All dark brown; underparts darker.

Soft Parts: Bill blackish; iris dark brown; feet blackish.

Measurements: Wing 51; tail 45; bill 13; tarsus 12.

Range: Borneo and Cagayan Sulu.

JAVA SPARROW PLATE 84

Padda oryzivora (Linnaeus, 1758)

1758 *Loxia oryzivora* Linnaeus, Syst. Nat., **1**:173, ("Asia and Ethiopia"= Java)

Description: Top of head black; back and wings light blue-gray; rump and tail black; sides of face white; chin black; throat and breast light blue-gray; belly purplish gray; under tail-coverts white lightly washed with purple.

Soft Parts: Bill pink; iris brown; feet pinkish.

Measurements: Wing 68; tail 50; bill 18; tarsus 19.

Range: Introduced on many islands from Indonesia.

Family FRINGILLIDAE   FINCHES, GROSBEAKS

BRAMBLING PLATE 85

Fringilla montifringilla Linnaeus, 1758

1758 *Fringilla montifringilla* Linnaeus, Syst. Nat., 1:179, (Sweden)

Description: Male—head, sides of throat, and back black with buffy edges to feathers; lower back and rump white; tail blackish brown; wing, bend of wing, scapulars, and ends of upper wing-coverts chestnut; rest of wing brownish black; chin and throat chestnut; lower breast, belly, and under tail-coverts white. Female—duller and upperparts browner.

Soft Parts: Bill blue-black; iris brown; feet pinkish brown.

Measurements: Wing 90; tail 64; bill 14; tarsus 18.

Range: Calayan (once); a straggler from Asia.

LITTLE BUNTING PLATE 85

Emberiza pusilla Pallas, 1776

1776 *Emberiza pusilla* Pallas, Reise Versch. Prov. Russ. Reichs, 3:647, (Daurian Range, southern Chita, southeastern Siberia)

Description: Top of head blackish brown with a chestnut stripe down the center; face chestnut; back, rump, and wings brown, streaked with dark brown; tail brown with white outer rectrices; chin chestnut; throat and upper breast white streaked with dark brown; belly and under tail-coverts white.

Soft Parts: Bill, upper mandible dark brown, lower mandible light brown; iris dark brown; feet light brown.

Measurements: Wing 66; tail 55; bill 10; tarsus 17.

Range: Recorded from Calayan and Luzon; a straggler from eastern Asia.

JAPANESE YELLOW BUNTING PLATE 85

Emberiza sulphurata Temminck and Schlegel, 1848

1848 *Emberiza sulphurata* Temminck and Schlegel, in Siebold's Faun. Jap., Aves, p. 100, (Japan)

Description: Crown and hind neck olive-green; back gray-green with dark brown stripes;

415

rump gray-green; tail dark brown with white outer rectrices; wings dark brown; throat, breast, and belly olive-yellow; under tail-coverts white.

Soft Parts: Bill black; iris brown; feet light brown.

Measurements: Wing 71; tail 60; bill 11; tarsus 19.

Range: Recorded from Calayan and Luzon; a migrant from eastern Asia.

BLACK-FACED BUNTING
PLATE 85

Emberiza spodocephala Pallas, 1776

1776 *Emberiza spodocephala* Pallas, Reise Versch. Prov. Russ. Reichs, 3:698, (Daurian Range, Siberia)

Description: Male—top of head gray with a few dark chestnut streaks; mantle brown streaked with dark brown; rump brown; tail dark brown with white outer rectrices; lores and chin black; throat and breast gray washed with olive; belly and under tail-coverts buffy white. Female—similar to male but lacks the black lores and chin and the gray on the throat and breast, which is replaced by brown and buff.

Soft Parts: Bill, upper mandible dark horn color; lower mandible cream; iris blackish; feet pale brown.

Measurements: Wing 73; tail 66; bill 13; tarsus 21.

Range: Recorded from Catanduanes (once); a straggler from eastern Asia.

MALAYSIAN FINCH
PLATE 85

Serinus estherae mindanensis Ripley and Rabor, 1961

1961 *Serinus mindanensis* Ripley and Rabor, Postilla, 50:13, (Mt. Katanglad, Mindanao)

Description: Male—forehead, forecrown, and sides of face golden yellow; lores olive-gray; hind crown and back dark olive-brown; lower back, rump, and ends of upper tail-coverts golden yellow; tail black; wings black with two yellow wing bars; chin and throat golden yellow; breast and flanks gray-white streaked with dark brown; belly and under tail-coverts dirty white.

Soft Parts: Bill olive-horn; iris unknown; feet dark brown.

Measurements: Wing 70; tail 49; bill 9; tarsus 15.

Range: Mt. Katanglad, Mindanao. (Endemic.)

EUROPEAN SISKIN
PLATE 85

Carduelis spinus (Linnaeus, 1758)

1758 *Fringilla spinus* Linnaeus, Syst. Nat., 1:181, (Sweden)

Description: Male—crown black; mantle dark olive-green; rump yellow; tail with dark brown central rectrices and basal two thirds of outer rectrices yellow; wing dark brown with a yellow bar; chin and center of throat black; sides of face and throat, breast, and flanks greenish yellow; belly and under tail-coverts white. Female—lacks black on crown and chin; paler yellow below, with heavier streaking.

Soft Parts: Bill, upper mandible dark brown, lower mandible light brown; iris black; feet dark brown.

Measurements: Wing 71; tail 50; bill 14; tarsus 13.

Range: Calayan (once); a straggler from Asia.

PHILIPPINE   BULLFINCH   PLATE 85

Pyrrhula leucogenys steerei Mearns, 1909

1909   *Pyrrhula steerei* Mearns, Proc. U. S. Nat. Mus., **36**:445, (Mt. Bliss, Mindanao)

1941   *Pyrrhula leucogenys apo* Hachisuka, Tori, **11**:88, (Mt. Apo, Mindanao)

1961   *Pyrrhula leucogenys coriaria* Ripley and Rabor, Postilla, 50:17, (Mt. Katanglad, Mindanao)

Description: Top of head, lores, and chin black with a bluish gloss; ear-coverts white; mantle brown; rump whitish; tail black with a blue gloss; wings mostly black with a blue gloss; ends of wing-coverts brown; outer margin of innermost scapular red; throat, breast, and belly brown; under tail-coverts rufous-brown.

Soft Parts: Bill black; iris brown; feet brown.

Measurements: Wing 77; tail 65; bill 11; tarsus 17.

Range: Mindanao. (Endemic.)

Pyrrhula leucogenys leucogenys Ogilvie-Grant, 1895

1895   *Pyrrhula leucogenys* Ogilvie-Grant, Bull. Brit. Orn. Cl., 4:41, (Lepanto, northern Luzon)

Description: Differs from *steerei* by being larger (wing 79; tail 66; bill 12).

Range: Northern Luzon. (Endemic.)

RED   CROSSBILL   PLATE 85

Loxia curvirostra luzoniensis Ogilvie-Grant, 1894

1894   *Loxia luzoniensis* Ogilvie-Grant, Bull. Brit. Orn. Cl., 3:51, (mountains of northern Luzon = Benguet)

Description: Top of head reddish; mantle, wings, and tail very dark olive-brown; rump reddish; throat and breast mottled red and gray; belly white streaked with dark brown.

Soft Parts: Bill dark brown; iris dark brown; feet brown.

Measurements: Wing 82; tail 55; bill 17; tail 54.

Range: Northern Luzon. (Endemic.)

PLATE 85

A   BRAMBLING
     (Fringilla montifringilla)—page 415

B   LITTLE BUNTING
     (Emberiza pusilla)—page 415

C   JAPANESE YELLOW BUNTING
     (Emberiza sulphurata)—page 415

D   BLACK-FACED BUNTING
     (Emberiza spodocephala)—page 416

E   MALAYSIAN FINCH
     (Serinus estherae)—page 416

F   EUROPEAN SISKIN
     (Carduelis spinus)—page 416

G   PHILIPPINE BULLFINCH
     (Pyrrhula leucogenys)—page 417

H   RED CROSSBILL
     (Loxia curvirostra)—page 417

418

PLATE 85

Bibliography

ALCASID, G. L., AND P. GONZALES

    1968   A new race of naked-faced spider-hunter (*Arachnothera clarae*) from Luzon. Bull. Brit. Orn. Cl., **88**:129–130.

AMADON, D.

    1942   Birds collected during the Whitney South Sea Expedition, XLIX. Am. Mus. Novit., 1175:1–11.

    1951   Notes on Chinese egret, *Egretta eulophotes* (Swinhoe). Phil. Journ. Sci., **80**:53–54.

    1952   A new bird to Palawan. Phil. Journ. Sci., **81**:139.

    1962   A new genus and species of Philippine bird. Condor, **64**:3–5.

AMADON, D., AND J. E. duPONT

    1970   Notes on Philippine birds. Nemouria, 1:1–14.

AMADON, D., AND S. G. JEWETT, JR.

    1946   Notes on Philippine birds. Auk, **63**:541–559.

BAIRD, S. F., J. CASSIN, AND
G. N. LAWRENCE

    1858   Rep. Expl. and Surv. R. R. Pac., **9**:1–1005.

BANGS, O.

    1922   Notes on Philippine birds collected by Governor W. Cameron Forbes. Bull. Mus. Comp. Zool., **65**:77–84.

BOURNS, F. S., AND D. C. WORCESTER

    1894   Preliminary notes on the birds and mammals collected by the Menage Scientific Expedition to the Philippine Islands. Occ. Papers Minn. Acad. Nat. Sci., 1:1–64.

BRODKORB, P., D. EMPESO, AND
R. GONZALEZ

    1969   White-tailed tropic-bird, an addition to the Philippine avifauna. Auk, **86**:357.

CAIN, A. J.

1954   Subdivision of the genus *Ptilinopus* (Aves, Columbae). Bull.
       Brit. Mus. (Nat. Hist.), Zool., **2**:267–284.

CHASEN, F. N.

1940   Notes on some Javan birds. Treubia, **17**:263–264.

CHASEN, F. N., AND C. B. KLOSS

1929   Two new Malaysian birds. Bull. Raffles Mus., **2**:22–23.

DEIGNAN, H. G.

1946   Races of the striated marsh warbler. Auk, **63**:381–383.
1947   A new canary flycatcher from the Philippine Islands. Proc.
       Biol. Soc. Wash., **60**:61–62.
1950   The races of the collared scops owl, *Otus bakkamoena* Pen-
       nant. Auk, **67**:189–201.
1951   A new race of the hawk-owl, *Ninox scutulata*, from the Philip-
       pines. Proc. Biol. Soc. Wash., **68**:41–42.
1955   Four new races of birds from east Asia. Proc. Biol. Soc. Wash.,
       64:145–147.
1955   The long-tailed nightjars of North Borneo and Palawan.
       Sarawak Mus. Journ., **6**:314–315.
1961   Type specimens of birds in the United States National Mu-
       seum. Proc. U. S. Nat. Mus., **221**:1–718.

DELACOUR, J.

1941   On the species of *Otus scops*. Zoologica, **26**:133–142.
1943   A revision of the subfamily Estrildinae of the family Ploceidae.
       Zoologica, **28**:69–86.
1946   The name of the white-faced titmouse of the Philippines.
       Auk, **63**:433.

DELACOUR, J., AND P. JABOUILLE

1940   Liste des Oiseau de L'Indochina Francaise. Ois. et Rev. Fran.
       d' Orn., **10**:89–220.

DELACOUR, J., AND E. MAYR

1945   Notes on the taxonomy of the birds of the Philippines. Zoo-
       logica, **30**:105–107.
1946   Birds of the Philippines, pp. 1–309.

DE SCHAUENSEE, R. M.

 1957 Notes on Philippine birds. Not. Nat., 303:1–12.

DE SCHAUENSEE, R. M., AND
 J. E. DUPONT

 1959 Notes on Philippine birds. Not. Nat., 322:1–5.
 1962 Birds from the Philippine Islands. Proc. Acad. Nat. Sci. Phila., **114**:149–173.

DUPONT, J. E.

 1971 Notes on Philippine birds (no. 1). Nemouria, 3:1–6.

EDWARDS, G.

 1743 A Natural History of Uncommon Birds, **1**:1–52.

FINSCH, O.

 1902 Notes Leyden Mus., **23**:151.

GILLIARD, E. T.

 1949 A study of the coleto or bald starling (*Sarcops Calvus*). Am. Mus. Novit., 1429:1–6..
 1949 Five new birds from the Philippines. Auk, **66**:275–280.
 1949 Two new orioles from the Philippines. Proc. Biol. Soc. Wash., **62**:155–158.
 1950 Notes on a collection of birds from Bataan, Luzon, Philippine Islands. Bull. Am. Mus. Nat. Hist., **94**:461–504.

GRANT, O. W. R.

 1896 On the birds of the Philippine Islands, part VIII; the highlands of Negros, with fieldnotes by John Whitehead. Ibis, pp. 525–565.

GRANT, O. W. R., AND J. WHITEHEAD

 1898 On the nests and eggs of some rare Philippine birds. Ibis, pp. 231–247.

HACHISUKA, M.

 1929 Contributions to the birds of the Philippines, no. 1. Orn. Soc. Japan, suppl. 13:1–137.

1930   Contributions to the birds of the Philippines, no. 2, part VI. Orn. Soc. Japan, suppl. 14:141–222.

1931–35   The Birds of the Philippine Islands. Parts 1 and 2, pp. 1–439; parts 3 and 4, pp. 1–469.

1939   A new race of bronze-winged dove. Bull. Brit. Orn. Cl., **59**: 45–47.

1939   The red jungle fowl from the Pacific Islands. Tori, **10**:596– 601.

1941   Further contributions to the ornithology of the Philippines. Tori, **11**:61–89.

HARRISSON, T.

1962   Hoopoe *Upupa epops* in the Philippines. Ibis, **104**:417–418.

HARTERT, E.

1910   Vög. pal. Fauna, **1**:65–66.

1922   Types of birds in the Tring Museum; B, types in the general collection. Nov. Zool., **29**:365–412.

1929   On various forms of the genus *Tyto*. Nov. Zool., **35**:93–104.

HELLMAYR, C. E.

1914   Die Avifauna von Timor. Zoologie von Timor, **1**:1–112.

HOOGSTRAAL, H.

1951   Philippine zoological expedition 1946–1947 (narrative and itinerary). Fieldiana: Zoology, **33**:1–88.

HUMPHREY, P. S., AND K. C. PARKES

1959   An approach to the study of molts and plumages. Auk, **76**:1–31.

JOUY, P. L.

1910   The paradise flycatchers of Japan and Korea. Proc. U. S. Nat. Mus., **37**:651–655.

LINNAEUS, C.

1758   Systema Naturae per Regna Tria Naturae . . . , **1**:1–824.

LINT, K. C., AND K. STOTT, JR.

1948   Notes on the birds of the Philippines. Auk, **65**:41–46.

McGREGOR, R. C.

1903 On birds from Luzon, Mindoro, Masbate, Ticao, Cuyo, Culion, Cagayan Sulu and Palawan. Bull. Phil. Mus., 1:3–12.

1904 The birds from Benguet Province, Luzon, and from the islands of Lubang, Mindoro, Cuyo, and Cagayancillo. Bull. Phil. Mus., 3:13.

1904 The birds of Calayan and Fuga, Babuyan Group. Bull. Phil. Mus., 4:9.

1908 Notes on a collection of birds from Siquijor, Philippine Islands. Phil. Jour. Sci., 3:275–281.

1909 A Manual of Philippine Birds, pp. 1–769.

1910 Additional notes on birds from northern Mindanao, Philippine Islands. Phil. Journ. Sci., 5:197.

1914 Description of a new species of *Prionochilus* from the highlands of Luzon. Phil. Journ. Sci., 9:531–535.

1920 Some features of the Philippine ornis with notes on the vegetation in relation to the avifauna. Phil. Journ. Sci., 16:361–437.

1921 Birds of Antique Province, Panay, Philippine Islands. Phil. Journ. Sci., 18:537–557, 2 pls.

1921 New or noteworthy Philippine birds, III. Phil. Journ. Sci., 18:75–84.

1921 New or noteworthy Philippine birds, IV. Phil. Journ., Sci., 19:691–706.

1924 Birds of Ilocos Norte Province, Luzon. Phil. Journ. Sci., 25:111–121.

1927 New or noteworthy Philippine birds, V. Phil. Journ. Sci., 32:513–527, 2 pls.

1928 Birds of the Philippines. Distribution of Life in the Philippines, Bureau of Science Monograph 21, Manila Bureau of Printing, pp. 168–213, 2 pls.

1936 Birds new and rare in the Philippines. Phil. Journ. Sci., 59:317–326.

McGREGOR, R. C., AND
D. C. WORCESTER

1906 A hand-list of the birds of the Philippine Islands. Bur. Govt. Lab., Manila, 36:1–123.

MANUEL, C. G.

1934 Food and feeding habits of the barred ground dove. Phil.
      Journ. Sci., **55**:69–78.

1934 Observations on the Philippine weaver, *Munia jagori mar-
      tens*, II; foods and feeding habits. Phil. Journ. Sci.,
      53:393–419.

1935 New birds from northern Luzon, Philippine Islands. Phil.
      Journ. Sci., **56**:93–96.

1936 A review of Philippine pigeons, I; the genus *Phapitreron*.
      Phil. Journ. Sci., **59**:300–301.

1936 A review of Philippine pigeons, II; subfamily Ptilinopodinae.
      Phil. Journ. Sci., **59**:327–336.

1936 A review of Philippine pigeons, III; subfamily Treroninae.
      Phil. Journ. Sci., **60**:157–163.

1936 A review of Philippine pigeons, IV; subfamily Duculinae.
      Phil. Journ. Sci., **60**:407–420.

1936 New Philippine fruit pigeons. Phil. Journ. Sci., **59**:307–310.

1937 Avifauna of Catanduanes. Phil. Journ. Sci., **63**:185–189.

1937 Beneficial swiftlet and edible birds' nest industry in Bacuit,
      Palawan. Phil. Journ. Sci., **62**:379–392.

1937 A review of Philippine pigeons, V; subfamilies Columbinae.
      Geopeliinae, Phabinae and Caloenadinae. Phil. Journ.
      Sci., **63**:175–184.

1939 Notes on recent collections of birds from Palawan and Bus-
      uanga. Phil. Journ. Sci., **69**:101–123.

1939 Studies on Philippine kingfishers, I; genus *Ceyx*. Phil. Journ.
      Sci., **69**:377–388.

1941 Studies on Philippine kingfishers, II; genera *Alcedo, Halcyon*
      and *Ramphalcyon*, with additional notes on the genus
      Ceyx. Phil. Journ. Sci., **74**:367–384.

1956 (1957) Neotypes of some Philippine birds. Phil. Journ. Sci.,
      85:315–321.

1957 Resident birds of Polillo Island. Phil. Journ. Sci., **86**:1–12.

MANUEL, C. G., AND
E. T. GILLIARD

1952 Undescribed and newly recorded Philippine birds. Am. Mus.
      Novit., 1545:1–9.

MAYR, E.

1944   The birds of Timor and Sumba. Bull. Am. Mus. Nat. Hist., **83**:123–194.

1945   Tree swifts (family Hemiprocnidae) ; *in* Delacour and Mayr, Notes on the taxonomy of the birds of the Philippines. Zoologica, **30**:105–117.

1947   Notes on tailorbirds (*Orthotomus*) from the Philippine Islands. Journ. Wash. Acad. Sci., **37**:140–141.

1949   Geographical variation in *Accipiter trivirgatus*. Am. Mus. Novit., 1415:1–12.

1957   New species of birds described from 1941 to 1955. Journ. Orn., **98**:22–35.

MAYR, E., AND
D. AMADON

1941   Birds collected during the Whitney South Sea Expedition, XLVI. Am. Mus. Novit., 1144:1–11.

1947   A review of the Dicaeidae. Am. Mus. Novit., 1360:1–32.

MAYR, E., AND
C. VAURIE

1948   Evolution in the family Dicruridae (birds). Evolution, **2**:238–265.

MEARNS, E. A.

1905   Descriptions of eight new Philippine birds, with notes on other species new to the Islands. Proc. Biol. Soc. Wash., **18**:83–90.

1907   Description of a new genus and nine new species of Philippine birds. Phil. Journ. Sci., **2**:355–360.

1909   A list of birds collected by Dr. Paul Bartsch in the Philippine Islands, Borneo, Guam, and Midway Island, with descriptions of three new forms. Proc. U. S. Nat. Mus., **36**:463–478.

1909   Additions to the list of Philippine birds with descriptions of new and rare species. Proc. U. S. Nat. Mus., **36**:435–447.

1916   On the geographical forms of the Philippine elegant titmouse, *Pardaliparus elegans* (Lesson), with descriptions of three new subspecies. Proc. U. S. Nat. Mus., **51**:57–65.

427

MEDWAY, LORD

    1966   Field characters as a guide to the specific relations of swiftlets. Proc. Linn. Soc. London, **177**:151–172.

MEES, G. F.

    1957   A systematic review of the Indo-Australian Zosteropidae (part 1). Zool. Verhandelingen, 35:1–204.

    1961   A systematic review of the Indo-Australian Zosteropidae (part II). Zool. Verhandelingen, 50:1–168.

    1969   A systematic review of the Indo-Australian Zosteropidae (part III). Zool. Verhandelingen, 102:1–390.

    1971   The Philippine subspecies of *Centropus bengalensis* (Gmelin) (Aves, Cuculidae). Zool. Med., 45:189–191.

MEINERTZHAGEN, R.

    1923   A review of the genus *Oriolus*. Ibis, pp. 52–96.

MERRILL, E. D.

    1907   The ascent of Mount Halcon, Mindoro. Phil. Journ. Sci., 2:179–203.

MISHIMA, T.

    1956   Notes on *Ninox scutulata*. Japan Wildlife Bull., **15**:25–26.

OBERHOLSER, H. C.

    1915   A review of the subspecies of the ruddy kingfisher, *Entomothera Coromanda* (Linnaeus). Proc. U. S. Nat. Mus., **48**:639–657.

OGILVIE-GRANT, W. R.

    1896   On the birds of the Philippine Islands, part VII; the highlands of Mindoro. Ibis, pp. 457–477.

    1897   On the birds of the Philippine Islands, part IX; the islands of Samar and Leite. Ibis, pp. 209–250.

    1906   On the birds collected by Mr. Walter Goodfellow on the volcano of Apo and in its vicinity, in southeast Mindanao, P.I. Ibis, pp. 465–505, 2 pls.

OLIVIER, G.

1947 Note sur *Lanius validirostris* Gant 1874 des Iles Philippines. Ois. et Rev. Fran. d' Orn., **17**:182–185.

PARKES, K. C.

1949 *Rallus philippensis* on Mindoro, Philippine Islands. Auk, **66**:200–201.

1957 Taxonomic notes on the lesser coucal, *Centropus bengalensis*. Bull. Brit. Orn. Cl., **77**:115–116.

1957 The plumage sequence of the Philippine coucal, *Centropus viridis*. Ibis, **99**:518–520.

1958 Nomenclatorial notes on Philippine pygmy woodpeckers. Bull. Brit. Orn. Cl., **78**:6–7.

1958 Extra-limital records of the Australian whiskered tern. Emu, **58**:288.

1958 Taxonomy and nomenclature of three species of *Lonchura* (Aves: Estrildinae). Proc. U. S. Nat. Mus., **108**:279–293.

1958 A revision of the Philippine elegant titmouse (*Parus elegans*). Proc. Biol. Soc. Wash., **71**:95–106.

1958 A new race of the blue-headed fantail (*Rhipidura cyaniceps*) from northern Luzon, Philippine Islands. Am. Mus. Novit., 1891:1–5.

1958 Specific relationships in the genus *Elanus*. Condor, **60**:139–140.

1959 Notes on some non-passerine birds from the Philippines. Annals of Carnegie Museum, 35:331–340.

1959 Supspecific identity of introduced tree sparrows, *Passer montanus*, in the Philippine Islands. Ibis, **101**:243–244.

1960 Notes on some Philippine tailor-birds. Bull. Brit. Orn. Cl., **80**:76–78.

1960 New subspecies of Philippine birds. Proc. Biol. Soc. Wash., **73**:57–62.

1960 Geographic variation in the lesser treeswift. Condor, 62:3–6.

1960 A drongo new to the Philippine list. Condor, 62:296–297.

1960 The races of the citrine canary flycatcher, *Culicicapa helianthea*. Proc. Biol. Soc. Wash., **73**:215–220.

1961 A substitute name for a Philippine tailor-bird. Bull. Brit. Orn. Cl., **81**:33.

1961 The crested lizard hawk (*Aviceda jerdoni*) in the Philippines. Postilla, 51:1–10.

1962 The red junglefowl of the Philippines—native or introduced? Auk, **79**:479–481.

1962 New subspecies of birds from Luzon, Philippines. Postilla, 67:1–8.

1963 The races of the flaming sunbird (*Aethopyga flagrans*). Bull. Brit. Orn. Cl., **83**:7–8.

1963 Additional notes on the Philippine elegant titmouse, *Parus elegans*. Bull. Brit. Orn. Cl., **83**:148–150.

1963 A new subspecies of tree-babbler from the Philippines. Auk, **80**:543–544.

1963 A substitute name for the Luzon race of *Copsychus saularis*. Bull. Brit. Orn. Cl., **83**:50.

1965 A small collection of birds from the island of Buad, Philippines. Annals of Carnegie Museum, **38**:49–67.

1965 The races of the pompadour green pigeon, *Treron pompadora*, in the Philippine Islands. Bull. Brit. Orn. Cl., **85**:137–139.

1965 Character displacement in some Philippine cuckoos. The Living Bird, 4:89–98.

1966 Geographic variation in Winchell's kingfisher, *Halcyon winchelli*, of the Philippines. Bull. Brit. Orn. Cl., **86**:82–86.

1966 A new subspecies of the yellow-bellied whistler, *Pachycephala philippinensis*. Bull. Brit. Orn. Cl., **86**:170–171.

1967 A new subspecies of the wattled bulbul, *Pycnonotus urostictus*, of the Philippines. Bull. Brit. Orn. Cl., **87**:23–25.

1968 An undescribed subspecies of button-quail from the Philippines. Bull. Brit. Orn. Cl., **88**:24–25.

1969 Subspecific status of the small skylark, *Alauda gulgula*, in the Philippines, with notes on age characters and moult. Bull. Brit. Orn. Cl., **89**:117–119.

1970 The Philippine races of the rufous-capped grass warbler, *Megalurus timoriensis*. Bull. Brit. Orn. Cl., **90**:111–115.

1970 A revision of the Philippine trogon (*Harpactes ardens*). Nat. Hist. Bull. Siam Soc., **23**:345–352.

1971 Taxonomic and distributional notes on Philippine birds. Nemouria, 4:1–67.

PARKES, K. C., AND D. AMADON

1948 The winter range of the Kennicott willow warbler. Condor, **50**:86–87.

1959 A new species of rail from the Philippine Islands. Wil. Bull., **71**:303–306.

PETERS, J. L.

    1939   Collections from the Philippine Islands: birds. Bull. Mus. Comp. Zool., **86**:74–128.

POTTER, N. S., III

    1948   Notes on the yellow-breasted sunbird. Wil. Bull., **60**:159–163.

    1953   The birds of Calicoan, Philippine Islands. Wil. Bull., **65**: 252–270.

PUCHERAN, J.

    1854   Etudes sur les types peu connus du Musee de Paris (onzieme article. Passereaux conirostres.) Rev. et Mag. Zool., **6**:62–74.

RABOR, D. S.

    1936   Life histories of some common birds in the vicinity of No-valiches, Rizal Province, Luzon, I. Phil. Journ. Sci., **59**:337–356.

    1936   Life histories of some common birds in the vicinity of No-valiches, Rizal Province, Luzon, II. Phil. Journ. Sci., **60**:143–156.

    1938   Avifauna of the Gigante Islands. Phil. Journ. Sci., **66**:267–274.

    1938   Birds from Leyte. Phil. Journ. Sci., **66**:15–34.

    1952   Distributional notes on some Philippine birds. Auk, **69**:253–257.

    1954   Notes on the nesting of some Philippine swifts on Negros and Mindanao. Silliman Jour., **1**:45–58.

    1959   The impact of deforestation on birds of Cebu, Philippines, with new records for that island. Auk., **76**:37–43.

    1970   A list of land vertebrates of Negros Island. Silliman Jour., **17**:298–302.

RAND, A. L.

    1940   New birds from the 1938–1939 expedition. Am. Mus. Novit., 1072:1–14.

    1948   Five new birds from the Philippines. Fieldiana: Zoology, 31:201–205.

    1950   Three rare Philippine birds. Nat. His. Misc., 60:1–5.

    1950   A new race of the Philippine creeper, *Rhabdornis inornatus* (class Aves). Nat. His. Misc., 59:1–3.

1950 A new race of owl, *Otus bakkamoena*, from Negros, Philippine Islands. Nat. His. Misc., 72:1–5.

1951 Review of the subspecies of the sunbird, *Nectarinia jugularis*. Fieldiana: Zoology, **31**:597–607.

1951 Birds of Negros Island. Fieldiana: Zoology, **31**:571–596.

1958 The races of the shrike, *Lanius validirostris*. Fieldiana: Zoology, **39**:85.

1960 A new species of babbling thrush from the Philippines. Fieldiana: Zoology, **39**:377–378.

1970 Species formation in the blue monarch flycatchers, genus *Hypothymis*. Nat. Hist. Bull. Siam Soc., **23**:353–364.

RAND, A. L., AND R. L. FLEMING

1957 Birds from Nepal. Fieldiana: Zoology, **41**:1–218.

RAND, A. L., AND D. S. RABOR

1952 Two new birds from Philippine Islands. Nat. His. Misc., 100:1–3.

1952 Notes on Philippine birds. Nat. His. Misc., 107:1–5.

1957 New birds from the Philippines. Fieldiana: Zoology, **42**:13–18.

1959 Three new birds from the Philippine Islands. Fieldiana: Zoology, **39**:275–277.

1959 Notes on some Philippine birds. Auk, **76**:102–104.

1959 Notes on some Philippine bulbuls. Auk, **76**:102–104.

1960 Birds of the Philippine Islands: Siquijor, Mount Malindang, Bohol and Samar. Fieldiana: Zoology, **35**:221–441.

1961 A new race of crow, *Corvus enca*, from the Philippines. Fieldiana: Zoology, **39**:577–579.

1967 New birds from Luzon, Philippine Islands. Fieldiana: Zoology, **51**:85–89.

1969 New birds from Camiguin South, Philippines. Fieldiana: Zoology, **51**:157–168.

RICKETT, C. B.

1900 Additional notes on the birds of Fokien. Ibis, pp. 52–60.

RIPLEY, S. D.

1941 Notes on the genus *Coracina*. Auk, **58**:381–395.

1942 A revision of the kingfishers, *Ceyx erithacus* and *rufidorsus*. Zoologica, **27**:55–59.

432

1949 A new race of shrike from the Philippines. Bull. Brit. Orn. Cl., **69**:121–122.

1950 Comments on specimens in the Hachisuka Collection from the Philippine Islands. Condor, **52**:165–166.

1951 Remarks on the Philippine mallard. Wil. Bull., **63**:189–191.

1952 Additional comments on Philippine birds and a new record from the Archipelago. Condor, **54**:362.

RIPLEY, S. D., AND
J. T. MARSHALL, JR.

1967 A new subspecies of flycatcher from Luzon, Philippine Islands (Aves; Muscicapinae). Proc. Biol. Soc. Wash., **80**:243–244.

RIPLEY, S. D., AND D. S. RABOR

1955 A new fruit pigeon from the Philippines. Postilla, 21:1–2.

1956 Birds of Negros Island, Philippines. Condor, **48**:283–291.

1956 Birds from Canlaon Volcano in the highlands of Negros Island in the Philippines. Condor, **58**:283–291.

1958 Notes on a collection of birds from Mindoro Island, Philippines. Bull. Peabody Mus. Nat. Hist., **13**:1–83.

1961 The avifauna of Mount Katanglad. Postilla, 50:1–20.

1962 New birds from Palawan and Culion Islands, Philippines. Postilla, 73:1–16.

1966 *Dicaeum proprium*, new species (Aves; family Dicaeidae). Proc. Biol. Soc. Wash., **79**:305–306.

1968 Two new subspecies of birds from the Philippines and comments on the validity of two others. Proc. Biol. Soc. Wash., **81**:31–36.

SALOMONSEN, F.

1928 Two new Acrocephalus-forms from the Indo-Malayan region. Orn. Monatsb., **36**:119.

1952 Systematic notes on some Philippine birds. Vid. Medd. Dansk nat. Foren., **114**:341–364.

1953 Miscellaneous notes on Philippine birds. Vid. Medd. Dansk nat. Foren., **115**:205–281.

1960 Notes on flowerpeckers (Aves, Dicaeidae), 2; the primitive species of the genus *Dicaeum*. Am. Mus. Novit., 1991: 1–38.

1960 Notes on flowerpeckers (Aves, Dicaeidae), 3; the species group *Dicaeum concolor* and the superspecies *Dicaeum erythrothorax*. Am. Mus. Novit., 2016:1–36.

1961 A new tit-babbler (*Stachyris hypogrammica*, sp. nov.) from Palawan, Philippine Islands. Dansk Orn. Foren. Tidsskrift, **55**:219.

1962 The mountain bird fauna of Palawan, Philippine Islands. Dansk Orn. Foren. Tidsskrift, **56**:129–134.

SIMS, R. W.

1959 The *Ceyx erithacus* and *rufidorsus* species problem. Journ. Linn. Soc. London, Zool., **44**:212–221.

STEERE, J. B.

1890 A List of the Birds and Mammals Collected by the Steere Expedition to the Philippines, pp. 1–30.

1894 On the distribution of genera and species of non-migratory land-birds in the Philippines. Ibis, pp. 411–420.

STOTT, K., JR.

1947 Notes on the Philippine brown hornbill. Condor, **49**:35.

STRESEMANN, E.

1952 On the birds collected by Pierre Poivre in Canton, Manila, India and Madagascar (1751–1756). Ibis, **94**:499–523.

TEMMINCK, C. J., AND
L. DeCHARTROUSE

1824 Nouveau recueil de planches coloriees d'Oiseaux.

TICEHURST, C. B.

1938 A Systematic Review of the Genus *Phylloscopus*, pp. 1–193.

TWEEDDALE, MARQUIS OF
(see also WALDEN, A., VISCOUNT)

1878 Contributions to the ornithology of the Philippines, no. IX; on the collection made by Mr. A. H. Everett in the island of Palawan. Proc. Zool. Soc. London, pp. 611–624.

1878   Contributions to the ornithology of the Philippines, no. X; on the collection made by Mr. A. H. Everett in the island of Bohol. Proc. Zool. Soc. London, pp. 708–712.

VAURIE, C.

1947   Two new drongos from the Philippines. Am. Mus. Novit., 1335:1–3.

1949   Notes on some Ploceidae from western Asia. Am. Mus. Novit., 1406:1–41.

1949   Notes on some Asiatic finches. Am. Mus. Novit., 1424:8.

1951   A study of Asiatic larks. Bull. Am. Mus. Nat. Hist., **97**:431–526.

1951   A new species of flycatcher from Mindanao, Philippine Islands. Am. Mus. Novit., 1543:1–4.

1952   A review of the bird genus *Rhinomyias* (Muscicapini). Am. Mus. Novit., 1570:1–36.

1953   A generic revision of flycatchers of the tribe Muscicapini. Bull. Am. Mus. Nat. Hist., **100**:453–538.

1954   Systematic notes on Palearctic birds, no. 9; Sylviinae: the genus *Phylloscopus*. Am. Mus. Novit., 1685:1–23.

1959   The Birds of the Palearctic Fauna, Passeriformes, 1:1–762.

1965   The Birds of the Palearctic Fauna, Non-Passeriformes, 2:1–763.

VERHEYEN, R.

1953   Contribution a l'etude de la structure pneumatique du crane chez les oiseaux. Bulletin Institut Royal des Sciences Naturelles de Belgique, **29**:24.

WALDEN, A., VISCOUNT
(see also TWEEDDALE, MARQUIS OF)

1877   A list of the birds known to inhabit the Philippine Archipelago. Trans. Zool. Soc. London, **9**:125–252.

WHITEHEAD, J.

1890   Notes on the birds of Palawan. Ibis, pp. 38–61.

WHITFORD, H. N.

1906   The vegetation of the Lamao Forest Reserve. Phil. Journ. Sci., **1**:373–428, 637–679.

WOLFE, L. R.

    1938   Birds of central Luzon. Auk, **55**:198–224.

WORCESTER, D. C.

    1898   Contributions to Philippine ornithology, part II; notes on the distribution of Philippine birds. Proc. U. S. Nat. Mus., **20**:567–625, pls. 55–61.

WORCESTER, D. C. AND F. S. BOURNS

    1898   Contributions to Philippine ornithology, part I; a list of the birds known to inhabit the Philippine and Palawan Islands, showing their distribution within the limits of the two groups. Proc. U. S. Nat. Mus., **20**:549–625.

ZIMMER, J. T.

    1918   A few rare birds from Luzon and Mindoro. Phil. Journ. Sci., **13**:223–232.

Index

A

abbotti, Hirundo tahitica, 233
　　Hypurolepis javanica, 233
abraensis, Dicrurus balicassius, 245, 245
Abrornis olivacea, 319
Accipiter gularis, 43
Accipiter soloensis, 46
Accipiter trivirgatus castroi, 46, 46
Accipiter trivirgatus extimus, 46, 46
Accipiter trivirgatus palawanus, 46, 46
Accipiter virgatus confusus, 43, 43
ACCIPITRIDAE, *35, 38-39, 42-43, 46-47, 52*
Aceros leucocephalus leucocephalus, 212
Aceros leucocephalus waldeni, 211
Acmonorhynchus affinis, 387
Acridotheres cristatellus cristatellus, 368
Acrocephalus arundinaceus harterti, 317
Acrocephalus arundinaceus orientalis, 317
Acrocephalus fasciolatus, 316
Acrocephalus sorghophilus, 317
Acrocephalus stentoreus harterti, 317
Actenoides hombroni, 206
Actenoides moseleyi, 206
acuminata, Calidris, 101
acuminatus, Totanus, 101
acuta, Anas, 27, 27
Aegialites dealbatus, 79
Aegithina tiphia aequanimis, 286, 286
aegyptius, Cuculus, 162
aenea, Carpophaga, 124
　　Columba, 124
　　Ducula, 124, 124
　　Ducula aenea, 124
　　Muscadivores, 124
aequanimis, Aegithina tiphia, 286, 286
aeruginosum, Dicaeum, 386, 387, 387
　　Dicaeum aeruginosum, 386
　　Prionochilus, 386
aeruginosus, Circus, 42
aethiopica, Threskiornis, 22
Aethopyga arolasi, 383
Aethopyga bella, 383
Aethopyga boltoni boltoni, 379
Aethopyga boltoni malindangensis, 378, 378
Aethopyga bonita, 383
Aethopyga dubia, 382
Aethopyga flagrans, 379
Aethopyga flagrans daphoenonota, 382, 382
Aethopyga flagrans decolor, 379, 379
Aethopyga flagrans flagrans, 379
Aethopyga flagrans guimarasensis, 379
Aethopyga flavipectus, 383
Aethopyga magnifica, 384
Aethopyga minuta, 383
Aethopyga primigenius diuatae, 378, 378
Aethopyga primigenius primigenius, 378

Aethopyga pulcherrima, 382
Aethopyga pulcherrima decorosa, 382
Aethopyga pulcherrima jefferyi, 382
Aethopyga pulcherrima pulcherrima, 382
Aethopyga rubrinota, 383
Aethopyga shelleyi, 382
Aethopyga shelleyi arolasi, 383
Aethopyga shelleyi bella, 383
Aethopyga shelleyi bonita, 383
Aethopyga shelleyi flavipectus, 383
Aethopyga shelleyi rubrinota, 383
Aethopyga shelleyi shelleyi, 382
Aethopyga siparaja magnifica, 384
affine, Dicaeum aeruginosum, 387
affinis, Acmonorhynchus, 387
　　Apus, 188
　　Caprimulgus, 182
　　Penelopides, 211
　　Penelopides panini, 211
　　Stachyris capitalis, 266
　　Zosterornis, 266
agusanae, Hypothymis helenae, 349, 349
alaris, Rhabdornis inornatus, 262, 262
Alauda arvensis wolfei, 227
Alauda gulgula wolfei, 227
ALAUDIDAE, *227*
alba, Calidris, 100
　　Egretta, 20
　　Motacilla, 358
　　Trynga, 100
albescens, Pardaliparus, 255
　　Parus elegans, 255
albifrons, Phapitreron, 119
　　Sterna, 110
albigularis, Rhinomyias, 328
　　Rhinomyias gularis, 328
albiloris, Oriolus, 250
　　Oriolus xanthonotus, 250
albiventris, Hyloterpe, 351
　　Pachycephala cinerea, 351
　　Philentoma, 328
　　Rhipidura cyaniceps, 328
ALCEDINIDAE, *190-191, 198-203, 206*
Alcedo atthis bengalensis, 190
Alcedo bengalensis, 190
Alcedo collaris, 200
Alcedo (Halcyon) coromanda minor, 201
Alcedo gularis, 201
Alcedo melanura, 199
Alcedo meninting amadoni, 191, 191
Alcedo meninting verreauxii, 191
Alcedo pileata, 202
Alcedo verreauxii, 191
alexandrinus, Charadrius, 79
alfredi, Halcyon, 203
　　Halcyon winchelli, 203
alopex, Megalurus timoriensis, 310, 310

altera, Coracina coerulescens, 235
alterum, Edoliosoma, 235
amabilis, Parus, 256, 256
amadoni, Alcedo meninting, 191, 191
    Treron pompadora, 115, 115
amandava, Amandava, 409
    Fringilla, 409
Amandava amandava, 409
amauronota, Strix, 166
    Tyto capensis, 166
Amaurornis olivaceus olivaceus, 74
Amaurornis phoenicurus javanicus, 74
amaurotis, Hypsipetes, 286
amelis, Collocalia unicolor, 183
    Collocalia vanikorensis, 183
americanus, Merops, 206
    Merops viridis, 206
amethystina, Phapitreron, 118, 119, 119,
    120, 120
        Phapitreron amethystina, 119
amethystinus, Chrysococcyx xanthorhynchus,
    159
amurensis, Ardea (Butorides) virescens var., 18
    Butorides striatus, 18
anaethetus, Sterna, 111, 111
    Sterna anaethetus, 111
Anaimos plateni culionensis, 386
Anas acuta, 27, 27
Anas arcuata, 26
Anas clypeata, 31, 31
Anas coromandeliana, 34
Anas crecca, 27
Anas crecca crecca, 27
Anas ferina, 31
Anas fuligula, 31
Anas luzonica, 30, 30
Anas penelope, 30, 30
Anas poecilorhyncha zonorhyncha, 27
Anas querquedula, 30, 30
Anas tadorna, 26
Anas zonorhyncha, 27
ANATIDAE, 26-27, 30-31, 34
anderseni, Saxicola caprata, 296, 296
andersoni, Brachypteryx montana, 291, 291
andromedae, Myiothera, 300
    Zoothera, 300
Anhinga, Oriental, 5, pl. 2
Anhinga melanogaster, 5
Anhinga rufa melanogaster, 5
ANHINGAS, 5
ANHINGIDAE, 5
annectans, Bhuchanga, 245
    Dicrurus, 245
anonymous, Centropus sinensis, 162, 162
Anous stolidus pileatus, 114
Anous tenuirostris worcesteri, 114
anthonyi, Dicaeum, 388, 388
    Dicaeum anthonyi, 388
    Prionochilus, 388

Anthothreptus griseigularis, 373
Anthracoceros lemprieri, 212
Anthracoceros marchei, 212, 212
Anthracoceros montani, 212
Anthreptes cagayanensis, 373
Anthreptes chlorigaster, 372
Anthreptes malacensis basilanicus, 372
Anthreptes malacensis birgitae, 373, 373
Anthreptes malacensis cagayanensis, 373
Anthreptes malacensis chlorigaster, 372
Anthreptes malacensis griseigularis, 373
Anthreptes malacensis heliolusius, 372, 372
Anthreptes malacensis iris, 373, 373
Anthreptes malacensis paraguae, 372, 372
Anthreptes malacensis wiglesworthi, 372, 372
Anthus cervinus, 359
Anthus gustavi, 359
Anthus gustavi gustavi, 359
Anthus hodgsoni, 359
Anthus hodgsoni hodgsoni, 359
Anthus hodgsoni yunnanensis, 359
Anthus maculatus yunnanensis, 359
Anthus novaeseelandiae lugubris, 358
antigone, Grus, 66, 66
apicalis, Loriculus, 151
    Loriculus philippensis, 151
apivorus, Pernis, 38, 38
Aplonis minor todayensis, 364
Aplonis panayensis panayensis, 364
apo, Callisitta frontalis, 258
    Dicaeum, 399
    Dicaeum ignipectus, 399
    Dryobates moluccensis, 220
    Muscicapula melanoleuca, 338
    Pyrrhula leucogenys, 417
    Rhipidura superciliaris, 327, 327
    Sitta frontalis, 258
APODIDAE, 182-183, 186-188
apoensis, Collocalia, 182
    Hyloterpe, 354, 355
    Pachycephala philippinensis, 354
Apus affinis subfurcatus, 188
Apus pacificus pacificus, 188
Arachnothera clarae, 385
Arachnothera clarae clarae, 385
Arachnothera clarae luzonensis, 385, 385
Arachnothera clarae malindangensis, 385, 385
Arachnothera clarae philippinensis, 385
Arachnothera dilutor, 384
Arachnothera flammifera, 384
Arachnothera longirostra dilutor, 384
Arachnothera longirostra flammifera, 384
Arachnothera longirostra randi, 384
Arachnothera longirostris randi, 384
arcanus, Ptilinopus, 122, 122
arcuata, Anas, 26
    Dendrocygna, 26
    Dendrocygna arcuata, 26
Ardea cinerea jouyi, 21, 21

Ardea cinnamomea, 11
Ardea episcopus, 23
Ardea flavicollis, 10
Ardea intermedia, 20
Ardea javanica, 18
Ardea modesta, 20
Ardea nigripes, 20
Ardea nycticorax, 22
Ardea purpurea manilensis, *21*, 21
Ardea sacra, 19
Ardea sinensis, 10
Ardea stellaris, 10
Ardea sumatrana, 21
Ardea sumatrana sumatrana, *21*
Ardea (Butorides) virescens var. *amurensis*, 18
ARDEIDAE, *10-11*, *18-22*
ardens, Harpactes, *189*, 189, *190*, 190
    Harpactes ardens, *189*
    Trogon, 189
Ardeola bacchus, 19
Ardetta eurhythma, 11
Arenaria interpes interpes, *93*
argentatus, Ceyx, *198*, 198
    Ceyx argentatus, *198*
    Larus, *104*, 104
ariel, Atagen, 5
    Fregata, 5
    Fregata ariel, 5
arolasi, Aethopyga, 383
    Aethopyga shelleyi, 383
arquata, Numenius, 85
ARTAMIDAE, *360*
Artamides cebuensis, 235
Artamides mindanensis, 234
Artamides mindorensis, 234
Artamides panayensis, 234
Artamus leucorhynchus leucorhynchus, *360*
arundinaceus, Acrocephalus, 317
Arundinax canturians, 303
arvensis, Alauda, 227
Asio flammeus flammeus, 177
assimile, Dicaeum trigonostigma, 396
assimilis, Dicaeum, 396
    Oriolus, 250
    Oriolus xanthonotus, 250
astrologus, Ixobrychus sinensis, 10
Astur (Nisus) gularis, 43
Atagen ariel, 5
Athene florensis, 176
atra, Fulica, *76*, 76
    Fulica atra, 76
atricapilla, Pitta, 225
atricaudatus, Pycnonotus urostictus, *277*, 277
atriceps, Pycnonotus, 276
    Pycnonotus atriceps, 276
    Turdus, 276
atrocaudata, Terpsiphone, *350*
atrogularis, Orthotomus, *324*, 324, *325*

atthis, Alcedo, 190
aurea, Zoothera dauma, *300*
aureiloris, Zosterops, 407
    Zosterops nigrorum, *407*
aureus, Turdus, 300
aurora, Cyrtostomus, 378
    Nectarinia jugularis, *378*
australe, Dicaeum, 394
    Dicaeum australe, 394
    Pipra, 394
australis, Sphenocercus, *114*, 115
Avadavat, Red, *409*, pl. 84
Aviceda jerdoni magnirostris, 35
axillaris, Osmotreron, 115
    Treron pompadora, *115*
Aythya ferina, *31*
Aythya fuligula, 31
Aythya marila mariloides, 34
azurae [sic]*, Hypothymis*, 348
azurea, Hypothymis, *348*, 348
    Hypothymis azurea, *348*
    Muscicapa, 348

B

Babbler, Ashy-headed Ground-, *262*, pl. 56
    Bagobo, *262*, pl. 56
    Black-crowned Tree-, *265*, pl. 57
    Brown Tit-, *269*, pl. 58
    Falcated Ground-, *264*, pl. 56
    Gray-faced Tit-, *268*, pl. 58
    Luzon Wren-, *264*, pl. 56
    Miniature Tit-, *276*, pl. 58
    Negros Tree-, *268*, pl. 58
    Palawan Tree-, *268*, pl. 58
    Pygmy Tree-, *265*, pl. 57
    Red-headed Tree-, *263*, pl. 56
    Rough-templed Tree-, *267*, pl. 57
    Streaked Ground-, *263*, pl. 56
    Striped Tree-, *267*, pl. 58
    Whitehead's Tree-, *267*, pl. 57
BABBLERS, *262-269*, *276*
bacchus, Ardeola, 19
    Buphus, 19
badia, Strix, 166
badius, Phodilus, 166
    Phodilus badius, *166*
bagobo, Collocalia esculenta, *186*, 186
bakkamoena, Otus, 167, *168*, *169*, 169
Balicassiao, *244*, pl. 53
balicassius, Corvus, 244
    Dicrurus, 244, *244*, *245*, 245
    Dicrurus balicassius, 244
balukensis, Megapodius cumingi, 54
bangsi, Entomothera coromanda, 201
    Halcyon coromanda, 201
    Sterna dougallii, *110*, 110

bangueyensis, Ptilinopus melanospila, 123
    Ptilopus, 123
banken, Centropus melanops, 163
barbarae, Hemiprocne comata, 189
barbata, Perdix, 55, 55
    Perdix barbata, 55
Barbet, Crimson-breasted, *213,* pl. 46
BARBETS, *213, 216*
BARN OWLS, *166-167*
basilanica, Ceyx, 200
    Dendrobiastes, 337
    Ficedula, 337
    Ficedula basilanica, 337
    Hydrocorax hydrocorax, 213
    Hyloterpe apoensis, 355
    Pachycephala philippinensis, 355
    Penelopides, 211
    Penelopides panini, 211
    Phlegoenas crinigera, 138
    Ptilocichla mindanensis, 264
    Ptiocichla [sic], 264
    Rhinomyias ruficauda, 329
    Zosterops, 405
    Zosterops everetti, 405
basilanicus, Anthreptes malacensis, 372
    Oriolus, 249
    Oriolus xanthonotus, 249
    Poliolophus, 277
    Pycnonotus urostictus, 277
    Yungipicus, 219
Basilornis miranda, 368
batanensis, Hypsipetes, 286
    Hypsipetes amaurotis, 286
    Otus bakkamoena, 167
batanis, Zosterops, 399
    Zosterops meyeni, 399
Batrachostomus javensis chaseni, 178, 178
Batrachostomus menagei, 177
Batrachostomus microrhynchus, 177
Batrachostomus septimus, 178
Batrachostomus septimus menagei, 177
Batrachostomus septimus microrhynchus, 177
Batrachostomus septimus septimus, 178
baueri, Limosa, 88
    Limosa lapponica, 88
Baza leucopias, 35
Bee-eater, Blue-tailed, *206,* pl. 46
    Chestnut-headed, *206,* pl. 46
BEE-EATERS, *206-207*
bella, Aethopyga, 383
    Aethopyga shelleyi, 383
bengalensis, Alcedo, 190
    Alcedo atthis, 190
    Centropus, 166, 166
benghalensis, Rallus, 77
    Rostratula, 77
    Rostratula benghalensis, 77
benguetensis, Phylloscopus trivirgatus, 318

Turnix ocellata, 66, 66
bergii, Sterna, 111
    Thalasseus, 111
besti, Dicaeum, 396
    Dicaeum trigonostigma, 396
Bhuchanga annectans, 245
bicolor, Chimarrhornis [sic], 294
    Columba, 130
    Dicaeum, 389, 389
    Dicaeum bicolor, 389
    Ducula, 130
    Prionochilus, 389
    Rhyacornis, 294
birgitae, Anthreptes malacensis, 373, 373
bitorquata, Streptopelia, 132
Bittern, Black, *10,* pl. 3
    Chinese Least, *10,* pl. 3
    Cinnamon Least, *11,* pl. 3
    Common, *10,* pl. 3
    Japanese, *11,* pl. 3
    Malay, *18,* pl. 3
    Schrenck's Least, *11,* pl. 3
Bluebird, Palawan Fairy, *287,* pl. 61
    Philippine Fairy, *290,* pl. 61
boholensis, Coracina striata, 235, 235
    Macronous striaticeps, 269
    Otus, 169
    Pachycephala philippinensis, 354, 354
    Penelopides panini, 211
    Rhinomyias ruficauda, 329, 329
    Stachyris capitalis, 266
    Stachyris nigrocapitata, 266
    Zosterops, 405
    Zosterops everetti, 405
Bolbopsittacus intermedius, 149
Bolbopsittacus lunulatus callainipictus,
    149, 149
Bolbopsittacus lunulatus intermedius, 149
Bolbopsittacus lunulatus lunulatus, 148
Bolbopsittacus lunulatus mindanensis, 149
boltoni, Aethopyga, 378, 378, 379, 379
    Aethopyga boltoni, 379
bonapartei, Loriculus, 151
    Loriculus philippensis, 151
bonga, Dicaeum, 399
    Dicaeum ignipectus, 399
bongaoensis, Parus elegans, 256, 256
bonita, Aethopyga, 383
    Aethopyga shelleyi, 383
bonthaina, Muscicapa, 337
BOOBIES, *3-4*
Booby, Blue-faced, *3,* pl. 1
    Brown, *4,* pl. 1
    Red-footed, *4,* pl. 1
borealis, Cettia diphone, 308
    Cettia minuta, 308
    Phyllopneuste, 320
    Phylloscopus, 320

Phylloscopus borealis, *320*
Botaurus stellaris stellaris, *10*
bournsi, *Loriculus*, 150
 Loriculus philippensis, *150*
bournsii, *Ceyx*, 198
Brachypteryx brunneiceps, 291
Brachypteryx malindangensis, 291
Brachypteryx mindanensis, 291
Brachypteryx montana andersoni, *291*, 291
Brachypteryx montana brunneiceps, *291*
Brachypteryx montana malindangensis, *291*
Brachypteryx montana mindanensis, *291*
Brachypteryx montana poliogyna, *290*
Brachypteryx montana sillimani, *291*, 291
Brachypteryx poliogyna, *290*
Brachypus cinereifrons, 277
Brachypus urostictus, 276
brachyura, *Pitta*, 226
Brachyurus mulleri, 226
Brachyurus propinquus, 225
Brachyurus steerii, 226
Bradypterus caudatus caudatus, 309
Bradypterus caudatus malindangensis, 309
Bradypterus caudatus unicolor, 309
Bradypterus luteoventris seebohmi, *308*, 308
Brambling, *415*, pl. 85
bres, *Criniger*, 278
brevipes, *Leucotreron occipitalis*, 121
 Totanus, 93
 Tringa incanas, 93
brevirostris, *Collocalia*, *182*, *183*
 Phabotreron, 119
 Phapitreron leucotis, *119*
Broadbill, Wattled, *224*, pl. 48
BROADBILLS, *224*
brunneiceps, *Brachypteryx*, 291
 Brachypteryx montana, *291*
 Cisticola juncidis, *311*
 Phabotreron, 121
 Phapitreron cinereiceps, 121
 Salicaria (Cisticola), 311
brunneiventris, *Chlorura*, 410
 Erythrura hyperythra, *410*
Bubo philippensis mindanensis, 174
Bubo philippensis philippensis, 174
Bubulcus ibis coromandus, *19*
bubutus, *Centropus*, 161
 Centropus sinensis, *161*
Bucco haemacephalus, 213
Bucco philippinensis, 213
Buceros hydrocorax, 212
Buceros hydrocorax hydrocorax, *212*
Buceros hydrocorax mindanensis, *213*
Buceros hydrocorax semigaleatus, *213*
Buceros leucocephalus, 212
Buceros manilloe, 210
Buceros mindanensis, 213
Buceros montani, 212

Buceros panini, 210
Buceros semigaleatus, 213
BUCEROTIDAE, *210-213*
Buchanga palawanensis, 244
Budytes taivanus, 358
Bulbul, Black-headed, *276*, pl. 59
 Chestnut-eared, *286*, pl. 60
 Mottled-breasted, *284*, pl. 60
 Olive, *279*, pl. 60
 Olive-brown, *277*, pl. 59
 Philippine, *279*, pl. 60
 Plain-throated, *285*, pl. 60
 Wattled, *276*, pl. 59
 White-throated, *278*, pl. 59
 Yellow-vented, *278*, pl. 59
 Zamboanga, *284*
BULBULS, *276-279*, *284-286*
Bullfinch, Philippine, *417*, pl. 85
Bunting, Black-faced, *416*, pl. 85
 Japanese Yellow, *415*, pl. 85
 Little, *415*, pl. 85
Buphus bacchus, 19
burbidgei, *Otus rufescens*, *168*, 168
burbidgii, *Tanygnathus*, 148
 Tanygnathus sumatranus, *148*
BURHINIDAE, *103*
Bush-warbler, *303*, pl. 65
 Mountain, *308*, pl. 65
Butastur indicus, *47*
buteo, *Buteo*, *47*
 Faclo [sic], 47
Buteo buteo japonensis, 47
Buteo holospilus, 42
Butio kutteri, 18
Butorides striatus amurensis, *18*
Butorides striatus carcinophilus, 18
Butorides striatus javensis, *18*, 19
BUTTON-QUAIL, *57-59*, *66*
Button-quail, Barred, *59*, pl. 16
 Spotted, *59*, pl. 16
 Striped, *57*, pl. 16
 Worcester's, *58*, pl. 16
Buzzard, Asiatic Honey, *38*, pl. 9
 Barred Honey, *35*, pl. 9
 Common, *47*, pl. 11
 Gray-faced, *47*, pl. 11

C

cabanisi, *Lonchura punctulata*, *411*
 Munia, 411
Cacomantis merulinus merulinus, *158*
Cacomantis sonneratii fasciolatus, *155*
Cacomantis variolosus everetti, *158*, 158
Cacomantis variolosus sepulcralis, *158*
caeruleus, *Elanus*, 38
cagayanensis, *Anthreptes*, 373
 Anthreptes malacensis, *373*
 Chibia, 248

cagayanensis (cont.)
  Dicaeum hypoleucum, 397, 397
  Macronous gularis, 269
  Mixornis, 269
  Orthotomus cineraceus, 326
  Orthotomus sepium, 326
  Phoenicophaeus superciliosus, 161, 161
Calamanthella tinnabulans, 311
Calamodyta sorghophila, 317
calayensis, Ficedula hyperythra, 336
  Muscicapula, 336
  Otus, 167
  Otus scops, 167
calcostetha, Nectarinia, 375, 375
caledonicus, Nycticorax, 22, 22
Calidris acuminata, 101
Calidris alba, 100
Calidris canutus canutus, 95
Calidris ferruginea, 101
Calidris ruficollis, 100
Calidris subminuta, 100
Calidris temminckii, 101
Calidris tenuirostris, 100
calidus, Falco, 54
  Falco peregrinus, 54
Callaeops periophthalmica, 350
*callainipictus, Bolbopsittacus lunulatus,
  149,* 149
calliope, Erithacus, 294
  Motacilla, 294
Callisitta frontalis apo, 258
Callisitta frontalis cebuensis, 257
Callisitta frontalis insignis, 257
Caloenas nicobarica nicobarica, 139
calva, Gracula, 368
calvus, Sarcops, 368, 369, 369
  Sarcops calvus, 368
camarinensis, Cyornis herioti, 339
  Muscicapa herioti, 339
camiguinensis, Hypsipetes, 286
  Hypsipetes amaurotis, 286
Camiguinia personata, 348
CAMPEPHAGIDAE, *234-235, 238-241, 244*
Cancroma Coromanda, 19
canescens, Treron pompadora, 118, 118
canorus, Cuculus, 155
canturians, Arundinax, 303
  Cettia diphone, 303
canutus, Calidris, 95
  Calidris canutus, 95
  Canutus, 95
  Tringa, 95
Canutus canutus rogersi, 95
capensis, Pelargopsis, 200
  Ramphalcyon, 200
  Tyto, 166
capitalis, Mixornis (?), 266
  Stachyris, 265, 266, 266

Stachyris capitalis, 266
CAPITONIDAE, *213, 216*
caprata, Motacilla, 296
  Saxicola, 296, 296
  Saxicola caprata, 296
CAPRIMULGIDAE, *178-179, 182*
Caprimulgus affinis griseatus, 182
Caprimulgus affinis mindanensis, 182, 182
Caprimulgus griseatus, 182
Caprimulgus indicus jotaka, 179
Caprimulgus jotaka, 179
Caprimulgus macrotis, 178
Caprimulgus macrurus delacouri, 179, 179
Caprimulgus macrurus johnsoni, 179, 179
Caprimulgus macrurus manillensis, 179
Caprimulgus manillensis, 179
carbo, Phalacrocorax, 4
carcinophilus, Butorides striatus, 18
Carduelis spinus, 416
carola, Ducula, 130, 131
  Ducula carola, 130
  Ptilocolpa, 130
carpenteri, Centropus, 163
  Centropus viridis, 163
Carpophaga aenea palawanensis, 124
Carpophaga chalybura, 124
Carpophaga mindorensis, 130
Carpophaga nuchalis, 124
Carpophaga pickeringii, 125
Carpophaga poliocephala, 125
caspia, Hydroprogne, 105
  Sterna, 105
castaneiceps, Orthotomus, 324
  Orthotomus atrogularis, 324
castroi, Accipiter trivirgatus, 46, 46
catarmanensis, Hypothymis azurae [sic], 348
  Hypothymis azurea, 348
  Hypsipetes everetti, 285, 285
  Zosterops nigrorum, 408, 408
caudacuta, Chaetura, 187
  Chaetura caudacuta, 187
  Hirundo, 187
caudatus, Bradypterus, 309
  Bradypterus caudatus, 309
  Pseudotharrhaleus, 309
Ceblepyris chilensis, 240
Ceblepyris coerulescens, 235
cebuensis, Artamides, 235
  Callisitta frontalis, 257
  Cittocincla, 296
  Collocalia, 186
  Copsychus, 296
  Coracina striata, 235
  Cryptolopha, 319
  Phylloscopus, 319, 320, 320
  Phylloscopus cebuensis, 319
celebensis, Pernis, 35, 35
celestinoi, Megalaema haemacephala, 213

Megalaima haemacephala, 213
Phapitreron amethystina, 119
Turnix, 58
Turnix sylvatica, 58
centralis, Ninox philippensis, 175, 175
Centrococcyx mindorensis, 163
Centropus bengalensis philippinensis,
166, 166
Centropus bubutus, 161
Centropus carpenteri, 163
Centropus melanops, 163, 163
Centropus melanops banken, 163
Centropus molkenboeri, 162
Centropus nigrifrons, 163
Centropus rufipennis, 162
Centropus sinensis anonymous, 162, 162
Centropus sinensis bubutus, 161
Centropus steerii, 162, 162
Centropus unirufus, 163
Centropus unirufus polillensis, 163
Centropus viridis carpenteri, 163
Centropus viridis mindorensis, 163
Centropus viridis viridis, 162
Cephalophoneus suluensis, 361
Certhia jugularis, 375
Certhia sperata, 373
certhiola, Locustella, 316
cervina, Motacilla, 359
cervinus, Anthus, 359
Cettia diphone borealis, 308
Cettia diphone canturians, 303
Cettia diphone seebohmi, 308
Cettia minuta borealis, 308
Cettia montana palawana, 308, 308
Cettia seebohmi, 308
ceylonensis, Culicicapa, 347
 Culicicapa ceylonensis, 347
 Platyrhynchus, 347
Ceyx argentatus, 198
Ceyx argentatus argentatus, 198
Ceyx argentatus flumenicola, 198
Ceyx basilanica, 200
Ceyx bournsii, 198
Ceyx cyano-pectus, 191
Ceyx cyanopectus cyanopectus, 191
Ceyx cyanopectus nigrirostris, 191
Ceyx erithacus motleyi, 199, 199
Ceyx erithacus rufidorsum, 198
Ceyx erithacus vargasi, 199
Ceyx euerythra, 199
Ceyx flumenicola, 198
Ceyx goodfellowi, 198
Ceyx goodfellowi virgicapitus, 198
Ceyx lepidus margarethae, 198
Ceyx malamaui, 198
Ceyx margarethae, 198
Ceyx melanurus melanurus, 199
Ceyx melanurus platenae, 200

Ceyx melanurus samarensis, 199
Ceyx mindanensis, 200
Ceyx nigrirostris, 191
Ceyx platenae, 200
Ceyx rufidorsa, 198
Ceyx samarensis, 199
Ceyx steerii, 191
Ceyx suluensis, 198
Chaetura caudacuta caudacuta, 187
Chaetura dubius, 187
Chaetura gigantea dubia, 187
Chaetura gigantea gigantea, 187
Chaetura gigantea manobo, 187, 187
Chaetura picina, 187, 187
Chalcites xanthorhynchus, 159
Chalcophaps indica indica, 133
chalybaeus, Surniculus lugubris, 159, 159
chalybura, Carpophaga, 124
CHARADRIIDAE, *77-79,* 84
Charadrius alexandrinus dealbatus, 79
Charadrius curonicus, 78
Charadrius dubius, 78
Charadrius dubius curonicus, 78
Charadrius dubius dubius, 78
Charadrius fulvus, 78
Charadrius leschenaultii, 84, 84
Charadrius magnirostris, 103
Charadrius mongolus, 79
Charadrius mongolus mongolus, 79
Charadrius peronii, 79, 79
Charadrius veredus, 84, 84
chaseni, Batrachostomus javensis, 178, 178
Chat, Pied, *296,* pl. 63
cheela, Spilornis, 42
Chelidon dasypus, 233
Chibia cagayanensis, 248
Chibia cuyensis, 248
Chibia menagei, 248
Chibia worcesteri, 248
chilensis, Ceblepyris, 240
 Lalage nigra, 240
Chimarrhornis [sic] *bicolor,* 294
chinensis, Coturnix, 56
 Oriolus, 250, 250, 251
 Oriolus chinensis, 250
 Riparia, 232
 Streptopelia, 133, 133
chirurgus, Hydrophasianus, 76
 Tringa, 76
Chlidonias hybrida fluviatilis, 105
Chlidonias hybrida javanica, 105
Chlidonias leucoptera, 104
chlorigaster, Anthreptes, 372
 Anthreptes malacensis, 372
chloris, Halcyon, 200
chloronotus, Orthotomus, 324
 Orthotomus atrogularis, 324
Chloropsis flavipennis flavipennis, 287

Chloropsis flavipennis mindanensis, 287, 287
Chloropsis palawanensis, 287
chloropus, Gallinula, 75, 75
chlororhynchus, Puffinus, 2
    Puffinus pacificus, 2
Chlorura brunneiventris, 410
Chrysococcyx malayanus malayanus, 158
Chrysococcyx xanthorhynchus amethystinus, 159
Chrysococcyx xanthorhynchus xanthorhynchus, 159
Chrysocolaptes erythrocephalus, 221
Chrysocolaptes lucidus erythrocephalus, 221
Chrysocolaptes lucidus grandis, 221, 221
Chrysocolaptes lucidus haematribon, 220
Chrysocolaptes lucidus lucidus, 221
Chrysocolaptes lucidus montanus, 221
Chrysocolaptes lucidus montium, 220
Chrysocolaptes lucidus ramosi, 220
Chrysocolaptes lucidus rufopunctatus, 221
Chrysocolaptes lucidus xanthocephalus, 221
Chrysocolaptes maculiceps, 221
Chrysocolaptes montanus, 221
Chrysocolaptes rufopunctatus, 221
Chrysocolaptes xanthocephalus, 221
chrysolaus, Turdus, 302, 302
    Turdus chrysolaus, 302
chrysonotus, Loriculus, 150
    Loriculus philippensis, 150
Ciconia episcopus episcopus, 23
Ciconiidae, *23*
cineraceus, Dicrurus, 244
    Orthotomus, 326
    Sturnus, 368, 368
cinerea, Ardea, 21, 21
    Fulica, 75
    Gallicrex, 75
    Geocichla, 300
    Motacilla, 358
    Pachycephala, 350, 351
    Scolopax, 93
    Zoothera, 300
cinereiceps, Drymocataphus, 262
    Hemichelidon, 341
    Hypsipetes siquijorensis, 285
    Iole, 285
    Muscicapa, 341
    Orthotomus, 325, 325
    Phabotreron, 120
    Phapitreron, 120, 121
    Phapitreron cinereiceps, 120
    Trichastoma, 262
cinereifrons, Brachypus, 277
    Pycnonotus plumosus, 277
cinereigulare, Dicaeum, 395
    Dicaeum trigonostigma, 395
cinereogenys, Oriolus, 249
    Oriolus xanthonotus, 249

cinereus, Pericrocotus, 240
    Pluvianus, 77
    Poliolimnas, 74, 74
    Vanellus, 77
    Xenus, 93
cinnamomea, Ardea, 11
    Terpsiphone, 349
    Terpsiphone cinnamomea, 349
cinnamomeus, Hypocryptadius, 408, 408
    Ixobrychus, 11
    Pericrocotus, 241
    Zeocephus, 349
Cinnyris excellens, 379
Cinnyris guimarasensis, 379
Cinnyris henkei, 374
Cinnyris obscurior, 375
Cinnyris picta, 375
Cinnyris sperata manueli, 373
Cinnyris sperata minima, 373
Cinnyris sperata trochilus, 373
Cinnyris whiteheadi, 374
Circus aeruginosus spilonotus, 42
Circus melanoleucus, 43
Circus spilonotus, 42
cirrhatus, Spizaetus, 52
Cisticola exilis semirufa, 311
Cisticola juncidis brunneiceps, 311
Cisticola juncidis mcgregori, 311
Cisticola juncidis nigrostriatus, 311, 311
Cisticola juncidis tinnabulans, 311
Cisticola semirufa, 311
Cittocincla cebuensis, 296
Cittocincla niger, 295
Cittocincla superciliaris, 295
Clamator coromandus, 151
clarae, Arachnothera, 385, 385
    Arachnothera clarae, 385
Clivicola riparia ijimae, 232
clypeata, Anas, 31, 31
Cockatoo, Philippine, *140*, pl. 33
coelestis, Hypothymis, 349, 349
    Pitta steerii, 226, 226
coerulescens, Ceblepyris, 235
    Coracina, 235
    Coracina coerulescens, 235
Coleto, *368*, pl. 77
Collaris, Alcedo, 200
    Halcyon chloris, 200
collingwoodi, Poliolimnas cinereus, 74
Collocalia apoensis, 182
Collocalia brevirostris origenis, 182
Collocalia brevirostris palawanensis, 183
Collocalia brevirostris whiteheadi, 182
Collocalia cebuensis, 186
Collocalia esculenta bagobo, 186, 186
Collocalia esculenta isonota, 186
Collocalia esculenta marginata, 186
Collocalia esculenta septentrionalis, 186

Collocalia fuciphaga germani, 183
Collocalia germani, 183
Collocalia linchi isonota, 186
Collocalia lowi palawanensis, 183
Collocalia marginata, 186
Collocalia origenis, 182
Collocalia troglodytes, 186, 186
Collocalia unicolor amelis, 183
Collocalia vanikorensis amelis, 183
Collocalia vestita mearnsi, 183
Collocalia whiteheadi, 182
Collocalia whiteheadi tsubame, 183
coloria, Erythrura, 410, 410
Columba aenea, 124
Columba bicolor, 130
Columba dusumieri, 132
Columba humilis, 132
Columba indica, 133
Columba leucotis, 118
Columba luzonica, 138
Columba nicobarica, 139
Columba striata, 133
Columba tigrina, 133
Columba vernans, 118
Columba vitiensis griseogularis, 131
COLUMBIDAE, *114-115, 118-125, 130-133,*
    138-139
Colymbus Philippensis, 1
comata, Hemiprocne, 189, 189
    Macropteryx, 189
compilator, Hypothymis azurea, 348
confusus, Accipiter virgatus, 43, 43
    Dryocopus javensis, 217
    Thriponax javensis, 217
Coot, Black, *76,* pl. 18
Copsychus cebuensis, 296
Copsychus luzoniensis luzoniensis, 295
Copsychus luzoniensis parvimaculata, 295
Copsychus luzoniensis superciliaris, 295
Copsychus niger, 295
Copsychus saularis deuteronymus, 294, 294
Copsychus saularis heterogynus, 294
Copsychus saularis mindanensis, 295
CORACIIDAE, 207
Coracina coerulescens altera, 235
Coracina coerulescens coerulescens, 235
Coracina mcgregori, 239
Coracina morio elusa, 238
Coracina morio everetti, 238
Coracina morio lecroyae, 238, 238
Coracina morio mindanensis, 238
Coracina morio ripleyi, 238, 238
Coracina ostenta, 239, 239
Coracina striata boholensis, 235, 235
Coracina striata cebuensis, 235
Coracina striata difficilis, 234
Coracina striata guillemardi, 235
Coracina striata kochii, 234

Coracina striata mindorensis, 234
Coracina striata panayensis, 234
Coracina striata striata, 234
coriaria, Pyrrhula leucogenys, 417
Cormorant, Great, *4,* pl. 2
CORMORANTS, *4*
Cornix philippinus, 254
coromanda, Alcedo (Halcyon), 201
    Cancroma, 19
    Entomothera, 201
    Halcyon, 201
coromandeliana, Anas, 34
coromandelianus, Nettapus, 34
    Nettapus coromandelianus, 34
coromandus, Bubulcus ibis, 19
    Clamator, 151
    Cuculus, 151
CORVIDAE, *251, 254*
Corvus balicassius, 244
Corvus enca pusillus, 251
Corvus enca samarensis, 251
Corvus enca sierramadrensis, 251, 251
Corvus macrorhynchos philippinus, 254
Corvus pusillus, 251
Corvus samarensis, 251
Corvus striatus, 234
Corydalla lugubris, 358
Corydonix pyrrhopterus, 162
cotabato, Podiceps ruficollis, 1
coturnix, Coturnix, 56
Coturnix chinensis lineata, 56
Coturnix coturnix japonica, 56
Coturnix vulgaris japonica, 56
Coucal, Black-faced, *163,* pl. 37
    Common, *161,* pl. 37
    Lesser, *166,* pl. 37
    Philippine, *162,* pl. 37
    Rufous, *163,* pl. 37
    Steere's, *162,* pl. 37
Crake, Chinese Banded, *69,* pl. 18
    Malay Banded, *68,* pl. 17
    Philippine Banded, *68,* pl. 17
    Ruddy, *69,* pl. 18
Crane, Eastern Sarus, *66,* pl. 6
CRANES, *66*
Craniorrhinus [sic] *waldeni,* 211
crecca, Anas, 27, 27
    Anas crecca, 27
Creeper, Plain-headed, *259,* pl. 55
    Striped-headed, *258,* pl. 55
CREEPERS, *258-259, 262*
Crested-cuckoo, Red-winged, *151,* pl. 35
crex, Megalurus timoriensis, 310, 310
criniger, Gallicolumba luzonica, 138
    Pampusanna, 138
    Phlegoenas, 139
Criniger bres frater, 278
Criniger everetti, 285

Criniger frater, 278
Criniger haynaldi, 285
Criniger palawanensis, 279
crinigera, Phlegoenas, 138
crissalis, Hyloterpe, 350
    Pachycephala cinerea, 350
cristata, Sterna, 111
    Sterna bergii, 111
cristatella, Gracula, 368
cristatellus, Acridotheres, 368
    Acridotheres cristatellus, 368
cristatus, Lanius, 360, 361, 361
    Lanius cristatus, 361
Crossbill, Red, *417*, pl. 85
Crow, Large-billed, *254*, pl. 54
    Little, *251*, pl. 54
CROWS, *251, 254*
crypta, Ficedula, 337
    Ficedula crypta, 337
    Muscicapa, 337
Cryptolopha cebuensis, 319
Cryptolopha flavigularis, 319
Cryptolopha malindangensis, 318
Cryptolopha mindanensis, 318
Cryptolopha nigrorum, 317
Cryptolopha xanthopygia, 320
Cuckoo, Bay-banded, *155*, pl. 36
    Brush, *158*, pl. 36
    Common, *155*, pl. 35
    Drongo, *159*, pl. 36
    Horsfield's Hawk-, *154*, pl. 35
    Large Hawk-, *154*, pl. 35
    Malay Bronze, *158*, pl. 35
    Oriental, *155*, pl. 35
    Plaintive, *158*, pl. 36
    Red-winged Crested-, *151*, pl. 35
    Rough-crested, *161*, pl. 36
    Scale-feathered, *161*, pl. 36
    Short-winged, *154*, pl. 35
    Violet, *159*, pl. 35
CUCKOOS, *151, 154-155, 158-163, 166*
CUCKOO-SHRIKES, *234-235, 238-241, 244*
CUCULIDAE, *151, 154-155, 158-163, 166*
cucullatus, Orthotomus, 321, 321
Cuculus aegyptius, 162
Cuculus canorus telephonus, 155
Cuculus coromandus, 151
Cuculus fasciolatus, 155
Cuculus fugax hyperythrus, 154
Cuculus fugax pectoralis, 154
Cuculus horsfieldi, 155
Cuculus hyperythrus, 154
Cuculus malayanus, 158
Cuculus merulinus, 158
Cuculus micropterus, 154
Cuculus micropterus micropterus, 154
Cuculus mindanensis, 160
Cuculus philippensis, 162

Cuculus saturatus horsfieldi, 155
Cuculus sepulcralis, 158
Cuculus sparverioides, 154
Cuculus sparverioides sparverioides, 154
Cuculus telephonus, 155
Cuculus viridis, 162
Culicicapa ceylonensis ceylonensis, 347
Culicicapa helianthea mayri, 347, 347
Culicicapa helianthea panayensis, 347
Culicicapa helianthea septentrionalis,
    347, 347
Culicicapa helianthea zimmeri, 347, 347
culionensis, Anaimos plateni, 386
cumingi, Megapodius, 54
    Megapodius freycinet, 55
    Minodoria striaticeps, 269
    Phoenicophaeus, 161
    Phoenicophaus, 161
cumingii, Megapodius, 55
Curlew, Common, *85*, pl. 21
    Long-billed, *85*, pl. 21
    Pygmy, *84*, pl. 21
curonicus, Charadrius, 78
    Charadrius dubius, 78
curvirostra, Loxia, 417
    Treron, 115, 115
curvirostris, Phoenicophaeus, 160
cuyensis, Chibia, 248
    Dicrurus hottentottus, 248
    Otus, 168
    Otus scops, 168
cyanescens, Terpsiphone, 350
    Zeocephus, 350
cyaniceps, Muscipeta, 327
    Prioniturus, 142
    Rhipidura, 327, 327, 328
    Rhipidura cyaniceps, 327
cyanocollis, Eurystomus, 207
    Eurystomus orientalis, 207
cyanogaster, Irena, 290, 290
    Irena cyanogaster, 290
cyanomelana, Ficedula, 339
    Ficedula cyanomelana, 339
    Muscicapa, 339
Cyanomyias helenae, 348
cyanopectus, Ceyx, 191, 191
    Ceyx cyanopectus, 191
Cyclopsitta mindanensis, 149
Cyornis herioti, 339
Cyornis herioti camarinensis, 339
Cyornis herioti herioti, 339
Cyornis lemprieri, 339, 339
Cyornis mindorensis, 340
Cyornis paraguae, 338
Cyornis philippinensis, 340
Cyornis rufigaster litoralis, 340
Cyornis rufigaster mindorensis, 340
Cyornis rufigaster philippinensis, 340

446

Cyornis rufigaster simplex, 340
Cyornis rufigastra litoralis, 340
Cyornis simplex, 340
Cypselus giganteus, 187
Cypselus subfurcatus, 188
Cypsiurus parvus pallidior, 188
Cyrtostomus aurora, 378
Cyrtostomus dinagatensis, 375
Cyrtostomus jugularis mindanensis, 375
Cyrtostomus jugularis woodi, 378

D

Dabchick, Common, *1*, pl. 1
Dacelo lindsayi, 203
dactylatra, Sula, 3
daggayana, Ficedula hyperythra, 336, 336
daphoenonota, Aethopyga flagrans, 382, 382
Dasycrotapha speciosa, 267
dasypus, Chelidon, 233
  Delichon, 233
  Delichon dasypus, 233
dauma, Zoothera, 300
davao, Dicaeum, 398
  Dicaeum pygmaeum, 398
  Orthotomus atrogularis, 324
davaoensis, Nectarinia sperata, 374, 374
dealbatus, Aegialites, 79
  Charadrius alexandrinus, 79
decolor, Aethopyga flagrans, 379, 379
decorosa, Aethopyga pulcherrima, 382
  Eudrepanis, 382
delacouri, Caprimulgus macrurus, 179, 179
Delichon dasypus dasypus, 233
Dendrobiastes basilanica, 337
Dendrocopos maculatus fulvifasciatus, 219
Dendrocopos maculatus leytensis, 219
Dendrocopos maculatus maculatus, 219
Dendrocopos maculatus menagei, 220
Dendrocopos maculatus ramsayi, 220
Dendrocopos maculatus siasiensis, 220
Dendrocopos maculatus validirostris, 219
Dendrocopus moluccensis igorotus, 219
Dendrocygna arcuata arcuata, 26
Dendrocygna guttata, 26, 26
Dendronanthus indicus, 355
Dendrophassa vernans nesophasma, 118
Dendrophila lilacea, 258
Dendrophila mesoleuca, 257
Dendrophila oenochlamys, 257
dennistouni, Stachyris capitalis, 266
  Zosterornis, 266
derbianus, Orthotomus, 321, 321
deuteronymus, Copsychus saularis, 294, 294
DICAEIDAE, *385-389, 394-399*
Dicaeum aeruginosum aeruginosum, 386
Dicaeum aeruginosum affine, 387
Dicaeum aeruginosum striatissimum, 387, 387
Dicaeum anthonyi anthonyi, 388

Dicaeum anthonyi kampalili, 388
Dicaeum anthonyi masawan, 388, 388
Dicaeum apo, 399
Dicaeum assimilis, 396
Dicaeum australe australe, 394
Dicaeum australe haematostictum, 394
Dicaeum besti, 396
Dicaeum bicolor bicolor, 389
Dicaeum bicolor inexpectatum, 389
Dicaeum bicolor viridissimum, 389, 389
Dicaeum bonga, 399
Dicaeum cinereigulare, 395
Dicaeum davao, 398
Dicaeum dorsale, 395
Dicaeum dorsale hanadori, 396
Dicaeum everetti, 397
Dicaeum flaviventer, 394
D(icaeum) flavum, 399
Dicaeum haematostictum, 394
Dicaeum haematostictum whiteheadi, 394
Dicaeum hypoleucum, 397
Dicaeum hypoleucum cagayanensis, 397, 397
Dicaeum hypoleucum hypoleucum, 397
Dicaeum hypoleucum lagunae, 396
Dicaeum hypoleucum obscurum, 396
Dicaeum hypoleucum pontifex, 397, 397
Dicaeum ignipectus apo, 399
Dicaeum ignipectus bonga, 399
Dicaeum ignipectus luzoniense, 398
Dicaeum intermedia, 395
Dicaeum isag, 387
Dicaeum kampalili, 388
Dicaeum luzoniense, 398
Dicaeum mindanense, 397
Dicaeum modestum, 397
Dicaeum nigrilore, 387, 387
Dicaeum nigrilore diuatae, 388
Dicaeum obscurum, 396
Dicaeum pallidior, 395
Dicaeum proprium, 387, 387
Dicaeum pygmaeum davao, 398
Dicaeum pygmaeum palawanorum, 398, 398
Dicaeum pygmaeum pygmaeum, 397
Dicaeum pygmaeum salomonseni, 398, 398
Dicaeum quadricolor, 389
Dicaeum retrocinctum, 394, 394
Dicaeum rubricapilla, 388
Dicaeum sibutuense, 396
Dicaeum sibuyanica, 395
Dicaeum trigonostigma assimile, 396
Dicaeum trigonostigma besti, 396
Dicaeum trigonostigma cinereigulare, 395
Dicaeum trigonostigma dorsale, 395
Dicaeum trigonostigma intermedia, 395
Dicaeum trigonostigma isidroi, 396, 396
Dicaeum trigonostigma pallidius, 395
Dicaeum trigonostigma sibutuense, 396
Dicaeum trigonostigma sibuyanicum, 395

447

Dicaeum trigonostigma xanthopygium, 394
Dicaeum xanthopygium, 394
DICRURIDAE, *244-245, 248*
Dicrurus annectans, 245
Dicrurus balicassius abraensis, 245, 245
Dicrurus balicassius balicassius, 244
Dicrurus balicassius mindorensis, 244
Dicrurus balicassius mirabilis, 245
Dicrurus cineraceus rebaptizatus, 244
Dicrurus hottentottus cuyensis, 248
Dicrurus hottentottus menagei, 248
Dicrurus hottentottus palawanensis, 248
Dicrurus hottentottus samarensis, 248, 248
Dicrurus hottentottus striatus, 245
Dicrurus hottentottus suluensis, 248
Dicrurus leucophaeus, 244
Dicrurus leucophaeus leucophaeus, 244
Dicrurus leucophaeus var. whiteheadi, 244
Dicrurus mirabilis, 245
Dicrurus palawanensis, 248
Dicrurus striatus, 245
Dicrurus suluensis, 248
difficilis, Coracina striata, 234
    Graucalus sumatrensis, 234
dillwyni, Megapodius, 54
dilutor, Arachnothera, 384
    Arachnothera longirostra, 384
dinagatensis, Cyrtostomus, 375
Dinopium javanense everetti, 216
diphone, Cettia, 303, 308
discurus, Prioniturus, 140, 140, *141,* 141
    Prioniturus discurus, 140
    Psittacus, 140
disposita, Ficedula crypta, 337
    Muscicapa bonthaina, 337
Dissoura neglecta, 23
diuatae, Aethopyga primigenius, 378, 378
    Dicaeum nigrilore, 388
    Phylloscopus trivirgatus, 318, 318
    Zosterops montana, 405, 405
divaricatus, Lanius, 240
    Pericrocotus, 240
    Pericrocotus divaricatus, 240
diversum, Piprisoma, 387
dohertyi, Loriculus philippensis, 151, 151
Dollar Bird, *207,* pl. 46
dominica, Pluvialis, 78
dorotheae, Phaethon lepturus, 3, 3
dorsale, Dicaeum, 395, 396
    Dicaeum trigonostigma, 395
Dotterel, Oriental, *84,* pl. 20
dougallii, Sterna, 110, 110
Dove, Amethyst Brown Fruit, *119,* pl. 28
    Black-chinned Fruit, *122,* pl. 29
    Black-naped Fruit, *123,* pl. 29
    Dwarf Turtle, *132,* pl. 31
    Green-winged Ground, *133,* pl. 32
    Marche's Fruit, *122,* pl. 29

    Merrill's Fruit, *121,* pl. 29
    Negros Fruit, *122,* pl. 29
    Philippine Turtle, *132,* pl. 31
    Slender-billed Cuckoo, *131,* pl. 31
    Southern Brown Fruit, *120*
    Spotted, *133,* pl. 31
    Superb Fruit, *123,* pl. 29
    White-eared Brown Fruit, *118,* pl. 28
    Yellow-breasted Fruit, *121,* pl. 29
    Zebra, *133,* pl. 32
DOVES, *114-115, 118-125, 130-133, 138-139*
Dowitcher, Oriental, *94,* pl. 23
Drongo, Crow-billed, *245,* pl. 53
    Gray, *244,* pl. 53
    Spangled, *245,* pl. 53
DRONGOS, *244-245, 248*
Drymocataphus cinereiceps, 262
Dryobates moluccensis apo, 220
Dryococcyx harringtoni, 160
Dryocopus javensis confusus, 217
Dryocopus javensis estholterus, 218, 218
Dryocopus javensis hargitti, 218
Dryocopus javensis mindorensis, 218
Dryocopus javensis multilunatus, 218
Dryocopus javensis pectoralis, 218
Dryocopus javensis philippensis, 218
Dryocopus javensis samarensis, 218
Dryocopus javensis suluensis, 219
dubia, Aethopyga, 382
    Chaetura gigantea, 187
dubius, Chaetura, 187
    Charadrius, 78, 78
    Charadrius dubius, 78
Duck, Greater Scaup, *34,* pl. 8
    Spotbill, 27, pl. 7
    Spotted Whistling-, 26, pl. 7
    Tufted, *31,* pl. 8
    Wandering Whistling-, *26,* pl. 7
DUCKS, *26-27, 30-31, 34*
Ducula aenea aenea, 124
Ducula aenea fugaensis, 124
Ducula aenea glaucocauda, 124
Ducula aenea nuchalis, 124
Ducula aenea palawanensis, 124
Ducula bicolor, 130
Ducula carola carola, 130
Ducula carola mindanensis, 131
Ducula carola nigrorum, 131
Ducula mindorensis, 130
Ducula pickeringii langhornei, 125
Ducula pickeringii palmasensis, 125
Ducula pickeringii pickeringii, 125
Ducula poliocephala nobilis, 130
Ducula poliocephala poliocephala, 125
Dupetor flavicollis flavicollis, 10
duponti, Tanygnathus sumatranus, 148, 148
dusumieri, Columba, 132
    Streptopelia, 132

dusumieri (cont.)
  Streptopelia bitorquata, 132

E

Eagle, Changeable Hawk, *52*, pl. 13
  Gray-headed Fishing, *42*, pl. 10
  Monkey-eating, *47*, pl. 12
  Philippine Hawk, *52*, pl. 13
  Rufous-bellied, *52*, pl. 13
  Serpent, *42*, pl. 10
  White-breasted Sea, *39*, pl. 10
EAGLES, *35, 38-39, 42-43, 46-47, 52*
edithae, Pardaliparus, 254
  Parus elegans, 254
Edoliisoma elusum, 238
Edoliisoma everetti, 238
Edoliisoma (Graucalus) panayensis, 239
Edoliosoma alterum, 235
Edolisoma mcgregori peterseni, 239
Egret, Cattle, *19*, pl. 4
  Chinese, *20*, pl. 4
  Greater, *20*, pl. 4
  Lesser, *20*, pl. 4
  Little, *20*, pl. 4
  Reef, *19*, pl. 4
Egretta alba modesta, 20
Egretta eulophotes, 20
Egretta garzetta nigripes, 20
Egretta intermedia intermedia, 20
Egretta sacra sacra, 19, pl. 4
Elanus caeruleus hypoleucus, 38
Elanus hypoleucus, 38
elegans, Pardaliparus, 254, 255
  Parus, 254, 254, 255, 255, 256, 256
  Parus elegans, 254
ellae, Irena, 290
  Irena cyanogaster, 290
elusa, Coracina morio, 238
elusum, Edoliisoma, 238
Emberiza pusilla, 415, 415
Emberiza spodocephala, 416, 416
Emberiza sulphurata, 415, 415
emphanum, Polyplectron, 57, 57
enantia, Haemataena melanocephala, 123
enca, Corvus, 251, 251
enganensis, Siphia, 339
Entomothera coromanda bangsi, 201
Entomothera coromanda ochrothorectis, 201
episcopus, Ardea, 23
  Ciconia, 23
  Ciconia episcopus, 23
epops (?), *Upupa, 207*
erimacra, Treron curvirostra, 115, 115
erithacus, Ceyx, 198, 199, 199
  Siphia, 338
Erithacus calliope, 294
ernesti, Falco, 54
  Falco peregrinus, 54
erythrocephalus, Chrysocolaptes, 221

Chrysocolaptes lucidus, 221
erythrogaster, Pitta, 224, 224, 225, 225
  Pitta erythrogaster, 224
erythrogastra, Pitta, 224
erythrogonys, Hierax, 53
  Microhierax, 53
  Microhierax erythrogonys, 53
Erythrura coloria, 410, 410
Erythrura hyperythra brunneiventris, 410
Erythrura viridifacies, 410, 410
Esacus magnirostris, 103
esculenta, Collocalia, 186, 186
estherae, Serinus, 416
estholterus, Dryocopus javensis, 218, 218
ESTRILDIDAE, *409-411, 414-415*
Eudrepanis decorosa, 382
Eudrepanis jefferyi, 382
Eudynamis [sic] *frater, 160*
Eudynamys scolopacea frater, 160
Eudynamys scolopacea mindanensis, 160
Eudynamys scolopacea onikakko, 160
Eudynamys scolopacea paraguena, 160
euerythra, Ceyx, 199
eulophotes, Egretta, 20
  Herodias, 20
Eumyias panayensis, 346
eurhina, Tringa totanus, 88
eurhinus, Totanus totanus, 88
eurhythma, Ardetta, 11
eurhythmus, Ixobrychus, 11
eurizonoides, Gallinula, 68
  Rallina, 68
  Rallina eurizonoides, 68
Eurostopodus macrotis macrotis, 178
EURYLAIMIDAE, *224*
Eurylaimus steerei mayri, 224
Eurylaimus steerii, 224
Eurylaimus steerii mayri, 224
Eurylaimus steerii samarensis, 224
Eurylaimus steerii steerii, 224
Eurystomus cyanocollis, 207
Eurystomus orientalis cyanocollis, 207
everetti, Cacomantis variolosus, 158, 158
  Coracina morio, 238
  Criniger, 285
  Dicaeum, 397
  Dinopium javanense, 216
  Edoliisoma, 238
  Hypsipetes, 285, 285
  Hypsipetes everetti, 285
  Lonchura leucogastra, 411
  Ninox, 175
  Orycerca, 411
  Osmotreron, 118
  Otus bakkamoena, 169
  Scops, 169
  Tanygnathus, 148
  Tanygnathus sumatranus, 148
  Tigra, 216

everetti (cont.)
    Treron pompadora, 118
    Zosterops, 405, 406, 406
    Zosterops everetti, 406
excellens, Cinnyris, 379
exilis, Cisticola, 311
extimus, Accipiter trivirgatus, 46, 46

F

Faclo [sic] *buteo japonensis,* 47
falcata, Ptilocichla, 264, 264
falcinellus, Limicola, 102
    Plegadis, 23
Falco calidus, 54
Falco ernesti, 54
Falco guttatus, 53
Falco haliaetus, 34
Falco ichthyaetus, 42
Falco indicus, 47
Falco interstinctus, 53
Falco leucogaster, 39
Falco limnaeetus, 52
Falco melanoleucus, 43
Falco peregrinus calidus, 54
Falco peregrinus ernesti, 54
Falco severus, 53
Falco severus severus, 53
Falco soloensis, 46
Falco tinnunculus interstinctus, 53
Falcon, Peregrine, *54,* pl. 13
Falconet, Philippine, *53,* pl. 13
FALCONIDAE, *53-54*
FALCONS, *53-54*
fallax, Hyloterpe, 354
    Pachycephala philippinensis, 354
Fantail, Black and Cinnamon, *328,* pl. 69
    Blue, *326,* pl. 69
    Blue-headed, *327,* pl. 69
    Malaysian, *328,* pl. 69
fasciata, Rallina, 68, 68
    Turnix suscitator, 59
fasciatus, Hemipodius, 59
fasciolata, Locustella, 316
fasciolatus, Acrocephalus, 316
    Cacomantis sonneratii, 155
    Cuculus, 155
fastosa, Pitta, 226
faustinoi, Neoleucotreron merrilli, 122
    Ptilinopus merrilli, 122
ferina, Anas, 31
    Aythya, 31
ferruginea, Calidris, 101
    Tringa, 101
Ficedula basilanica basilanica, 337
Ficedula basilanica samarensis, 337
Ficedula crypta crypta, 337
Ficedula crypta disposita, 337

Ficedula cyanomelana cyanomelana, 339
Ficedula hyperythra calayensis, 336
Ficedula hyperythra daggayana, 336, 336
Ficedula hyperythra luzoniensis, 331
Ficedula hyperythra malindangensis, 336, 336
Ficedula hyperythra montigena, 336
Ficedula hyperythra nigrorum, 336
Ficedula mugimaki, 331
Ficedula narcissina narcissina, 330
Ficedula platenae, 338
Ficedula westermanni palawanensis, 338
Ficedula westermanni westermanni, 338
filipina, Porzana plumbea, 69
    Treron formosae, 114, 114
Finch, Green-faced Parrot-, *410,* pl. 84
    Green-tailed Parrot-, *410,* pl. 84
    Malaysian, *416,* pl. 85
    Mindanao Parrot-, *410,* pl. 84
FINCHES, *415-417*
FINCHES, GRASS, *409-411, 414-415*
finitima, Zosterops montana, 404
flagrans, Aethopyga, 379, 379, *382,* 382
    Aethopyga flagrans, 379
flammea, Strix, 177
flammeus, Asio, 177
    Asio flammeus, 177
    Pericrocotus, 241, 244, 244
    Pericrocotus johnstoniae, 241
flammifera, Arachnothera, 384
    Arachnothera longirostra, 384
flava, Motacilla, 355, 355, *358*
flavicollis, Ardea, 10
    Dupetor, 10
    Dupetor flavicollis, 10
flavigularis, Cryptolopha, 319
flavipectus, Aethopyga, 383
    Aethopyga shelleyi, 383
flavipennis, Chloropsis, 287, 287
    Chloropsis flavipennis, 287
    Phyllornis, 287
flavissima, Zosterops, 407
flaviventer, Dicaeum, 394
flavostriatus, Phylloscopus trivirgatus,
    318, 318
flavum, D(icaeum), 399
florensis, Athene, 176
    Ninox scutalata, 176
Flowerpecker, Bicolored, *389,* p. 81
    Fire-throated, *398,* pl. 82
    Four-colored, *389,* pl. 81
    Gray-breasted, *387,* pl. 81
    Mindoro, *394,* pl. 82
    Olive-backed, *385,* pl. 81
    Olive-capped, *387,* pl. 81
    Orange-breasted, *394,* pl. 82
    Palawan Yellow-rumped, *386,* pl. 81
    Philippine, *394,* pl. 82

Pygmy, *397*, pl. 82
Striped, *386*, pl. 81
White-bellied, *396*, pl. 82
Yellow-crowned, *388*, pl. 81
FLOWERPECKERS, *385-389, 394-399*
flumenicola, Ceyx, 198
Ceyx argentatus, 198
fluviatilis, Chlidonias hybrida, 105
Hydrochelidon, 105
Flycatcher, Black and Orange, *331*, pl. 70
Black Paradise, *350*, pl. 73
Blue Paradise, *350*, pl. 73
Blue-breasted, *339*, pl. 71
Brown, *346*, pl. 72
Citrine Canary, *347*, pl. 72
Ferruginous, *341*, pl. 72
Goodfellow's Jungle, *330*, pl. 69
Gray-headed Canary, *347*, pl. 71
Gray-spotted, *341*, pl. 72
Hill Blue, *339*, pl. 71
Japanese Blue, *339*, pl. 71
Little Pied, *338*, pl. 70
Little Slaty, *337*, pl. 70
Luzon Jungle, *330*, pl. 69
Mangrove Blue, *340*, pl. 71
Narcissus, *330*, pl. 70
Palawan, *338*, pl. 70
Rufous Paradise, *349*, pl. 73
Rufous-tailed Jungle, *329*, pl. 69
Sooty, *341*, pl. 72
Thicket, *331*, pl. 70
Vaurie's, *337*, pl. 70
Verditer, *346*, pl. 72
White-throated Jungle, *328*, pl. 69
FLYCATCHERS, OLD WORLD *326-331, 336-341,*
346-351, 354-355
forbesi, Megalurus palustris, 309, 309
Zosterops, 405
formosae, Treron, 114, 114, 115
formosana, Lonchura malacca, 414
Munia, 414
formosus, Hieraaetus kieneri, 52, 52
fortichi, Ptilocichla mindanensis, 263, 263
Fowl, Jungle, *56*, pl. 14
Francolin, Chinese, *55*, pl. 14
Francolinus pintadeanus pintadeanus, 55
frater, Criniger, 278
Criniger bres, 278
Eudynamis [sic], 160
Eudynamys scolopacea, 160
freeri, Tanygnathus, 148
Tanygnathus sumatranus, 148
Fregata ariel ariel, 5
Fregata minor minor, 5
FREGATIDAE, 5
freycinet, Megapodius, 54, 54, 55
Frigatebird, Greater, *5*, pl. 2
Lesser, *5*, pl. 2

FRIGATEBIRDS, 5
Fringilla amandava, 409
Fringilla minuta, 414
Fringilla montifringilla, 415, 415
Fringilla spinus, 416
FRINGILLIDAE, *415-417*
Frogmouth, Java, *178*, pl. 40
Philippine, *177*, pl. 40
FROGMOUTHS, *177-178*
frontalis, Callisitta, 257, 258
Orthotomus, 324
Orthotomus atrogularis, 324
Phabotreron, 120
Phapitreron amethystina, 120
Sitta, 257, 257, *258,* 258
fuciphaga, Collocalia, 183
fugaensis, Ducula aenea, 124
Muscadivores aenea, 124
Oriolus chinensis, 251
fugax, Cuculus, 154
fugensis, Hypsipetes, 286
Hypsipetes amaurotis, 286
Fulica atra, 76
Fulica atra atra, 76
Fulica cinerea, 75
fuliginosus, Mulleripicus, 217
Mulleripicus funebris, 217
Otus bakkamoena, 169
Scops, 169
fuligula, Anas, 31
Aythya, 31
mariloides, 34
fulva, Pluvialis dominica, 78
fulvifasciatus, Dendrocopos maculatus, 219
Iyngipicus, 219
fulvus, Charadrius, 78
funebris, Mulleripicus, 217, 217
Mulleripicus funebris, 217
Picus, 217
fusca, Porzana, 69
Porzana fusca, 69
fuscans, Lonchura, 414
Spermestes, 414
fuscata, Sterna, 111
fuscus, Rallus, 69

G

G(algulus) philippinensis, 279
Gallicolumba luzonica criniger, 138
Gallicolumba luzonica griseolateralis,
138, 138
Gallicolumba luzonica keayi, 138
Gallicolumba luzonica leytensis, 139
Gallicolumba luzonica luzonica, 138
Gallicolumba luzonica menagei, 139
Gallicolumba luzonica platenae, 138
Gallicrex cinerea, 75

gallinacea, Irediparra, 76, 76
    Irediparra gallinacea, 76
    Parra, 76
gallinago, Gallinago, 95
    Gallinago gallinago, 95
    Scolopax, 95
Gallinago gallinago gallinago, 95
Gallinago megala, 94, 94
Gallinago stenura, 95
Gallinula chloropus lozanoi, 75, 75
Gallinula eurizonoides, 68
Gallinula javanica, 74
Gallinula olivacea, 74
Gallinule, 75, pl. 18
gallus, Gallus, 56, 56
    Gallus gallus, 56
    Phasianus, 56
Gallus gallus gallus, 56
Gallus gallus philippensis, 56
garzetta, Egretta, 20
Gelochelidon nilotica nilotica, 105
Geocichla cinerea, 300
Geocichla mindanensis, 300
Geokichla interpres minima, 297
Geopelia striata striata, 133
germani, Collocalia, 183
    Collocalia fuciphaga, 183
Gerygone rhizophorae, 303
Gerygone simplex, 303
Gerygone sulphurea simplex, 303
gigantea, Chaetura, 187, 187
    Chaetura gigantea, 187
    Pelargopsis, 200
    Pelargopsis capensis, 200
giganteus, Cypselus, 187
gilli, Zosterops montana, 404, 404
gilliardi, Parus elegans, 255, 255
gironieri, Leucotreron, 123
    Ptilinopus leclancheri, 123
glareola, Tringa, 92, 92
Glareola maldivarum, 103, 103
GLAREOLIDAE, 103
glaucocauda, Ducula aenea, 124
Godwit, Bar-tailed, 88, pl. 21
    Black-tailed, 88, pl. 21
goiavier, Muscicapa, 278
    Pycnonotus, 278, 278
    Pycnonotus goiavier, 278
goisagi, Gorsachius, 11
    Nycticorax, 11
gonzalesi, Pericrocotus flammeus, 244, 244
goodfellowi, Ceyx, 198
    Lophozosterops, 408, 408
    Lophozosterops goodfellowi, 408
    Rhinomyias, 330, 330
    Zosterops, 408
Goodfellowia miranda, 368
Gorsachius goisagi, 11

Gorsachius melanolophus kutteri, 18, 18
Gorsachius melanolophus rufolineatus, 18, 18
Goshawk, Crested, 46, pl. 11
gouldi, Pelargopsis, 200
    Pelargopsis capensis, 200
gracilis, Lophozosterops goodfellowi, 408
Gracula calva, 368
Gracula cristatella, 368
Gracula religiosa palawanensis, 369
grandis, Chrysocolaptes lucidus, 221, 221
    Rhabdornis, 259
    Rhabdornis inornatus, 259
GRASS FINCHES, 409-411, 414-415
Graucalus guillemardi, 235
Graucalus kochii, 234
Graucalus sumatrensis difficilis, 234
Graybird, Barred, 234, pl. 51
    Black, 235, pl. 51
    Moluccan, 238, pl. 51
    Sharp-tailed, 239, pl. 51
    White-winged, 239, pl. 51
Grebe, Black-necked, 1, pl. 1
    Eared, 1, pl. 1
GREBES, 1
Greenshank, 89, pl. 22
    Spotted, 89, pl. 22
gregalis, Lonchura malacca, 414
griseatus, Caprimulgus, 182
    Caprimulgus affinis, 182
griseigularis, Anthothreptus, 373
    Anthreptes malacensis, 373
griseipectus, Pseudotharrhaleus, 309
    Ptilocolpa, 130
griseisticta, Hemichelidon, 341
    Muscicapa, 341
griseogularis, Columba vitiensis, 131
    Ianthoenas, 131
griseolateralis, Gallicolumba luzonica, 138, 138
GROSBEAKS, 415-417
Ground-babbler, Ashy-headed, 262, pl. 56
    Falcated, 264, pl. 56
    Streaked, 263, pl. 56
GRUIDAE, 66
Grus antigone sharpii, 66, 66
Guaiabero, 148, pl. 34
guillemardi, Coracina striata, 235
    Graucalus, 235
guimarasensis, Aethopyga flagrans, 379
    Cinnyris, 379
    Hypsipetes philippinus, 284
    Iole, 284
    Pardaliparus elegans, 255
gularis, Accipiter, 43
    Alcedo, 201
    Astur (Nisus), 43
    Halcyon smyrnensis, 201

Macronous, 268, 269
    Philedon, 279
    Rhinomyias, 328
gulgula, Alauda, 227
Gull, Black-headed, *104*, pl. 26
    Herring, *104*, pl. 26
GULLS, *104-105, 110-111, 114*
gurneyi, Mimizuku, 169
    Pseudoptynx, 169
gustavi, Anthus, 359, 359
    Anthus gustavi, 359
gutierrezi, Streptopelia dusumieri, 132
guttata, Dendrocygna, 26, 26
guttatus, Falco, 53
guttifer, Totanus, 89
guttifera, Tringa, 89
gutturalis, Hirundo, 232
    Hirundo rustica, 232

H

hachisuka, Lanius validirostris, 364, 364
haemacephala, Megalaema, 213, 216
    Megalaima, 213, 216
    Megalaima haemacephala, 213
haemacephalus, Bucco, 213
Haemataena melanocephala enantia, 123
haematostictum, Dicaeum, 394
    Dicaeum australe, 394
haematribon, Chrysocolaptes lucidus, 220
    Picus, 220
haematuropygia, Kakatoe, 140, 140
haematuropygius, Psittacus, 140
halconensis, Zosterops, 404
    Zosterops montana, 404
Halcyon alfredi, 203
Halcyon chloris collaris, 200
Halcyon coromanda bangsi, 201
Halcyon coromanda major, 201
Halcyon coromanda minor, 201
Halcyon hombroni, 206
Halcyon lindsayi lindsayi, 203
Halcyon lindsayi moseleyi, 206
Halcyon pileata, 202
Halcyon pileata palawanensis, 202
Halcyon smyrnensis gularis, 201
Halcyon winchelli, 202
Halcyon winchelli alfredi, 203
Halcyon winchelli mindanensis, 202, 202
Halcyon winchelli nesydrionetes, 203, 203
Halcyon winchelli nigrorum, 203, 203
Halcyon winchelli winchelli, 202
Haliaeetus leucogaster, 39
haliaetus, Falco, 34
    Pandion, 34, 35, 35
    Pandion haliaetus, 34
Haliaetus lineatus, 39
Haliastur intermedius, 39
Haliastus indus intermedius, 39

halodramus, Thalasseus bergii, 111
hanadori, Dicaeum dorsale, 396
hargitti, Dryocopus javensis, 218
    Thriponax, 218
Harpactes ardens ardens, 189
Harpactes ardens herberti, 190, 190
Harpactes ardens linae, 189, 189
Harpactes ardens luzoniensis, 190, 190
Harpactes ardens minor, 190, 190
Harpactes rodiosternus, 189
Harrier, Marsh, *42*, pl. 10
    Pied, *43*, pl. 10
harringtoni, Dryococcyx, 160
    Phoenicophaeus curvirostris, 160
harterti, Acrocephalus arundinaceus, 317
    Acrocephalus stentoreus, 317
hartlaubi, Loriculus, 151
Hawk, Asiatic Sparrow, *43*, pl. 11
    Crested Lizard, *35*, pl. 9
    Gray Frog, *46*, pl. 11
    Philippine Sparrow, *43*, pl. 11
Hawk-cuckoo, Horsfield's, *154*, pl. 35
    Large, *154*, pl. 35
    Short-winged, *154*, pl. 35
HAWKS, *35, 38-39, 42-43, 46-47, 52*
haynaldi, Criniger, 285
    Hypsipetes everetti, 285
    Turnix, 59
helenae, Cyanomyias, 348
    Hypothymis, 348, 349, 349
    Hypothymis helenae, 348
helianthea, Culicicapa, 347, 347
heliolusius, Anthreptes malacensis, 372, 372
Hemichelidon cinereiceps, 341
Hemichelidon griseisticta, 341
Hemipodius fasciatus, 59
Hemiprocne comata barbarae, 189
Hemiprocne comata major, 189
Hemiprocne comata nakamurai, 189
HEMIPROCNIDAE, *189*
henkei, Cinnyris, 374
    Nectarinia sperata, 374
herberti, Harpactes ardens, 190, 190
herioti, Cyornis, 339, 339
    Cyornis herioti, 339
    Muscicapa, 339
Herodias eulophotes, 20
Heron, Black-crowned Night, *22*, pl. 5
    Chinese Pond, *19*, pl. 4
    Giant, *21*, pl. 5
    Gray, *21*, pl. 5
    Little Mangrove, *18*, pl. 4
    Purple, *21*, pl. 5
    Rufous Night, *22*, pl. 5
HERONS, *10-11, 18-22*
heterogynus, Copsychus saularis, 294
heterolaemus, Orthotomus atrogularis, 324
    Orthotomus cucullatus, 321

heterolaemus (cont.)

   Phyllergates, 321

Hieraaetus kieneri formosus, 52, 52

Hierax erythrogonys, 53

himantopus, Himantopus, 102

Himantopus himantopus leucocephalus, 102

Himantopus leucocephalus, 102

Hiracococcyx pectoralis, 154

hirsuta, Strix, 176

HIRUNDINIDAE, *232-233*

hirundo, Sterna, 110

Hirundo caudacuta, 187

Hirundo gutturalis, 232

Hirundo pacificus, 188

Hirundo rustica gutturalis, 232

Hirundo rustica saturata, 232

Hirundo saturata, 232

Hirundo striolata, 233

Hirundo striolata striolata, 233

Hirundo tahitica abbotti, 233

Hobby, Oriental, *53*, pl. 13

hodgsoni, Anthus, 359, 359

   Anthus hodgsoni, 359

holospilus, Buteo, 42

   Spilornis, 42

hombroni, Actenoides, 206

   Halcyon, 206

homeyeri, Hyloterpe, 351

   Pachycephala cinerea, 351

hoogstraali, Irena cyanogaster, 290, 290

Hoopoe, *207*, pl. 46

HOOPOES, 207

Hornbill, Palawan, *212*, pl. 47

   Rufous, *212*, pl. 47

   Sulu, *212*, pl. 47

   Tarictic, *210*, pl. 47

   Writhed-billed, *211*, pl. 47

HORNBILLS, *210-213*

horrisonus, Tanygnathus lucionensis, 142

horsfieldi, Cuculus, 155

   Cuculus saturatus, 155

hottentottus, Dicrurus, 245, 248, 248

humilis, Columba, 132

   Streptopelia tranquebarica, 132

hutchinsoni, Rhipidura, 328

   Rhipidura nigrocinnamomea, 328

hybrida, Chlidonias, 105

hybridus, Tanygnathus lucionensis, 143, 143

Hydrochelidon fluviatilis, 105

hydrocorax, Buceros, 212, 212, 213

   Buceros hydrocorax, 212

   Hydrocorax, 213

Hydrocorax hydrocorax basilanica, 213

Hydrophasianus chirurgus, 76

Hydroprogne caspia, 105

Hyloterpe albiventris, 351

Hyloterpe apoensis, 354

Hyloterpe apoensis basilanica, 355

Hyloterpe crissalis, 350

Hyloterpe fallax, 354

Hyloterpe homeyeri, 351

Hyloterpe illex, 354

Hyloterpe major, 351

Hyloterpe mindorensis, 351

Hyloterpe philippinensis, 354

Hyloterpe plateni, 351

Hyloterpe whiteheadi, 351

Hyloterpe winchelli, 351

hyperythra, Erythrura, 410

   Ficedula, 331, 336, 336

   Muscicapa, 331

   Muscicapula, 331

hyperythrus, Cuculus, 154

   Cuculus fugax, 154

Hypocryptadius cinnamomeus, 408, 408

Hypocryptadius cinnamomeus malindangensis,
   408

Hypocryptadius cinnamomeus pallidigula,
   408

hypogrammica, Stachyris, 268, 268

hypoleucos, Tringa, 92, 92

hypoleucum, Dicaeum, 396, 396, 397, 397

   Dicaeum hypoleucum, 397

hypoleucus, Elanus, 38

   Elanus caeruleus, 38

Hypotaenidia striata paraterma, 66

Hypothymis azurae [sic]*catarmanensis*, 348

Hypothymis azurea azurea, 348

Hypothymis azurea catarmanensis, 348

Hypothymis azurea compilator, 348

Hypothymis coelestis, 349, 349

Hypothymis coelestis rabori, 349

Hypothymis helenae agusanae, 349, 349

Hypothymis helenae helenae, 348

Hypothymis occipitalis, 348

Hypothymis samarensis, 327

Hypothymis superciliaris, 326

Hypsipetes amaurotis batanensis, 286

Hypsipetes amaurotis camiguinensis, 286

Hypsipetes amaurotis fugensis, 286

Hypsipetes batanensis, 286

Hypsipetes camiguinensis, 286

Hypsipetes everetti catarmanensis, 285, 285

Hypsipetes everetti everetti, 285

Hypsipetes everetti haynaldi, 285

Hypsipetes everetti samarensis, 285, 285

Hypsipetes fugensis, 286

Hypsipetes palawanensis, 279

Hypsipetes philippensis, 279

Hypsipetes philippinus guimarasensis, 284

Hypsipetes philippinus mindorensis, 284

Hypsipetes philippinus philippinus, 279

Hypsipetes rufigularis, 284, 284

Hypsipetes siquijorensis cinereiceps, 285

Hypsipetes siquijorensis monticola, 284

Hypsipetes siquijorensis siquijorensis, 284

Hyptiopus magnirostris, 35
Hypurolepis javanica abbotti, 233
Hypurolepis javanica mallopega, 233

I

Ianthoenas griseogularis, 131
ibis, Bubulcus, 19
Ibis, Glossy, *23*, pl. 6
    White, *22*, pl. 6
Ibis peregrina, 23
IBISES, *22-23*
ichthyaetus, Falco, 42
    Ichthyophaga, 42
    Ichthyophaga ichthyaetus, 42
igneus, P(ericrocotus), 241
    Pericrocotus cinnamomeus, 241
ignipectus, Dicaeum, 398, 399
igorotus, Dendrocopus moluccensis, 219
ijimae, Clivicola riparia, 232
    Riparia riparia, 232
illex, Hyloterpe, 354
    Pachycephala philippinensis, 354
ilokensis, Pycnonotus urostictus, 277, 277
incanas, Tringa, 93
INCERTAE SEDIS, *408-409*
incognita, Ptilopus, 121
indica, Chalcophaps, 133
    Chalcophaps indica, 133
    Columba, 133
    Motacilla, 355
indicus, Butastur, 47
    Caprimulgus, 179
    Dendronanthus, 355
    Falco, 47
indus, Haliastus, 39
inexpectatum, Dicaeum bicolor, 389
inexpectatus, Prionochilus, 389
inornatus, Rhabdornis, 259, 259, 260, 260
    Rhabdornis inornatus, 259
insignis, Callisitta frontalis, 257
    Rhinomyias, 330, 330
intermedia, Ardea, 20
    Dicaeum, 395
    Dicaeum trigonostigma, 395
    Egretta, 20
    Egretta intermedia, 20
    Megalaima haemacephala, 216
    Xantholaema, 216
intermedius, Bolbopsittacus, 149
    Bolbopsittacus lunulatus, 149
    Haliastur, 39
    Haliastus indus, 39
interpes, Arenaria, 93
    Arenaria interpes, 93
    Tringa, 93
interpres, Geokichla, 297
    Turdus, 297
    Zoothera, 297

    Zoothera interpres, 297
interstinctus, Falco, 53
    Falco tinnunculus, 53
Iole cinereiceps, 285
Iole guimarasensis, 284
Iole mindorensis, 284
Iole monticola, 284
Iole philippinus saturatior, 279
Iole siquijorensis, 284
Iole striaticeps, 279
Iora, Black-winged, *286*, pl. 61
Irediparra gallinacea gallinacea, 76
Irediparra gallinacea nakamurai, 76
Irena cyanogaster, 290
Irena cyanogaster cyanogaster, 290
Irena cyanogaster ellae, 290
Irena cyanogaster hoogstraali, 290, 290
Irena cyanogaster melanochlamys, 290
Irena ellae, 290
Irena melanochlamys, 290
Irena puella tweeddalei, 287
Irena tweeddalei, 287
IRENIDAE, *286-287*, 290
iris, Anthreptes malacensis, 373, 373
isabelae, Stachyris capitalis, 266, 266
isabellae, Oriolus, 250, 250
isag, Dicaeum, 387
isarog, Sitta frontalis, 257, 257
isidroi, Dicaeum trigonostigma, 396, 396
isonota, Collocalia esculenta, 186
    Collocalia linchi, 186
Ixobrychus cinnamomeus, 11
Ixobrychus eurhythmus, 11
Ixobrychus sinensis astrologus, 10
Ixobrychus sinensis sinensis, 10
Iyngipicus fulvifasciatus, 219
Iyngipicus menagei, 220
Iyngipicus ramsayi, 220

J

Jacana, Comb-crested, 76, pl. 19
    Pheasant-tailed, 76, pl. 19
JACANAS, *76*
JACANIDAE, *76*
Jaeger, Pomarine, *103*, pl. 25
jagori, Lonchura malacca, 414
    Munia (Dermophrys), 414
    Oxycerca (Uroloncha), 411
japonensis, Buteo buteo, 47
    Faclo [sic] *buteo, 47*
japonica, Coturnix coturnix, 56
    Coturnix vulgaris, 56
    Ninox scutulata, 176
    Strix hirsuta, 176
javanense, Dinopium, 216
javanica, Ardea, 18
    Chlidonias hybrida, 105
    Gallinula, 74

javanica (cont.)
    Hypurolepis, 233
    Mirafra, 227
    Rhipidura, *328*
    Sterna, 105
javanicus, Amaurornis phoenicurus, 74
javensis, Batrachostomus, 178, 178
    Butorides striatus, 18, 19
    Dryocopus, 217, 218, 218, *219*
    Thriponax, 217, 219
jefferyi, Aethopyga pulcherrima, 382
    Eudrepanis, 382
    Pithecophaga, 47, 47
jerdoni, Aviceda, 35
johannae, Prionochilus, 386
johnsoni, Caprimulgus macrurus, 179, 179
johnstoniae, Pericrocotus, 241
    Pericrocotus flammeus, 241
    Trichoglossus, 139, 139, *140*, 140
    Trichoglossus johnstoniae, 139
Jole schmackeri, 284
jotaka, Caprimulgus, 179
    Caprimulgus indicus, 179
jouyi, Ardea cinerea, 21, 21
jugularis, Certhia, 375
    Cyrtostomus, 375, *378*
    Nectarinia, 375, *378*
    Nectarinia jugularis, 375
juliae, Nectarinia sperata, 374
    Nectarophila, 374
juncidis, Cisticola, 311, 311
Jungle Fowl, *56*, pl. 14

K

Kakatoe haematuropygia, 140
Kakatoe haematuropygia mcgregori, 140
kampalili, Dicaeum anthonyi, 388
katanglad, Turdus poliocephalus, 302, 302
keayi, Gallicolumba luzonica, 138
    Phlegoenas, 138
kelleri, Merula, 302
    Turdus poliocephalus, 302
Kestrel, *53*, pl. 13
kettlewelli, Macronous, 269
    Macronous striaticeps, 269
kieneri, Hieraaetus, 52, 52
Kingfisher, Black-capped, *202*, pl. 45
    Dwarf River, *191*, pl. 44
    Hombron's, *206*, pl. 45
    Malay Forest, *198*, pl. 44
    Malaysian, *191*, pl. 44
    Philippine Forest, *199*, pl. 44
    River, *190*, pl. 44
    Ruddy, *201*, pl. 45
    Silvery, *198*, pl. 44
    Spotted Wood, *203*, pl. 45
    Stork-billed, *200*, pl. 45
    Variable Forest, *198*, pl. 44

    White-collared, *200*, pl. 45
    White-throated, *201*, pl. 45
    Winchell's, *202*, pl. 45
KINGFISHERS, *190-191, 198-203, 206*
Kite, Black-eared, *39*, pl. 9
    Black-winged, *38*, pl. 9
    Brahminy, *39*, pl. 10
Kittacincla parvimaculata, 295
Knot, *95*, pl. 23
    Great, *100*, pl. 23
kochi, Pitta, 225, 225
kochii, Coracina striata, 234
    Graucalus, 234
Koel, *160*, pl. 36
koikei, Tanygnathus lucionensis, 143
Kurukuru temminckii, 123
kutteri, Butio, 18
    Gorsachius melanolophus, 18, 18

L

laeta, Zosterops, 405
lagunae, Dicaeum hypoleucum, 396
Lalage melanoleuca melanoleuca, 239
Lalage melanoleuca minor, 240
Lalage nigra chilensis, 240
Lalage nigra mitifica, 240
Lalage schisticeps, 240
Lamprocorax todayensis, 364
lanceolata, Locustella, 316
    Sylvia, 316
langhornei, Ducula pickeringii, 125
    Muscadivora, 125
LANIIDAE, *360-361, 364*
Lanius cristatus, 361
Lanius cristatus cristatus, 361
Lanius cristatus lucionensis, 360
Lanius cristatus superciliosus, 361
Lanius divaricatus, 240
Lanius leucoryn(chus), 360
Lanius lucionensis, 360
Lanius nasutus, 361
Lanius schach nasutus, 361
Lanius schach suluensis, 361
Lanius superciliosus, 361
Lanius tigrinus, 360, 360
Lanius validirostris, 361
Lanius validirostris hachisuka, 364, 364
Lanius validirostris quartus, 364
Lanius validirostris tertius, 364, 364
Lanius validirostris validirostris, 361
lapponica, Limosa, 88
Lapwing, Gray-headed, *77*, pl. 19
LARIDAE, *104-105, 110-111, 114*
Lark, Bush, 227, pl. 50
LARKS, *227*
Larus argentatus, 104
Larus argentatus vegae, 104
Larus ridibundus, 104, 104

latirostris, Muscicapa, *346*, 346
Leafbird, Palawan, *287*, pl. 61
    Yellow-billed, *287*, pl. 61
LEAFBIRDS, 286-287, 290
leclancheri, Leucotreron, 123
    Ptilinopus, 122, 123
    Ptilinopus leclancheri, 122
    Tererolaema, 122
lecroyae, Coracina morio, *238*, 238
Lempijius megalotis, 168
lemprieri, Anthracoceros, 212
    Cyornis, *339*, 339
Leonardina woodi, *262*, 262
lepidus, Ceyx, *198*
lepturus, Phaethon, *3*, 3
leschenaultii, Charadrius, *84*, 84
Lestris pomarinus, 103
leucocephalus, Aceros, *211*, 212
    Aceros leucocephalus, 212
    Buceros, 212
    Himantopus, 102
    Himantopus himantopus, 102
leucogaster, Falco, 39
    Haliaeetus, 39
    Sula, 4
leucogastra, Lonchura, *411*, 411
leucogenys, Pyrrhula, *417*, 417
    Pyrrhula leucogenys, 417
leucomelas, Procellaria, 1
    Puffinus, 1
leucophaeus, Dicrurus, *244*, 244
    Dicrurus leucophaeus, 244
leucopias, Baza, 35
leucoptera, Chlidonias, 104
    Sterna, 104
leucorhynchus, Artamus, *360*
    Artamus leucorhynchus, 360
leucoryn(chus), Lanius, 360
leucotis, Columba, 118
    Phapitreron, *118*, 118, *119*, 119
    Phapitreron leucotis, 118
Leucotreron gironieri, 123
Leucotreron leclancheri longialis, 123
Leucotreron leclancheri palawana, 123
Leucotreron merrilli, 121
Leucotreron occipitalis brevipes, 121
leytensis, Dendrocopos maculatus, 219
    Gallicolumba luzonica, 139
    Micromacronus, *276*, 276
    Micromacronus leytensis, 276
    Penelopides panini, 211
    Pericrocotus, 241
    Pericrocotus flammeus, 241
    Phlegoenas criniger, 139
    Yungipicus, 219
lilacea, Dendrophila, 258
    Sitta frontalis, 258
Limicola falcinellus sibirica, 102

Limicola sibirica, 102
limnaeetus, Falco, 52
    Spizaetus cirrhatus, 52
Limnocryptes minimus, 94
Limnodromus semipalmatus, 94
limosa, Limosa, 88
Limosa baueri, 88
Limosa lapponica baueri, 88
Limosa limosa melanuroides, 88
Limosa melanuroides, 88
limucon, Phapitreron leucotis, 119
linae, Harpactes ardens, *189*, 189
linchi, Collocalia, 186
lindsayi, Dacelo, 203
    Halcyon, *203*, 206
    Halcyon lindsayi, 203
lineata, Coturnix chinensis, 56
lineatus, Haliaetus, 39
    Milvus migrans, 39
    Oriolus, 56
litoralis, Cyornis rufigaster, 340
    Cyornis rufigastra, 340
lobatus, Phalaropus, 102
Locustella certhiola ochotensis, 316
Locustella fasciolata, 316
Locustella lanceolata, 316
Lonchura fuscans, 414
Lonchura leucogastra everetti, 411
Lonchura leucogastra manueli, *411*, 411
Lonchura leucogastra palawana, *411*, 411
Lonchura malacca formosana, 414
Lonchura malacca gregalis, 414
Lonchura malacca jagori, 414
Lonchura punctulata cabanisi, 411
longialis, Leucotreron leclancheri, 123
    Ptilinopus leclancheri, 123
longicornis, Otus scops, *167*
    Scops, 167
longipennis, Sterna, 110
    Sterna hirundo, 110
longirostra, Arachnothera, 384
longirostris, Arachnothera, 384
    Rhabdornis, 258, 259
    Upupa, 207
    Upupa epops (?), 207
Lophozosterops goodfellowi goodfellowi, *408*
Lophozosterops goodfellowi gracilis, 408
Lophozosterops goodfellowi malindangensis, 408
Loriculus apicalis, 151
Loriculus bonapartei, 151
Loriculus bournsi, 150
Loriculus chrysonotus, 150
Loriculus hartlaubi, 151
Loriculus mindorensis, 149
Loriculus panayensis, 150
Loriculus philippensis apicalis, *151*
Loriculus philippensis bonapartei, *151*

Loriculus philippensis bournsi, 150
Loriculus philippensis chrysonotus, 150
Loriculus philippensis dohertyi, *151*, 151
Loriculus philippensis mindorensis, *149*
Loriculus philippensis panayensis, 150
Loriculus philippensis philippensis, *149*
Loriculus philippensis regulus, 150
Loriculus philippensis siquijorensis, 150
Loriculus philippensis worcesteri, 150
Loriculus regulus, 150
Loriculus salvadorii, 151
Loriculus siquijorensis, 150
Loriculus worcesteri, 150
Lorikeet, Mindanao, *139*, pl.33
lowi, *Collocalia*, 183
lowii, *Megapodius*, 55
    Sarcops, 369
    Sarcops calvus, *369*
Loxia curvirostra luzoniensis, *417*
Loxia luzoniensis, 417
Loxia oryzivora, 414
lozanoi, *Gallinula chloropus*, 75, *75*
lucidus, *Chrysocolaptes*, 220, *220*, *221*, 221
    Chrysocolaptes lucidus, 221
    Picus, 221
lucionensis, *Lanius*, 360
    Lanius cristatus, *360*
    Psittacus, 143
    Tanygnathus, *142*, 142, *143*, 143
    Tanygnathus lucionensis, *143*
luconensis, *Prionturus*, *142*, 142
lugubris, *Anthus novaeseelandiae*, *358*
    Corydalla, 358
    Surniculus, *159*, 159, *160*, 160
lunulatus, *Bolbopsittacus*, *148*, *149*, 149
    Bolbopsittacus lunulatus, 148
    Psittacus, 148
luteoventris, *Bradypterus*, *308*, 308
luzonensis, *Arachnothera clarae*, *385*, 385
    Phylloscopus cebuensis, *319*
    Phylloscopus olivaceus, 319
luzonica, *Anas*, *30*, 30
    Columba, 138
    Gallicolumba, *138*, 138, *139*
    Gallicolumba luzonica, *138*
    Zosterops, 406
    Zosterops nigrorum, *406*
luzoniense, *Dicaeum*, 398
    Dicaeum ignipectus, *398*
luzoniensis, *Copsychus*, 295
    Copsychus luzoniensis, 295
    Ficedula hyperythra, 331
    Harpactes ardens, *190*, 190
    Loxia, 417
    Loxia curvirostra, *417*
    Muscicapula, 331
    Turdus, 295
Lyncornis mindanensis, 178

M

mcgregori, *Cisticola juncidis*, 311
    Coracina, 239
    Edolisoma, 239
    Kakatoe haematuropygia, 140
    Malindangia, 239
mcgregorii, *Treron formosae*, 115
Macronous gularis cagayanensis, 269
Macronous gularis woodi, 268
Macronous kettlewelli, 269
Macronous mindanensis, 269
Macronous mindanensis montanus, 269
Macronous striaticeps, 269
Macronous striaticeps boholensis, 269
Macronous striaticeps kettlewelli, 269
Macronous striaticeps mearnsi, 269
Macronous striaticeps mindanensis, 269
Macronous striaticeps striaticeps, 269
Macropteryx comata major, 189
Macropygia phaea, 132
Macropygia phasianella phaea, *132*
Macropygia phasianella tenuirostris, 131
Macropygia tenuirostris, 131
Macropygia tenuirostris septentrionalis, 132
Macrorhamphus semipalmatus, 94
macrorhynchos, *Corvus*, 254
macrotis, *Caprimulgus*, 178
    Eurostopodus, 178
    Eurostopodus macrotis, 178
macrurus, *Caprimulgus*, *179*, 179
maculatus, *Anthus*, 359
    Dendrocopos, 219, *220*
    Dendrocopos maculatus, 219
    Picus, 219
maculiceps, *Chrysocolaptes*, 221
maculipectus, *Phabotreron*, 120
    Phapitreron amethystina, *120*
madagascariensis, *Numenius*, 85
    Scolopax, 85
magnifica, *Aethopyga*, 384
    Aethopyga siparaja, *384*
magnirostris, *Aviceda jerdoni*, 35
    Charadrius, 103
    Esacus, *103*
    Hyptiopus, 35
Mainatus palawanensis, 369
major, *Halcyon coromanda*, *201*
    Hemiprocne comata, *189*
    Hyloterpe, 351
    Macropteryx comata, 189
    Nycticorax caledonicus, 22
malacca, *Lonchura*, *414*, 414
malaccensis, *Passer montanus*, *409*, 409
malacensis, *Anthreptes*, *372*, 372, *373*, 373
Malacopteron palawanense, *263*, 263
malamaui, *Ceyx*, 198
malayanus, *Chrysococcyx*, 158
    Chrysococcyx malayanus, *158*

Cuculus, 158
Malcoha, Palawan, *160*, pl. 36
maldivarum, Glareola, 103
    Glareola (Pratincola), 103
malindangensis, Aethopyga boltoni, 378, 378
    Arachnothera clarae, 385, 385
    Brachypteryx, 291
    Brachypteryx montana, 291
    Bradypterus caudatus, 309
    Cryptolopha, 318
    Ficedula hyperythra, 336, 336
    Hypocryptadius cinnamomeus, 408
    Lophozosterops goodfellowi, 408
    Merula, 301
    Phylloscopus trivirgatus, 318
    Prioniturus, 141
    Pseudotharrhaleus, 309
    Turdus poliocephalus, 301
    Zosterops goodfellowi, 408
Malindangia mcgregori, 239
Mallard, Philippine, *30*, pl. 7
mallopega, Hypurolepis javanica, 233
mandibularis, Zosterops everetti, 406, 406
manilensis, Ardea purpurea, 21, 21
manillensis, Caprimulgus, 179
    Caprimulgus macrurus, 179
    Nycticorax, 22
    Nycticorax caledonicus, 22
    Passer montanus, 409
manilloe, Buceros, 210
    Penelopides panini, 210
Mannikin, Chestnut, *414*, pl. 84
    Dusky, *414*, pl. 84
    Nutmeg, *411*, pl. 84
    White-breasted, *411*, pl. 84
MANNIKINS, *409-411, 414-415*
manobo, Chaetura gigantea, 187, 187
manueli, Cinnyris sperata, 373
    Lonchura leucogastra, 411, 411
marchei, Anthracoceros, 212, 212
    Ptilinopus, 122
    Ptilopus (Rhamphilculus), 122
marchesae, Pericrocotus, 244
    Pericrocotus flammeus, 244
margarethae, Ceyx, 198
    Ceyx lepidus, 198
marginata, Collocalia, 186
    Collocalia esculenta, 186
marila, Aythya, 34
mariloides, Aythya marila, 34
    Fuligula, 34
marinduquensis, Nectarinia sperata, 374, 374
Martin, Asiatic House, *233*, pl. 50
    Gray-breasted Sand, *232*, pl. 50
masaaki, Turnix sylvatica, 58, 58
masawan, Dicaeum anthonyi, 388, 388
mayonensis, Merula, 301
    Turdus poliocephalus, 301

mayri, Culicicapa helianthea, 347, 347
    Eurylaimus steerei, 224
    Eurylaimus steerii, 224
    Mulleripicus funebris, 217
mearnsi, Collocalia vestita, 183
    Macronous striaticeps, 269
    Orthotomus, 325
    Orthotomus atrogularis, 325
megala, Gallinago, 94, 94
Megalaema haemacephala celestinoi, 213
Megalaema haemacephala mindanensis, 216
Megalaima haemacephala celestinoi, 213
Megalaima haemacephala haemacephala, 213
Megalaima haemacephala intermedia, 216
Megalaima haemacephala mindanensis, 216
megalorynchos, Psittacus, 143
    Tanygnathus, 143
    Tanygnathus megalorynchos, 143
megalotis, Lempijius, 168
    Otus bakkamoena, 168
Megalurus palustris forbesi, 309, 309
Megalurus ruficeps, 310
Megalurus timoriensis alopex, 310, 310
Megalurus timoriensis crex, 310, 310
Megalurus timoriensis mindorensis, 310, 310
Megalurus timoriensis tweeddalei, 310
Megalurus tweeddalei, 310
Megapode, *54*, pl. 14
MEGAPODES, *54-55*
MEGAPODIIDAE, *54-55*
Megapodius cumingi balukensis, 54
Megapodius cumingii, 55
Megapodius dillwyni, 54
Megapodius freycinet cumingi, 55
Megapodius freycinet pusillus, 54
Megapodius freycinet tabon, 54
Megapodius lowii, 55
Megapodius pusillus, 54
Melaniparus semilarvatus, 256
melanocephala, Haemataena, 123
    Threskiornis aethiopica, 22
melanocephalus, Tantalus, 22
melanochlamys, Irena, 290
    Irena cyanogaster, 290
melanogaster, Anhinga, 5
    Anhinga rufa, 5
melanoleuca, Lalage, 239, 240
    Lalage melanoleuca, 239
    Muscicapula, 338
    Pseudolalage, 239
melanoleucus, Circus, 43
    Falco, 43
melanolophus, Gorsachius, 18, 18
melanonotus, Sarcops, 369
    Sarcops calvus, 369
melanops, Centropus, 163, 163
melanospila, Ptilinopus, 123
melanura, Alcedo, 199

melanuroides, Limosa, 88
    Limosa limosa, 88
melanurus, Ceyx, *199, 200*
    Ceyx melanurus, 199
Meliphaga mysticalis, 258
melvillensis, Pandion haliaetus, 35, 35
menagei, Batrachostomus, 177
    Batrachostomus septimus, 177
    Chibia, 248
    Dendrocopos maculatus, 220
    Dicrurus hottentottus, 248
    Gallicolumba luzonica, 139
    Iyngipicus, 220
    Phlogoenas, 139
meninting, Alcedo, 191, 191
meridionalis, Microhierax, 53
    Microhierax erythrogonys, 53
MEROPIDAE, *206-207*
Merops americanus, 206
Merops philippinus, 206
Merops philippinus philippinus, 206
Merops viridis americanus, 206
merrilli, Leucotreron, 121
    Neoleucotreron, 122
    Ptilinopus, 121, 122
    Ptilinopus merrilli, 121
Merula kelleri, 302
Merula malindangensis, 301
Merula mayonensis, 301
Merula thomassoni, 301
merulinus, Cacomantis, 158
    Cacomantis merulinus, 158
    Cuculus, 158
mesoleuca, Dendrophila, 257
    Sitta frontalis, 257
mesoluzonica, Napothera rabori, 264, 264
meyeni, Zosterops, 399, 399
    Zosterops meyeni, 399
meyleri, Zosterops, 407
    Zosterops nigrorum, 407
Micranous worcesteri, 114
Microhierax erythrogonys erythrogonys, 53
Microhierax erythrogonys meridionalis, 53
Microhierax meridionalis, 53
Micromacronus leytensis, 276
Micromacronus leytensis leytensis, 276
Micromacronus leytensis sordidus, 276, 276
micropterus, Cuculus, 154, 154
    Cuculus micropterus, 154
Micropus nehrkorni, 257
microrhynchus, Batrachostomus, 177
    Batrachostomus septimus, 177
migrans, Milvus, 39
Milvus migrans lineatus, 39
Mimizuku gurneyi, 169
mindanaoensis, Phapitreron amethystina, 120, 120
mindanense, Dicaeum, 397

mindanensis, Artamides, 234
    Bolbopsittacus lunulatus, 149
    Brachypteryx, 291
    Brachypteryx montana, 291
    Bubo philippensis, 174
    Buceros, 213
    Buceros hydrocorax, 213
    Caprimulgus affinis, 182, 182
    Ceyx, 200
    Chloropsis flavipennis, 287, 287
    Copsychus saularis, 295
    Coracina morio, 238
    Cryptolopha, 318
    Cuculus, 160
    Cyclopsitta, 149
    Cyrtostomus jugularis, 375
    Ducula carola, 131
    Eudynamys scolopacea, 160
    Geocichla, 300
    Halcyon winchelli, 202, 202
    Lyncornis, 178
    Macronous, 269
    Macronous striaticeps, 269
    Megalaema haemacephala, 216
    Megalaima haemacephala, 216
    Mirafra javanica, 227
    Mirafra philippensis, 227
    Muscicapula, 337
    Pardaliparus elegans, 255
    Parus elegans, 255
    Phylloscopus trivirgatus, 318
    Ptilocichla, 263, 263, *264*
    Ptilocichla mindanensis, 263
    Ptilocolpa, 131
    Ptilopyga, 263
    Rhinomyias ruficauda, 329
    Serinus, 416
    Serinus estherae, 416
    Turdus, 295
    Volvocivora, 238
mindorensis, Artamides, 234
    Carpophaga, 130
    Centrococcyx, 163
    Centropus viridis, 163
    Coracina striata, 234
    Cyornis, 340
    Cyornis rufigaster, 340
    Dicrurus balicassius, 244
    Dryocopus javensis, 218
    Ducula, 130
    Hyloterpe, 351
    Hypsipetes philippinus, 284
    Iole, 284
    Loriculus, 149
    Loriculus philippensis, 149
    Megalurus timoriensis, 310, 310
    Muscicapula hyperythra, 331
    Ninox, 175

Ninox philippensis, 175
Otus scops, 167
Pachycephala cinerea, 351
Penelopides, 210
Penelopides panini, 210
Phapitreron leucotis, 118
Prioniturus, 141
Prioniturus discurus, 141
Sarcops calvus, 369
Scops, 167
Surniculus lugubris, 159
Thriponax, 218
Turdus, 301
Turdus poliocephalus, 301
Zosterops nigrorum, 407, 407
minima, Cinnyris sperata, 373
Geokichla interpres, 297
Scolopax, 94
minimus, Limnocryptes, 94
Surniculus lugubris, 160, 160
Minivet, Ashy, *240,* pl. 52
Fiery, *241,* pl. 52
Flame, *241,* pl. 52
Minodoria striaticeps cumingi, 269
minor, Alcedo (Halcyon) coromanda, 201
Aplonis, 364
Fregata, 5
Fregata minor, 5
Halcyon coromanda, 201
Harpactes ardens, 190, 190
Lalage melanoleuca, 240
Pelecanus, 5
Platalea, 23, 23
Pseudolalage, 240
Rhabdornis, 259
Rhabdornis mysticalis, 259
Sarcops calvus, 369
minuta, Aethopyga, 383
Cettia, 308
Fringilla, 414
Ptilocichla, 263
Ptilocichla mindanensis, 263
minutus, Numenius, 84, 84
mirabilis, Dicrurus, 245
Dicrurus balicassius, 245
Mirafra javanica mindanensis, 227
Mirafra javanica philippensis, 227
Mirafra philippensis, 227
Mirafra philippensis mindanensis, 227
miranda, Basilornis, 368
Goodfellowia, 368
mirificus, Rallus, 67, 67
mirus, Otus scops, 168, 168
mitifica, Lalage nigra, 240
Mixornis cagayanensis, 269
Mixornis (?) capitalis, 266
Mixornis nigrocapitatus, 265
Mixornis plateni, 265

Mixornis woodi, 268
modesta, Ardea, 20
Egretta alba, 20
modestum, Dicaeum, 397
molkenboeri, Centropus, 162
moluccensis, Dryobates, 220
Pitta brachyura, 226
Turdus, 226
Monarch, Black-naped Blue, *348,* pl. 72
Celestial Blue, *349,* pl. 72
Short-crested Blue, *348,* pl. 72
mongolus, Charadrius, 79, 79
Charadrius mongolus, 79
montana, Brachypteryx, 290, 291, 291
Cettia, 308, 308
Zosterops, 404, 404, 405, 405
montani, Anthracoceros, 212
Buceros, 212
montanus, Chrysocolaptes, 221
Chrysocolaptes lucidus, 221
Macronous mindanensis, 269
Passer, 409, 409
Prioniturus, 141, 141, 142
Prioniturus montanus, 141
monticola, Hypsipetes siquijorensis, 284
Iole, 284
Monticola solitarius philippensis, 297
montifringilla, Fringilla, 415, 415
montigena, Ficedula hyperythra, 336
Muscicapula, 336
montigenus, Pardaliparus elegans, 254
Parus elegans, 254
montis, Seicercus, 320
montium, Chrysocolaptes lucidus, 220
morio, Coracina, 238, 238
moro, Tanygnathus lucionensis, 143
moseleyi, Actenoides, 206
Halcyon lindsayi, 206
Motacilla alba ocularis, 358
Motacilla calliope, 294
Motacilla caprata, 296
Motacilla cervina, 359
Motacilla cinerea robusta, 358
Motacilla flava simillima, 355, 355
Motacilla flava taivana, 358
Motacilla indica, 355
Motacilla ocularis, 358
Motacilla oenanthe, 297
Motacilla philippensis, 365
Motacilla violacea, 365
MOTACILLIDAE, *355, 358-360*
motleyi, Ceyx erithacus, 199, 199
mugimaki, Ficedula, 331
Muscicapa, 331
mulleri, Brachyurus, 226
Pitta sordida, 226
Mulleripicus fuliginosus, 217
Mulleripicus funebris fuliginosus, 217

Mulleripicus funebris funebris, 217
Mulleripicus funebris mayri, 217
Mulleripicus funebris parkesi, 217, 217
Mulleripicus pulverulentus pulverulentus, 216
multilunatus, Dryocopus javensis, 218
    Thriponax, 218
Munia cabanisi, 411
Munia formosana, 414
Munia (Dermophrys) jagori, 414
Muscadivora langhornei, 125
Muscadivores aenea fugaensis, 124
Muscadivores palmasensis, 125
Muscicapa azurea, 348
Muscicapa bonthaina disposita, 337
Muscicapa cinereiceps, 341
Muscicapa crypta, 337
Muscicapa cyanomelana, 339
Muscicapa goiavier, 278
Muscicapa griseisticta, 341
Muscicapa herioti camarinensis, 339
Muscicapa hyperytha trinitatis, 331
Muscicapa latirostris randi, 346, 346
Muscicapa mugimaki, 331
Muscicapa narcissina, 330
Muscicapa panayensis, 364
Muscicapa panayensis nigriloris, 346
Muscicapa panayensis nigrimentalis, 346
Muscicapa panayensis panayensis, 346
Muscicapa rufigastra simplicior, 340
Muscicapa sibirica, 341
Muscicapa sibirica sibirica, 341
Muscicapa westermanni palawanensis, 338
Muscicapa westermanni rabori, 338
Muscicapidae, *326-331, 336-341, 346-351, 354-355*
Muscicapula calayensis, 336
Muscicapula hyperytha mindorensis, 331
Muscicapula luzoniensis, 331
Muscicapula melanoleuca apo, 338
Muscicapula mindanensis, 337
Muscicapula montigena, 336
Muscicapula nigrorum, 336
Muscicapula samarensis, 337
Muscicapula westermanni, 338
Muscipeta cyaniceps, 327
Myiothera andromedae, 300
Myna, Crested, *368*, pl. 77
    Mount Apo, *368*, pl. 77
    Talking, *369*, pl. 77
mysticalis, Meliphaga, 258
    Rhabdornis, 258, 259
    Rhabdornis mysticalis, 258

N

nakamurai, Hemiprocne comata, 189
    Irediparra gallinacea, 76
napoleonis, Polyplectron, 57

Napothera rabori, 265
Napothera rabori mesoluzonica, 264, 264
Napothera rabori rabori, 265
Napothera rabori sorsogonensis, 265
Napothera sorsogonensis, 265
narcissina, Ficedula, 330
    Ficedula narcissina, 330
    Muscicapa, 330
nasutus, Lanius, 361
    Lanius schach, 361
nebularia, Scolopax, 89
    Tringa, 89
Nectarinia calcostetha, 375, 375
Nectarinia jugularis aurora, 378
Nectarinia jugularis jugularis, 375
Nectarinia jugularis obscurior, 375
Nectarinia jugularis woodi, 378
Nectarinia pygmaea, 397
Nectarinia pygmea, 397
Nectarinia sperata davaoensis, 374, 374
Nectarinia sperata henkei, 374
Nectarinia sperata juliae, 374
Nectarinia sperata marinduquensis, 374, 374
Nectarinia sperata sperata, 373
Nectarinia sperata theresae, 374, 374
Nectariniidae, *372-375, 378-379, 382-385*
Nectarophila juliae, 374
neglecta, Dissoura, 23
nehrkornae, Polyplectron, 57
nehrkorni, Micropus, 257
    Parus semilarvatus, 257
Neoleucotreron merrilli faustinoi, 122
nesophasma, Dendrophassa vernans, 118
nesophilus, Prioniturus discurus, 141, 141
nesydrionetes, Halcyon winchelli, 203, 203
Nettapus coromandelianus coromandelianus, 34
nicobarica, Caloenas, 139
    Caloenas nicobarica, 139
    Columba, 139
niger, Cittocincla, 295
    Copsychus, 295
Nightjar, Japanese, *179*, pl. 40
    Long-tailed, *179*, pl. 40
    Philippine Eared, *178*, pl. 40
    Savanna, *182*, pl. 40
Nightjars, *178-179, 182*
nigra, Lalage, 240, 240
    Terpsiphone, 350
nigrescens, Turnix, 59
    Turnix suscitator, 59
nigriceps, Orthotomus, 325, 325
    Orthotomus nigriceps, 325
nigricollis, Podiceps, 1, 1
    Podiceps nigricollis, 1
nigrifrons, Centropus, 163
nigrilore, Dicaeum, 387, 387, 388
nigriloris, Muscicapa panayensis, 346

Stoparola panayensis, 346
nigrimentalis, Muscicapa panayensis, 346
    Stoparola, 346
nigripes, Ardea, 20
    Egretta garzetta, 20
nigrirostris, Ceyx, 191
    Ceyx cyanopectus, 191
nigritorquis, Rhipidura, 328
    Rhipidura javanica, 328
nigrocapitata, Stachyris, 266
    Stachyris capitalis, 265
nigrocapitatus, Mixornis, 265
nigrocinnamomea, Rhipidura, 328, 328
    Rhipidura nigrocinnamomea, 328
nigrorum, Cryptolopha, 317
    Ducula carola, 131
    Ficedula hyperythra, 336
    Halcyon winchelli, 203, 203
    Muscicapula, 336
    Otus bakkamoena, 169, 169
    Phabotreron, 119
    Phapitreron leucotis, 119
    Phylloscopus trivirgatus, 317
    Ptilocolpa, 131
    Stachyris, 268, 268
    Tanygnathus lucionensis, 143
    Turdus, 301
    Turdus poliocephalus, 301
    Zosterops, 406,407, 407, *408,* 408
    Zosterops nigrorum, 407
nigrostriatus, Cisticola juncidis, 311, 311
    Oriolus, 249
nilotica, Gelochelidon, 105
    Gelochelidon nilotica, 105
    Sterna, 105
Ninox everetti, 175
Ninox mindorensis, 175
Ninox philippensis, 174
Ninox philippensis centralis, 175, 175
Ninox philippensis mindorensis, 175
Ninox philippensis philippensis, 174
Ninox philippensis proxima, 174, 174
Ninox philippensis reyi, 175
Ninox philippensis spilocephala, 175
Ninox philippensis spilonota, 175
Ninox plateni, 175
Ninox reyi, 175
Ninox scutulata florensis, 176
Ninox scutulata japonica, 176
Ninox scutulata palawanensis, 176, 176
Ninox scutulata randi, 176, 176
Ninox spilocephala, 175
Ninox spilonotus, 175
nobilis, Ducula poliocephala, 130
    Zonophaps poliocephala, 130
Noddy, Common, *114*, pl. 27
    White-capped, *114*, pl. 27
novaeseelandiae, Anthus, 358

novus, Pericrocotus, 241
    Pericrocotus flammeus, 241
nubilosa, Sterna, 111
    Sterna fuscata, 111
nuchalis, Carpophaga, 124
    Ducula aenea, 124
Numenius arquata orientalis, 85
Numenius madagascariensis, 85
Numenius minutus, 84, 84
Numenius orientalis, 85
Numenius phaeopus variegatus, 85
nuntius, Orthotomus ruficeps, 326
    Orthotomus sericeus, 326
Nuthatch, Velvet-fronted, *257*, pl. 55
NUTHATCHES, 257-258
nycticorax, Ardea, 22
    Nycticorax, 22
    Nycticorax nycticorax, 22
Nycticorax caledonicus major, 22
Nycticorax caledonicus manillensis, 22
Nycticorax goisagi, 11
Nycticorax manillensis, 22
Nycticorax nycticorax nycticorax, 22

O

obscurior, Cinnyris, 375
    Nectarinia jugularis, 375
obscurum, Dicaeum, 396
    Dicaeum hypoleucum, 396
obscurus, Turdus, 303, 303
occipitalis, Hypothymis, 348
    Leucotreron, 121
    Phabotreron, 119
    Phapitreron leucotis, 119
    Ptilinopus, 121
    Ptilonopus, 121
occularis, Rhinomyias, 330
    Rhinomyias ruficauda, 330
ocellata, Turnix, 59, 66, 66
    Turnix ocellata, 59
ocellatus, Oriolus, 59
ochotensis, Locustella certhiola, 316
    Sylvia (Locustella), 316
ochrophus, Tringa, 92, 92
ochrothorectis, Entomothera coromanda, 201
ocularis, Motacilla, 358
    Motacilla alba, 358
    Poliolimnas cinereus, 74, 74
oenanthe, Motacilla, 297
    Oenanthe, 297
    Oenanthe oenanthe, 297
Oenanthe oenanthe oenanthe, 297
oenochlamys, Dendrophila, 257
    Sitta frontalis, 257
Oestrelata sandwichensis, 2
OLD WORLD FLYCATCHERS, 326-331, 336-341,
    346-351, 354-355

463

OLD WORLD WARBLERS, *303, 308-311, 316-321,*
324-326
olivacea, Abrornis, 319
Gallinula, 74
olivaceus, Amaurornis, 74
Amaurornis olivaceus, 74
Phylloscopus, 319, 319
Prionochilus, 385, 386, 386
Prionochilus olivaceus, 386
onikakko, Eudynamys scolopacea, 160
orientalis, Acrocephalus arundinaceus, 317
Eurystomus, 207
Numenius, 85
Numenius arquata, 85
Pernis apivorus, 38, 38
Salicaria turdina, 317
origenis, Collocalia, 182
Collocalia brevirostris, 182
Oriole, Black-naped, *250,* pl. 54
Dark-throated, *248,* pl. 54
Isabella, *250,* pl. 54
ORIOLES, *248-251*
ORIOLIDAE, *248-251*
Oriolus albiloris, 250
Oriolus assimilis, 250
Oriolus basilanicus, 249
Oriolus chinensis, 250
Oriolus chinensis chinensis, 250
Oriolus chinensis fugaensis, 251
Oriolus chinensis palawanensis, 250
Oriolus chinensis sorsogonensis, 251
Oriolus chinensis yamamurae, 250
Oriolus cinereogenys, 249
Oriolus isabellae, 250, 250
Oriolus lineatus, 56
Oriolus nigrostriatus, 249
Oriolus ocellatus, 59
Oriolus poliogenys, 249
Oriolus samarensis, 248
Oriolus sinensis, 365
Oriolus steerii, 249
Oriolus suluensis, 250
Oriolus xanthonotus albiloris, 250
Oriolus xanthonotus assimilis, 250
Oriolus xanthonotus basilanicus, 249
Oriolus xanthonotus cinereogenys, 249
Oriolus xanthonotus palawanus, 249
Oriolus xanthonotus persuasus, 249, 249,
pl. 54
Oriolus xanthonotus samarensis, 248
Oriolus xanthonotus steerii, 249
Orthotomus atrogularis castaneiceps, 324
Orthotomus atrogularis chloronotus, 324
Orthotomus atrogularis davao, 324
Orthotomus atrogularis frontalis, 324
Orthotomus atrogularis heterolaemus, 324
Orthotomus atrogularis mearnsi, 325
Orthotomus atrogularis rabori, 324, 324

Orthotomus castaneiceps, 324
Orthotomus chloronotus, 324
Orthotomus cineraceus cagayanensis, 326
Orthotomus cinereiceps, 325, 325
Orthotomus cucullatus heterolaemus, 321
Orthotomus cucullatus philippinus, 321
Orthotomus cucullatus viridicollis, 321, 321
Orthotomus derbianus, 321, 321
Orthotomus frontalis, 324
Orthotomus mearnsi, 325
Orthotomus nigriceps, 325
Orthotomus nigriceps nigriceps, 325
Orthotomus nigriceps samarensis, 325
Orthotomus panayensis, 324
Orthotomus ruficeps nuntius, 326
Orthotomus samarensis, 325
Orthotomus sepium cagayanensis, 326
Orthotomus sericeus nuntius, 326
Orycerca everetti, 411
oryzivora, Loxia, 414
Padda, 414
Osmotreron axillaris, 115
Osmotreron everetti, 118
Osprey, *34,* pl. 9
OSPREYS, *34-35*
ostenta, Coracina, 239, 239
Otus bakkamoena batanensis, 167
Otus bakkamoena everetti, 169
Otus bakkamoena fuliginosus, 169
Otus bakkamoena megalotis, 168
Otus bakkamoena nigrorum, 169, 169
Otus boholensis, 169
Otus calayensis, 167
Otus cuyensis, 168
Otus romblonis, 167
Otus rufescens burbidgei, 168, 168
Otus scops calayensis, 167
Otus scops cuyensis, 168
Otus scops longicornis, 167
Otus scops mindorensis, 167
Otus scops mirus, 168, 168
Otus scops romblonis, 167
Otus scops sibutuensis, 168
Otus steerei, 168
Owl, Bay, *166,* pl. 38
Giant Scops, *169,* pl. 38
Grass, *166,* pl. 39
Oriental Screech, *168,* pl. 38
Philippine Boobook, *174,* pl. 38
Philippine Hawk, *176,* pl. 38
Philippine Horned, *174,* pl. 39
Rufous Scops, *168,* pl. 38
Scops, *167,* pl. 38
Seloputo, *176,* pl. 39
Short-eared, *177,* pl. 39
OWLS, BARN, *166-167*
TYPICAL, *167-169, 174-177*
Oxycerca (Uroloncha) jagori, 411

P

Pachycephala cinerea albiventris, 351
Pachycephala cinerea crissalis, 350
Pachycephala cinerea homeyeri, 351
Pachycephala cinerea mindorensis, 351
Pachycephala cinerea plateni, 351
Pachycephala cinerea winchelli, 351
Pachycephala philippinensis apoensis, 354
Pachycephala philippinensis basilanica, 355
Pachycephala philippinensis boholensis,
   354, 354
Pachycephala philippinensis fallax, 354
Pachycephala philippinensis illex, 354
Pachycephala philippinensis philippinensis,
   354
Pachycephala philippinensis siquijorensis,
   354, 354
pacificus, Apus, 188
   Apus pacificus, 188
   Hirundo, 188
   Puffinus, 2
Padda oryzivora, 414
Painted-snipe, 77, pl. 19
PAINTED-SNIPES, 77
palawana, Cettia montana, 308, 308
   Leucotreron leclancheri, 123
   Lonchura leucogastra, 411, 411
   Sitta frontalis, 258, 258
   Streptopelia chinensis, 133
palawanense, Malacopteron, 263, 263
palawanensis, Buchanga, 244
   Carpophaga aenea, 124
   Chloropsis, 287
   Collocalia brevirostris, 183
   Collocalia lowi, 183
   Cringer, 279
   Dicrurus, 248
   Dicrurus hottentottus, 248
   Ducula aenea, 124
   Ficedula westermanni, 338
   Gracula religiosa, 369
   Halcyon pileata, 202
   Hypsipetes, 279
   Mainatus, 369
   Muscicapa westermanni, 338
   Ninox scutulata, 176, 176
   Oriolus chinensis, 250
   Pernis apivorus, 38, 38
   Phyllornis, 287
   Pitta sordida, 226, 226
   Spilornis cheela, 42
palawanorum, Dicaeum pygmaeum, 398, 398
palawanus, Accipiter trivirgatus, 46, 46
   Oriolus xanthonotus, 249
Pallenura robusta, 358
pallidigula, Hypocryptadius cinnamomeus,
   408
pallidior, Cypsiurus parvus, 188

   Dicaeum, 395
   Tachornis, 188
pallidius, Dicaeum trigonostigma, 395
pallidus, Turdus, 302, 302
palmasensis, Ducula pickeringii, 125
   Muscadivores, 125
paludicola, Riparia, 232
palustris, Megalurus, 309, 309
Pampusanna criniger, 138
panayensis, Aplonis, 364
   Aplonis panayensis, 364
   Artamides, 234
   Coracina striata, 234
   Culicicapa helianthea, 347
   Edoliisoma (Graucalus), 239
   Eumyias, 346
   Loriculus, 150
   Loriculus philippensis, 150
   Muscicapa, 346, 364
   Muscicapa panayensis, 346
   Orthotomus, 324
   Pardaliparus elegans, 254
   Spilornis, 42
   Stoparola, 346
   Xantholestes, 347
Pandion haliaetus haliaetus, 34
Pandion haliaetus melvillensis, 35, 35
PANDIONIDAE, *34-35*
panini, Buceros, 210
   Penelopides, 210, 211, 211
   Penelopides panini, 210
papuensis, Pipra, 394
paraguae, Anthreptes malacensis, 372, 372
   Cyornis, 338
paraguena, Eudynamys scolopacea, 160
paraguenus, Tanygnathus lucionensis, 143
Parakeet, Philippine Hanging, *149,* pl. 34
paraterma, Hypotaenidia striata, 66
Pardaliparus albescens, 255
Pardaliparus edithae, 254
Pardaliparus elegans guimarasensis, 255
Pardaliparus elegans mindanensis, 255
Pardaliparus elegans panayensis, 254
Pardaliparus elegans suluensis, 255
Pardaliparus elegans visayanus, 255
PARIDAE *254-257*
parkesi, Mulleripicus funebris, 217, 217
   Zosterops montana, 404, 404
Parra gallinacea, 76
Parrot, Blue-backed, *148,* pl. 34
   Blue-headed Racket-tailed, *140,* pl. 33
   Blue-naped, 142, pl. 34
   Crimson-spotted Racket-tailed, *141,* pl. 33
   Green-headed Racket-tailed, *142,* pl. 33
   Large-billed, *143,* pl. 34
   Palawan Racket-tailed, *142,* pl. 33
Parrot-finch, Green-faced, *410,* pl. 84
   Green-tailed, *410,* pl. 84

Parrot-finch *(cont.)*

Mindanao, *410,* pl. 84

PARROTS, 139-*143, 148-151*

parsonsi, Prionochilus, 385

　Prionochilus olivaceus, 385

Partridge, Bearded, *55,* pl. 14

Parus amabilis, 256, 256

Parus elegans, 254

Parus elegans albescens, 255

Parus elegans bongaoensis, 256, 256

Parus elegans edithae, 254

Parus elegans elegans, 254

Parus elegans gilliardi, 255, 255

Parus elegans mindanensis, 255

Parus elegans montigenus, 254, 254

Parus elegans suluensis, 255

Parus elegans visayanus, 255

Parus quadrivittatus, 254

Parus semilarvatus nehrkorni, 257

Parus semilarvatus semilarvatus, 256

Parus semilarvatus snowi, 256, 256

parvimaculata, Copsychus luzoniensis, *295*

　Kittacincla, 295

parvus, Cypsiurus, 188

Passer montanus malaccensis, 409, 409

Passer montanus manillensis, 409

Passer montanus saturatus, 409

Passer saturatus, 409

paykullii, Porzana, 69

　Rallus, 69

pectoralis, Cuculus fugax, 154

　Dryocopus javensis, 218

　Hiracococcyx, 154

　Thriponax, 218

　Zosterops montana, 404, 404

Pelargopsis capensis gigantea, 200

Pelargopsis capensis gouldi, 200

Pelargopsis capensis smithi, 200

Pelargopsis gigantea, 200

Pelargopsis gouldi, 200

PELECANIDAE, *3*

Pelecanus minor, 5

Pelecanus philippensis, 3, 3

Pelecanus plotus, 4

Pelecanus sinensis, 4

Pelican, Philippine, *3,* pl. 2

PELICANS, *3*

penelope, Anas, 30, 30

Penelopides affinis, 211

Penelopides basilanica, 211

Penelopides mindorensis, 210

Penelopides panini affinis, 211

Penelopides panini basilanica, 211

Penelopides panini boholensis, 211

Penelopides panini leytensis, 211

Penelopides panini manilloe, 210

Penelopides panini mindorensis, 210

Penelopides panini panini, 210

Penelopides panini samarensis, 211

Penelopides panini subnigra, 210

Penelopides panini ticaensis, 211, 211

Penelopides samarensis, 211

Penelopides schmackeri, 210

Penelopides subnigra, 210

Penelopides talisi, 210

Perdix barbata, 55

Perdix barbata barbata, 55

peregrina, Ibis, 23

peregrinus, Falco, 54

　Plegadis falcinellus, 23

Pericrocotus cinereus, 240

Pericrocotus cinnamomeus igneus, 241

Pericrocotus divaricatus divaricatus, 240

Pericrocotus flammeus gonzalesi, 244, 244

Pericrocotus flammeus johnstoniae, 241

Pericrocotus flammeus leytensis, 241

Pericrocotus flammeus marchesae, 244

Pericrocotus flammeus novus, 241

P(ericrocotus) igneus, 241

Pericrocotus johnstoniae, 241

Pericrocotus leytensis, 241

Pericrocotus marchesae, 244

Pericrocotus novus, 241

periophthalmica, Callaeops, 350

　Terpsiphone atrocaudata, 350

Pernis apivorus orientalis, 38, 38

Pernis apivorus palawanensis, 38, 38

Pernis apivorus philippensis, 38, 38

Pernis celebensis steerei, 35, 35

peronii, Charadrius, 79, 79

personata, Camiguinia, 348

　Sula, 3

　Sula dactylatra, 3

persuasus, Oriolus xanthonotus, 249,

　249, pl. 54

peterseni, Edolisoma mcgregori, 239

petersoni, Phylloscopus trivirgatus, 319, 319

Petrel, Dark-rumped, *2*

　Tahiti, *2*

Phabotreron brevirostris, 119

Phabotreron brunneiceps, 121

Phabotreron cinereiceps, 120

Phabotreron frontalis, 120

Phabotreron maculipectus, 120

Phabotreron nigrorum, 119

Phabotreron occipitalis, 119

phaea, Macropygia, 132

　Macropygia phasianella, 132

Phaenicophaus superciliosus, 161

phaeopus, Numenius, 85

phaeopygia, Pterodroma, 2

Phaethon lepturus dorotheae, 3, 3

PHAETHONTIDAE, *3*

PHALACROCORACIDAE, *4*

Phalacrocorax carbo sinensis, 4

Phalarope, Northern, *102,* pl. 25

PHALAROPES, *102-103*
PHALAROPODIDAE, *102-103*
Phalaropus lobatus, 102
Phapitreron albifrons, 119
Phapitreron amethystina, 119
Phapitreron amethystina amethystina, 119
Phapitreron amethystina celestinoi, 119
Phapitreron amethystina frontalis, 120
Phapitreron amethystina maculipectus, 120
Phapitreron amethystina mindanaoensis,
   120, 120
Phapitreron amethystina polillensis, 118, *119*
Phapitreron cinereiceps brunneiceps, 121
Phapitreron cinereiceps cinereiceps, 120
Phapitreron leucotis brevirostris, 119
Phapitreron leucotis leucotis, 118
Phapitreron leucotis limucon, 119
Phapitreron leucotis mindorensis, 118
Phapitreron leucotis nigrorum, 119
Phapitreron leucotis occipitalis, 119
Phapitreron samarensis, 119
phasianella, Macropygia, 131, 132
PHASIANIDAE, *55-57*
Phasianus gallus, 56
Pheasant, Palawan Peacock, *57,* pl. 15
PHEASANTS, *55-57*
Philedon gularis, 279
Philemon philippinensis, 385
Philentoma albiventris, 328
philippense, Syrnium, 174
philippensis, Bubo, 174
   Bubo philippensis, 174
   Colymbus, 1
   Cuculus, 162
   Dryocopus javensis, 218
   Gallus gallus, 56
   Hypsipetes, 279
   Loriculus, 149, 150, 151, 151
   Loriculus philippensis, 149
   Mirafra, 227
   Mirafra javanica, 227
   Monticola solitarius, 297
   Motacilla, 365
   Ninox, 174, 174, *175,* 175
   Ninox philippensis, 174
   Pelecanus, 3, 3
   Pernis apivorus, 38, 38
   Podiceps ruficollis, 1
   Poliolophus urostictus, 277
   Pseudoptynx, 174
   Psittacus, 149
   Pycnonotus urostictus, 277
   Rallus, 67, 67
   Rallus philippensis, 67
   Scops, 174
   Spizaetus, 52, 52
   Sturnus, 365
   Thriponax, 218

   Turdus, 297
philippinensis, Arachnothera clarae, 385
   Bucco, 213
   Centropus bengalensis, 166, 166
   Cyornis, 340
   Cyornis rufigaster, 340
   G(algulus), 279
   Hyloterpe, 354
   Pachycephala, 354, 354, 355
   Pachycephala philippinensis, 354
   Philemon, 385
Philippinia primigenius, 378
philippinus, Cornix, 254
   Corvus macrorhynchos, 254
   Hypsipetes, 279, 284
   Hypsipetes philippinus, 279
   Iole, 279
   Merops, 206, 206
   Merops philippinus, 206
   Orthotomus cucullatus, 321
   Phyllergates, 321
   (Turdus), 279
Philomachus pugnax, 102
Phlegoenas criniger leytensis, 139
Phlegoenas crinigera basilanica, 138
Phlegoenas keayi, 138
Phlogoenas menagei, 139
Phlogoenas platenae, 138
Phodilus badius badius, 166
Phodilus riverae, 166
Phoenicophaeus cumingi, 161, 161
Phoenicophaeus curvirostris harringtoni, 160
Phoenicophaeus superciliosus cagayanensis,
   161, 161
Phoenicophaeus superciliosus superciliosus,
   161
Phoenicophaus cumingi, 161
phoenicurus, Amaurornis, 74
Phyllergates heterolaemus, 321
Phyllergates philippinus, 321
Phyllopneuste borealis, 320
Phyllopneuste xanthodryas, 320
Phyllornis flavipennis, 287
Phyllornis palawanensis, 287
Phylloscopus borealis borealis, 320
Phylloscopus borealis xanthodryas, 320
Phylloscopus cebuensis cebuensis, 319
Phylloscopus cebuensis luzonensis, 309
Phylloscopus cebuensis sorsogonensis, 320,
   320
Phylloscopus olivaceus, 319
Phylloscopus olivaceus luzonensis, 319
Phylloscopus trivirgatus benguetensis, 318
Phylloscopus trivirgatus diuatae, 318, 318
Phylloscopus trivirgatus flavostriatus, 318,
   318
Phylloscopus trivirgatus malindangensis, 318
Phylloscopus trivirgatus mindanensis, 318

Phylloscopus trivirgatus nigrorum, 317
Phylloscopus trivirgatus petersoni, 319, 319
PICIDAE, *216-221*
picina, Chaetura, 187, 187
pickeringii, Carpophaga, 125
    Ducula, 125
    Ducula pickeringii, 125
picta, Cinnyris, 375
Picus funebris, 217
Picus haematribon, 220
Picus lucidus, 221
Picus maculatus, 219
Picus pulverulentus, 216
Picus validirostris, 219
Pigeon, Bleeding-heart, *138*, pl. 32
    Gray Imperial, *125*, pl. 30
    Green Imperial, *124*, pl. 30
    Metallic Wood, *131*, pl. 31
    Mindoro Imperial, *130*, pl. 30
    Nicobar, *139*, pl. 32
    Nutmeg Imperial, *130*, pl. 30
    Pink-bellied Imperial, *125*, pl. 30
    Pink-necked Green, *118*, pl. 28
    Pompadour Green, *115*, pl. 28
    Spotted Imperial, *130*, pl. 30
    Thick-billed Green, *115*, pl. 28
    Whistling Green, *114*, pl. 28
PIGEONS, *114-115, 118-125, 130-133, 138-139*
pileata, Alcedo, 202
    Halcyon, 202, 202
pileatus, Anous stolidus, 114
    Sterna, 114
pinicola, Rhipidura cyaniceps, 327, 327
pintadeanus, Francolinus, 55
    Francolinus pintadeanus, 55
    Tetrao, 55
Pintail, *27*, pl. 7
Pipit, Oriental Tree, *359*, pl. 74
    Petchora, *359*, pl. 74
    Red-throated, *359*, pl. 74
    Richard's, *358*, pl. 74
PIPITS, *355, 358-360*
Pipra australe, 394
Pipra papuensis, 394
Piprisoma diversum, 387
pistra, Trichoglossus johnstoniae, 140, 140
Pithecophaga jefferyi, 47, 47
Pitta, Black-headed, *225*, pl. 49
    Blue-winged, *226*, pl. 49
    Koch's, *225*, pl. 49
    Red-breasted, *224*, pl. 49
    Steere's, *226*, pl. 49
Pitta atricapilla rothschildi, 225
Pitta brachyura moluccensis, 226
Pitta erythrogaster, 224
Pitta erythrogaster erythrogaster, 224
Pitta erythrogaster propinqua, 225
Pitta erythrogaster thompsoni, 225, 225

Pitta erythrogastra yairocho, 224
Pitta fastosa, 226
Pitta kochi, 225, 225
Pitta sordida mulleri, 226
Pitta sordida palawanensis, 226, 226
Pitta sordida sordida, 225
Pitta steerii coelestis, 226, 226
Pitta steerii steerii, 226
PITTAS, *224-227*
PITTIDAE, *224-227*
Platalea minor, 23, 23
platenae, Ceyx, 200
    Ceyx melanurus, 200
    Ficedula, 338
    Gallicolumba luzonica, 138
    Phlogoenas, 138
    Prioniturus, 142, 142
    Siphia, 338
plateni, Anaimos, 386
    Hyloterpe, 351
    Mixornis, 265
    Ninox, 175
    Pachycephala cinerea, 351
    Prionochilus, 386, 386
    Stachyris, 265
    Stachyris plateni, 265
Platyrhynchus ceylonensis, 347
Plegadis falcinellus peregrinus, 23
PLOCEIDAE, *409*
plotus, Pelecanus, 4
    Sula leucogaster, 4
Plover, Black-bellied, *77*, pl. 19
    Kentish, *79*, pl. 20
    Large Sand, *84*, pl. 20
    Malay, *79*, pl. 20
    Mongolian, *79*, pl. 20
    Pacific Golden, *78*, pl. 19
    Ring-necked, *78*, pl. 20
PLOVERS, *77-79, 84*
plumbea, Porzana, 69
plumosus, Pycnonotus, 277
Pluvialis dominica fulva, 78
Pluvialis squatarola, 77
Pluvianus cinereus, 77
Pochard, European, *31*, pl. 8
PODARGIDAE, *177-178*
Podiceps nigricollis, 1
Podiceps nigricollis nigricollis, 1
Podiceps ruficollis cotabato, 1
Podiceps ruficollis philippensis, 1
PODICIPEDIDAE, *1*
poecilorhyncha, Anas, 27
polillensis, Centropus unirufus, 163
    Phapitreron amethystina, 118, 119
poliocephala, Carpophaga, 125
    Ducula, 125, 130
    Ducula poliocephala, 125
    Zonophaps, 130

poliocephalus, Turdus, 301, 302, 302
poliogenys, Oriolus, 249
poliogyna, Brachypteryx, 290
    Brachypteryx montana, 290
Poliolimnas cinereus collingwoodi, 74
Poliolimnas cinereus ocularis, 74, 74
Poliolophus basilanicus, 277
Poliolophus urostictus philippensis, 277
Polyplectron emphanum, 57, 57
Polyplectron napoleonis, 57
Polyplectron nehrkornae, 57
pomarinus, Lestris, 103
    Stercorarius, 103
pompadora, Treron, 115, 115, *118,* 118
pontifex, Dicaeum hypoleucum, 397, 397
porphyrio, Porphyrio, 75
Porphyrio porphyrio pulverulentus, 75
Porphyrio pulverulentus, 75
Porzana fusca fusca, 69
Porzana paykullii, 69
Porzana plumbea filipina, 69
Porzana pusilla pusilla, 68
Porzana tabuensis, 69
Porzana tabuensis tabuensis, 69
Pratincole, *103,* pl. 25
Pratincoles, *103*
primigenius, Aethopyga, 378, 378
    Aethopyga primigenius, 378
    Philippinia, 378
Prioniturus cyaniceps, 142
Prioniturus discurus discurus, 140
Prioniturus discurus mindorensis, 141
Prioniturus discurus nesophilus, 141, 141
Prioniturus discurus var. *suluensis, 140*
Prioniturus discurus whiteheadi, 141, 141
Prioniturus luconensis, 142, 142
Prioniturus malindangensis, 141
Prioniturus mindorensis, 141
Prioniturus montanus, 141
Prioniturus montanus montanus, 141
Prioniturus montanus verticalis, 142
Prioniturus montanus waterstradti, 141
Prioniturus platenae, 142, 142
Prioniturus verticalis, 142
Prioniturus waterstradti, 141
Prionochilus aeruginosum, 386
Prionochilus anthonyi, 388
Prionochilus bicolor, 389
Prionochilus inexpectatus, 389
Prionochilus johannae, 386
Prionochilus olivaceus, 386
Prionochilus olivaceus olivaceus, 386
Prionochilus olivaceus parsonsi, 385
Prionochilus olivaceus samarensis, 386
Prionochilus parsonsi, 385
Prionochilus planteni, 386, 386
Prionochilus quadricolor, 389
Prionochilus samarensis, 386

Procellaria leucomelas, 1
Procellaria rostrata, 2
Procellariidae, *1-2*
propinqua, Pitta erythrogaster, 225
propinquus, Brachyurus, 225
proprium, Dicaeum, 387, 387
proxima, Ninox philippensis, 174, 174
Pseudolalage melanoleuca, 239
Pseudolalage minor, 240
Pseudoptynx gurneyi, 169
Pseudoptynx philippensis, 174
Pseudotharrhaleus caudatus, 309
Pseudotharrhaleus griseipectus, 309
Pseudotharrhaleus malindangensis, 309
Pseudotharrhaleus unicolor, 309
Psittacidae, *139-143, 148-151*
Psittacus discurus, 140
Psittacus haematuropygius, 140
Psittacus lucionensis, 143
Psittacus lunulatus, 148
Psittacus megalorynchos, 143
Psittacus philippensis, 149
Pterodroma phaeopygia sandwichensis, 2
Pterodroma rostrata rostrata, 2
Ptilinopus arcanus, 122, 122
Ptilinopus leclancheri gironieri, 123
Ptilinopus leclancheri leclancheri, 122
Ptilinopus leclancheri longialis, 123
Ptilinopus marchei, 122
Ptilinopus melanospila bangueyensis, 123
Ptilinopus merrilli faustinoi, 122
Ptilinopus merrilli merrilli, 121
Ptilinopus occipitalis, 121
Ptilinopus superbus temminckii, 123
Ptilocichla falcata, 264, 264
Ptilocichla (?) mindanensis, 263
Ptilocichla mindanensis basilanica, 264
Ptilocichla mindanensis fortichi, 263, 263
Ptilocichla mindanensis mindanensis, 263
Ptilocichla mindanensis minuta, 263
Ptilocichla minuta, 263
Ptilocolpa carola, 130
Ptilocolpa griseipectus, 130
Ptilocolpa mindanensis, 131
Ptilocolpa nigrorum, 131
Ptilonopus occipitalis, 121
Ptilopus bangueyensis, 123
Ptilopus incognita, 121
Ptilopus (Rhamphilculus) marchei, 122
Ptilopyga mindanensis, 263
Ptiocichla [sic] *basilanica,* 264
puella, Irena, 287
Puffinus chlororhynchus, 2
Puffinus leucomelas, 1
Puffinus pacificus chlororhynchus, 2
pugnax, Philomachus, 102
    Tringa, 102
pulcherrima, Aethopyga, 382, 382

pulcherrima (cont.)
 Aethopyga pulcherrima, 382
pulverulentus, Mulleripicus, *216*
 Mulleripicus pulverulentus, 216
 Picus, 216
 Porphyrio, 75
 Porphyrio porphyrio, 75
punctulata, Lonchura, *411*
purpurea, Ardea, *21,* 21
pusilla, Emberiza, *415,* 415
 Porzana, 68
 Porzana pusilla, 68
pusillus, Corvus, 251
 Corvus enca, 251
 Megapodius, 54
 Megapodius freycinet, 54
 Rallus, 68
PYCNONOTIDAE, *276-279, 284-286*
Pycnonotus atriceps atriceps, 276
Pycnonotus goiavier goiavier, 278
Pycnonotus goiavier samarensis, 278, 278
Pycnonotus goiavier suluensis, 278, 278
Pycnonotus plumosus cinereifrons, 277
Pycnonotus urostictus atricaudatus, 277, 277
Pycnonotus urostictus basilanicus, 277
Pycnonotus urostictus ilokensis, 277, 277
Pycnonotus urostictus philippensis, 277
Pycnonotus urostictus urostictus, 276
pygmaea, Nectarinia, *397*
 Stachyris plateni, 265, pl. 57
pygmaeum, Dicaeum *397, 398,* 398
 Dicaeum pygmaeum, 397
pygmaeus, Zosterornis, *265*
pygmea, Nectarinia, *397*
Pyrrhocentor unirufus, 163
pyrrhopterus, Corydonix, *162*
Pyrrhula leucogenys, 417
Pyrrhula leucogenys apo, 417
Pyrrhula leucogenys coriaria, 417
Pyrrhula leucogenys leucogenys, 417
Pyrrhula leucogenys steerei, 417
Pyrrhula steerei, 417

Q

quadricolor, Dicaeum, *389*
 Prionochilus, 389
quadrivittatus, Parus, 254
Quail, Asiatic Migratory, *56,* pl. 14
 Barred Button-, *59,* pl. 16
 Painted, *56,* pl. 14
 Spotted Button-, *59,* pl. 16
 Striped Button-, *57,* pl. 16
 Worcester's Button-, *58,* pl 16
quartus, Lanius validirostris, *364*
querquedula, Anas, *30,* 30
quisumbingi, Rallus torquatus, 67

R

rabori, Hypothymis coelestis, *349*
 Muscicapa westermanni, *338*
 Napothera, 264, 264, 265, 265
 Napothera rabori, 265
 Orthotomus atrogularis, 324, 324
 Rhabdornis inornatus, 259, 259
Rail, Banded, *67,* pl. 17
 Barred, *67,* pl. 17
 Brown-banded, *67,* pl. 17
 Dwarf, *68,* pl. 18
 Slaty-breasted, *66,* pl. 17
 Sooty, *69,* pl. 18
 White-browed, *74,* pl. 17
RAILS, *66-69, 74-76*
RALLIDAE, *66-69, 74-76*
Rallina eurizonoides eurizonoides, 68
Rallina fasciata, 68, 68
Rallus benghalensis, 77
Rallus fuscus, 69
Rallus mirificus, 67, 67
Rallus paykullii, 69
Rallus philippensis, 67
Rallus philippensis philippensis, 67
Rallus pusillus, 68
Rallus striatus, 66
Rallus striatus striatus, 66
Rallus torquatus, 67
Rallus torquatus quisumbingi, 67
Rallus torquatus sanfordi, 67
Rallus torquatus torquatus, 67
ramosi, Chrysocolaptes lucidus, 220
 Tersiphone unirufa, 349
Ramphalcyon capensis smithi, 200
ramsayi, Dendrocopos maculatus, *220*
 Iyngipicus, 220
 Siphia, 339
randi, Arachnothera longirostra, *384*
 Arachnothera longirostris, 384
 Muscicapa latirostris, 346, 346
 Ninox scutulata, 176, 176
 Saxicola caprata, 296, 296
rebaptizatus, Dicrurus cineraceus, 244
RECURVIROSTRIDAE, *102*
Redshank, *88,* pl. 21
Redstart, Philippine Water, *294,* pl. 62
regulus, Loriculus, 150
 Loriculus philippensis, 150
religiosa, Gracula, 369
retrocinctum, Dicaeum, *394,* 394
reyi, Ninox, 175
 Ninox philippensis, 175
Rhabdornis grandis, 259
Rhabdornis inornatus, 259
Rhabdornis inornatus alaris, 262, 262
Rhabdornis inornatus grandis, 259
Rhabdornis inornatus inornatus, 259
Rhabdornis inornatus rabori, 259, 259

Rhabdornis inornatus zamboanga, 262
Rhabdornis longirostris, 258, 259
Rhabdornis minor, 259
Rhabdornis mysticalis minor, 259
Rhabdornis mysticalis mysticalis, 258
RHABDORNITHIDAE, *258-259, 262*
Rhinomyias albigularis, 328
Rhinomyias goodfellowi, 330, 330
Rhinomyias gularis albigularis, 328
Rhinomyias insignis, 330, 330
Rhinomyias occularis, 330
Rhinomyias ruficauda basilanica, 329
Rhinomyias ruficauda boholensis, 329, 329
Rhinomyias ruficauda mindanensis, 329
Rhinomyias ruficauda occularis, 330
Rhinomyias ruficauda ruficauda, 329
Rhinomyias ruficauda samarensis, 329
Rhinomyias ruficauda zamboanga, 329, 329
Rhipidura cyaniceps albiventris, 328
Rhipidura cyaniceps cyaniceps, 327
Rhipidura cyaniceps pinicola, 327, 327
Rhipidura cyaniceps sauli, 327
Rhipidura hutchinsoni, 328
Rhipidura javanica nigritorquis, 328
Rhipidura nigritorquis, 328
Rhipidura nigrocinnamomea, 328
Rhipidura nigrocinnamomea hutchinsoni, 328
Rhipidura nigrocinnamomea nigrocinnamomea, 328
Rhipidura sauli, 327
Rhipidura superciliaris apo, 327, 327
Rhipidura superciliaris samarensis, 327
Rhipidura superciliaris superciliaris, 326
rhizophorae, Gerygone, 303
Rhyacornis bicolor, 294
richmondi, Zosterops, 407
    Zosterops nigrorum, 407
ridibundus, Larus, 104, 104
riparia, Clivicola, 232
    Riparia, 232
Riparia chinensis tantilla, 232
Riparia paludicola tantilla, 232
Riparia riparia ijimae, 232
ripleyi, Coracina morio, 238, 238
riverae, Phodilus, 166
robusta, Motacilla cinerea, 358
    Pallenura, 358
rodiosternus, Harpactes, 189
rogersi, Canutus canutus, 95
ROLLERS, *207*
romblonis, Otus, 167
    Otus scops, 167
rostrata, Procellaria, 2
    Pterodroma, 2
    Pterodroma rostrata, 2
Rostratula benghalensis benghalensis, 77
ROSTRATULIDAE, 77

rothschildi, Pitta atricapilla, 225
rubricapilla, Dicaeum, 388
rubrinota, Aethopyga, 383
    Aethopyga shelleyi, 383
rubripes, Sula, 4
    Sula sula, 4
Ruby-throat, *294*, pl. 62
rufa, Anhinga, 5
    Tchitrea, 349
rufescens, Otus, 168, 168
Ruff, *102*, pl. 24
ruficauda, Rhinomyias, 329, 329, 330
    Rhinomyias ruficauda, 329
    Setaria, 329
ruficeps, Megalurus, 310
    Orthotomus, 326
ruficollis, Calidris, 100
    Podiceps, 1, 1
    Trynga, 100
rufidorsa, Ceyx, 198
rufidorsum, Ceyx erithacus, 198
rufifrons, Trichostoma, 263
rufigaster, Cyornis, 340
rufigastra, Cyornis, 340
    Muscicapa, 340
rufigularis, Hypsipetes, 284, 284
rufipennis, Centropus, 162
rufolineatus, Gorsachius melanolophus, 18, 18
rufopunctatus, Chrysocolaptes, 221
    Chrysocolaptes lucidus, 221
rustica, Hirundo, 232
rusticola, Scolopax, 95, 95

S

sacra, Ardea, 19
    Egretta, 19
    Egretta sacra, 19
Salicaria (Cisticola) brunneiceps, 311
Salicaria turdina orientalis, 317
salomonseni, Dicaeum pygmaeum, 398, 398
salvadorii, Loriculus, 151
    Tanygnathus, 142
    Tanygnathus lucionensis, 142
samarensis, Ceyx, 199
    Ceyx melanurus, 199
    Corvus, 251
    Corvus enca, 251
    Dicrurus hottentottus, 248, 248
    Dryocopus javensis, 218
    Eurylaimus steerii, 224
    Ficedula basilanica, 337
    Hypothymis, 327
    Hypsipetes everetti, 285, 285
    Muscicapula, 337
    Oriolus, 248
    Oriolus xanthonotus, 248
    Orthotomus, 325
    Orthotomus nigriceps, 325

samarensis (cont.)
   Penelopides, 211
   Penelopides panini, 211
   Phapitreron, 119
   Prionochilus, 386
   Prionochilus olivaceus, 386
   Pycnonotus goiavier, 278, 278
   Rhinomyias ruficauda, 329
   Rhipidura superciliaris, 327
   Sarcophanops, 224
   Sarcops calvus, 369
   Setaria, 329
Sanderling, 100, pl. 24
Sandpiper, Broad-billed, 102, pl. 24
   Common, 92, pl. 22
   Curlew, 101, pl. 24
   Green, 92, pl. 22
   Least, 100, pl. 24
   Marsh, 89, pl. 21
   Sharp-tailed, 101, pl. 24
   Terek, 93, pl. 22
   Wood, 92, pl. 22
SANDPIPERS, 84-85, 88-89, 92-95, 100-102
sandwichensis, Oestrelata, 2
   Pterodroma phaeopygia, 2
sanfordi, Rallus torquatus, 67
Sarcophanops samarensis, 224
Sarcops calvus calvus, 368
Sarcops calvus lowii, 369
Sarcops calvus melanonotus, 369
Sarcops calvus mindorensis, 369
Sarcops calvus minor, 369
Sarcops calvus samarensis, 369
Sarcops calvus similis, 369
Sarcops lowii, 369
Sarcops melanonotus, 369
saturata, Hirundo, 232
   Hirundo rustica, 232
saturatior, Iole philippinus, 279
saturatus, Cuculus, 155
   Passer, 409
   Passer montanus, 409
saularis, Copsychus, 294, 294, 295
sauli, Rhipidura, 327
   Rhipidura cyaniceps, 327
Saxicola caprata anderseni, 296, 296
Saxicola caprata caprata, 296
Saxicola caprata randi, 296, 296
schach, Lanius, 361
schisticeps, Lalage, 240
schmackeri, Jole, 284
   Penelopides, 210
scolopacea, Eudynamys, 160, 160
SCOLOPACIDAE, 84-85, 88-89, 92-95, 100-102
Scolopax cinerea, 93
Scolopax gallinago, 95
Scolopax madagascariensis, 85
Scolopax minima, 94

Scolopax nebularia, 89
Scolopax rusticola, 95, 95
Scolopax stenura, 95
scops, Otus, 167, 168, 168
Scops everetti, 169
Scops fuliginosus, 169
Scops longicornis, 167
Scops mindorensis, 167
Scops philippensis, 174
Scops sibutuensis, 168
Scops whiteheadi, 168
scutulata, Ninox, 176, 176
seebohmi, Bradypterus luteoventris, 308, 308
   Cettia, 308
   Cettia diphone, 308
Seicercus montis xanthopygius, 320
seloputo, Strix, 176
semigaleatus, Buceros, 213
   Buceros hydrocorax, 213
semilarvatus, Melaniparus, 256
   Parus, 256, 256, 257
   Parus semilarvatus, 256
semipalmatus, Limnodromus, 94
   Macrorhamphus, 94
semirufa, Cisticola, 311
   Cisticola exilis, 311
sepium, Orthotomus, 326
septentrionalis, Collocalia esculenta, 186
   Culicicapa helianthea, 347, 347
   Macropygia tenuirostris, 132
septimus, Batrachostomus, 177, 178, 178
   Batrachostomus septimus, 178
sepulcralis, Cacomantis variolosus, 158
   Cuculus, 158
sericeus, Orthotomus, 326
   Sturnus, 365, 365
Serinus estherae mindanensis, 416
Serinus mindanensis, 416
Setaria ruficauda, 329
Setaria samarensis, 329
severus, Falco, 53, 53
   Falco severus, 53
Shama, Black, 296, pl. 62
   Palawan, 295, pl. 62
   White-eyebrowed, 295, pl. 62
sharpii, Grus antigone, 66, 66
Shearwater, Wedge-tailed, 2, pl. 1
   White-faced, 1, pl. 1
SHEARWATERS, 1-2
Sheldrake, 26, pl. 7
shelleyi, Aethopyga, 382, 382, 383
   Aethopyga shelleyi, 382
Shortwing, Blue, 290, pl. 62
Shoveler, Common, 31, pl. 8
Shrike, Brown, 360, pl. 75
   Schach, 361, pl. 75
   Strong-billed, 361, pl. 75
   Tiger, 360, pl. 75

SHRIKES, *360-361, 364*
siasiensis, *Dendrocopos maculatus*, 220
    Yungipicus, 220
sibirica, *Limicola*, 102
    Limicola falcinellus, 102
    Muscicapa, 341, 341
    Muscicapa sibirica, 341
sibutuense, *Dicaeum*, 396
    Dicaeum trigonostigma, 396
sibutuensis, *Otus scops, 168*
    Scops, 168
sibuyanica, *Dicaeum*, 395
sibuyanicum, *Dicaeum trigonostigma*, 395
sierramadrensis, *Corvus enca, 251*, 251
    Zosterops nigrorum, 407
sillimani, *Brachypteryx montana, 291*, 291
similis, *Sarcops calvus*, 369
simillima, *Motacilla flava, 355*, 355
simplex, *Cyornis*, 340
    Cyornis rufigaster, 340
    Gerygone, 303
    Gerygone sulphurea, 303
simplicior, *Muscicapa rufigastra*, 340
sinensis, *Ardea*, 10
    Centropus, 161, 162, 162
    Ixobrychus, 10, 10
    Ixobrychus sinensis, 10
    Oriolus, 365
    Pelecanus, 4
    Phalacrocorax carbo, 4
    Sterna, 110
    Sterna albifrons, 110
    Sturnus, 365
siparaja, *Aethopyga, 384*
Siphia enganensis, 339
Siphia erithacus, 338
Siphia platenae, 338
Siphia ramsayi, 339
siquijorensis, *Hypsipetes, 284, 285*
    Hypsipetes siquijorensis, 284
    Iole, 284
    Loriculus, 150
    Loriculus philippensis, 150
    Pachycephala philippinensis, 354, 354
    Tanygnathus lucionensis, 143
    Zosterops, 406
    Zosterops everetti, 406
Siskin, European, *416*, pl. 85
Sitta frontalis apo, 258
Sitta frontalis isarog, 257, 257
Sitta frontalis lilacea, 258
Sitta frontalis mesoleuca, 257
Sitta frontalis oenochlamys, 257
Sitta frontalis palawana, 258, 258
Sitta frontalis zamboanga, 258, 258
SITTIDAE, *257-258*
SKUAS, *103-104*
Skylark, Small, *227*, pl. 50

smithi, *Pelargopsis capensis*, 200
    Ramphalcyon capensis, 200
smyrnensis, *Halcyon, 201*
Snipe, Common, *95*, pl. 23
    Jack, *94*, pl. 23
    Marsh, *94*, pl. 23
    Painted-, 77, pl. 19
    Pintail, *95*, pl. 23
snowi, *Parus semilarvatus, 256*, 256
solitarius, *Monticola*, 297
soloensis, *Accipiter, 46*
    Falco, 46
sonneratii, *Cacomantis*, 155
sordida, *Pitta, 225, 226*, 226
    Pitta sordida, 225
    Turdus, 225
sordidus, *Micromacronus leytensis, 276*, 276
sorghophila, *Calamodyta*, 317
sorghophilus, *Acrocephalus*, 317
sorsogonensis, *Napothera*, 265
    Napothera rabori, 265
    Oriolus chinensis, 251
    Phylloscopus cebuensis, 320, 320
    Stachyris whiteheadi, 267
Sparrow, Java, *414*, pl. 84
    Tree, *409*, pl. 84
sparverioides, *Cuculus, 154*, 154
    Cuculus sparverioides, 154
speciosa, *Dasycrotapha*, 267
    Stachyris, 267
sperata, *Certhia, 373*
    Cinnyris, 373
    Nectarinia, 373, 374, 374
    Nectarinia sperata, 373
Spermestes fuscans, 414
Sphenocercus australis, 114, 115
Spider Hunter, Little, *384*, pl. 80
    Naked-faced, *385*, pl. 80
spilocephala, *Ninox*, 175
    Ninox philippensis, 175
spilonota, *Ninox philippensis*, 175
spilonotus, *Circus*, 42
    Circus aeruginosus, 42
    Ninox, 175
Spilornis cheela palawanensis, 42
Spilornis holospilus, 42
Spilornis panayensis, 42
spinus, *Carduelis, 416*
    Fringilla, 416
Spizaetus cirrhatus limnaeetus, 52
Spizaetus philippensis, 52, 52
spodocephala, *Emberiza, 416*, 416
Spoonbill, Lesser, *23*, pl. 6
squatarola, *Pluvialis*, 77
    Tringa, 77
Stachyris capitalis affinis, 266
Stachyris capitalis boholensis, 266
Stachyris capitalis capitalis, 266

Stachyris capitalis dennistouni, 266
Stachyris capitalis isabelae, 266, 266
Stachyris capitalis nigrocapitata, 265
Stachyris hypogrammica, 268, 268
Stachyris nigrocapitata boholensis, 266
Stachyris nigrorum, 268, 268
Stachyris plateni plateni, 265
Stachyris plateni pygmaea, 265, pl. 57
Stachyris speciosa, 267
Stachyris striata, 267
Stachyris whiteheadi, 267
Stachyris whiteheadi sorsogonensis, 267
stagnatilis, Totanus, 89
    Tringa, 89
Starling, Ashy, *368*, pl. 76
    Gray-backed, *365*, pl. 76
    Lesser Glossy, *364*, pl. 76
    Philippine Glossy, *364*, pl. 76
    Silky, *365*, pl. 76
    Violet-backed, *365*, pl. 76
STARLINGS, *364-365, 368-369*
steerei, Eurylaimus, 224
    Otus, 168
    Pernis celebensis, 35, 35
    Pyrrhula, 417
    Pyrrhula leucogenys, 417
steerii, Brachyurus, 226
    Centropus, 162, 162
    Ceyx, 191
    Eurylaimus, 224, 224
    Eurylaimus steerii, 224
    Oriolus, 249
    Oriolus xanthonotus, 249
    Pitta, 226, 226
    Pitta steerii, 226
stellaris, Ardea, 10
    Botaurus, 10
    Botaurus stellaris, 10
stentoreus, Acrocephalus, 317
stenura, Gallinago, 95
    Scolopax, 95
STERCORARIIDAE, *103-104*
Stercorarius pomarinus, 103
Sterna albifrons sinensis, 110
Sterna anaethetus, 111
Sterna anaethetus anaethetus, 111
Sterna bergii cristata, 111
Sterna caspia, 105
Sterna cristata, 111
Sterna dougallii bangsi, 110, 110
Sterna fuscata nubilosa, 111
Sterna hirundo longipennis, 110
Sterna javanica, 105
Sterna leucoptera, 104
Sterna longipennis, 110
Sterna nilotica, 105
Sterna nubilosa, 111
Sterna pileatus, 114

Sterna sinensis, 110
Sterna sumatrana, 110, 110
Sterna zimmermanni, 114, 114
Stilt, White-headed, *102*, pl. 25
STILTS, *102*
Stint, Little, *100*, pl. 24
    Temminck's, *101*, pl. 24
stolidus, Anous, 114
Stoparola nigrimentalis, 346
Stoparola panayensis nigriloris, 346
Stork, White-necked, *23*, pl. 6
STORKS, *23*
Streptopelia bitorquata dusumieri, 132
Streptopelia chinensis palawana, 133
Streptopelia chinensis tigrina, 133
Streptopelia dusumieri gutierrezi, 132
Streptopelia tranquebarica humilis, 132
striata, Columba, 133
    Coracina, 234, 235, 235
    Coracina striata, 234 .
    Geopelia, 133
    Geopelia striata, 133
    Hypotaenidia, 66
    Stachyris, 267
striaticeps, Iole, 279
    Macronous, 269, 269
    Macronous striaticeps, 269
    Minodoria, 269
striatissimum, Dicaeum aeruginosum, 387, 387
striatus, Butorides, 18, 18
    Corvus, 234
    Dicrurus, 245
    Dicrurus hottentottus, 245
    Rallus, 66, 66
    Rallus striatus, 66
    Zosterornis, 267
STRIGIDAE, *167-169, 174-177*
striolata, Hirundo, 233, 233
    Hirundo striolata, 233
Strix amauronota, 166
Strix badia, 166
Strix flammea, 177
Strix hirsuta japonica, 176
Strix seloputo wiepkeni, 176
STURNIDAE, *364-365, 368-369*
Sturnus chineraceus, 368, 368
Sturnus philippensis, 365
Sturnus sericeus, 365, 365
Sturnus sinensis, 365
subfurcatus, Apus affinis, 188
    Cypselus, 188
subminuta, Calidris, 100
    Tringa, 100
subnigra, Penelopides, 210
    Penelopides panini, 210
sula, Sula, 4
Sula dactylatra personata, 3
Sula leucogaster plotus, 4

Sula personata, 3
Sula rubripes, 4
Sula sula rubripes, 4
SULIDAE, *3-4*
sulphurata, Emberiza, 415, 415
sulphurea, Gerygone, 303
suluensis, Cephalophoneus, 361
    Ceyx, 198
    Dicrurus, 248
    Dicrurus hottentottus, 248
    Dryocopus javensis, 219
    Lanius schach, 361
    Oriolus, 250
    Pardaliparus elegans, 255
    Parus elegans, 255
    Prioniturus discurus, 140
    Pycnonotus goiavier, 278, 278
    Surniculus lugubris, 159
    Thriponax javensis, 219
    Turnix, 58
    Turnix sylvatica, 58
sumatrana, Ardea, 21, 21
    Ardea sumatrana, 21
    Sterna, 110, 110
sumatranus, Tanygnathus, 148, 148
sumatrensis, Graucalus, 234
Sunbird, Apo, *378,* pl. 79
    Flaming, *379,* pl. 79
    Hachisuka's, *378,* pl. 79
    Lovely, *383,* pl. 80
    Macklot's, *375,* pl. 78
    Mountain, *382,* pl. 79
    Olive-backed, *375,* pl. 78
    Plain-throated, *372,* pl. 78
    Van Hasselt's, *373,* pl. 78
    Yellow-backed, *384,* pl. 80
SUNBIRDS, *372-375, 378-379, 382-385*
superbus, Ptilinopus, 123
superciliaris, Cittocincla, 295
    Copsychus luzoniensis, 295
    Hypothymis, 326
    Rhipidura, 326, 327, 327
    Rhipidura superciliaris, 326
superciliosus, Lanius, 361
    Lanius cristatus, 361
    Phaenicophaus, 161
    Phoenicophaeus, 161, 161
    Phoenicophaeus superciliosus, 161
Surniculus lugubris chalybaeus, 159, 159
Surniculus lugubris mindorensis, 159
Surniculus lugubris minimus, 160, 160
Surniculus lugubris suluensis, 159
Surniculus lugubris velutinus, 159
Surniculus velutinus, 159
suscitator, Turnix, 59
Swallow, Bank, *232,* pl. 50
    Barn, *232,* pl. 50
    Mosque, *233,* pl. 50

    Pacific, *233,* pl. 50
SWALLOWS, *232-233*
    WOOD-, *360*
Swamphen, Plain, *74,* pl. 17
    Purple, *75,* pl. 18
    White-breasted, *74,* pl. 17
Swift, House, *188,* pl. 42
    Lesser Tree, *189,* pl. 42
    Malaysian Spine-tailed, *187,* pl. 42
    Northern Spine-tailed, *187,* pl. 42
    Palm, *188,* pl. 42
    Philippine Spine-tailed, *187,* pl. 42
    White-rumped, *188,* pl. 42
Swiftlet, Edible-nest, *183,* pl. 41
    Glossy, *186,* pl. 41
    Gray, *183,* pl. 41
    Himalayan, *182,* pl. 41
    Pygmy, *186,* pl. 41
SWIFTS, *182-183, 186-188*
    TREE, *189*
sylvatica, Turnix, 57, 58, 58
Sylvia lanceolata, 316
Sylvia (Locustella) ochotensis, 316
SYLVIIDAE, *303, 308-311, 316-321, 324-326*
Syrnium philippense, 174
Syrnium whiteheadi, 176
Syrnium wiepkeni, 176

T

tabon, Megapodius freycinet, 54
tabuensis, Porzana, 69, 69
    Porzana tabuensis, 69
Tachornis pallidior, 188
tadorna, Anas, 26
    Tadorna, 26
Tadorna tadorna, 26
tahitica, Hirundo, 233
Tailor-bird, Ashy, *326,* pl. 68
    Black-headed, *325,* pl. 68
    Common, *324,* pl. 68
    Luzon, *321,* pl. 68
    Mountain, *321,* pl. 68
    Rufous-crowned, *326,* pl. 68
    White-eared, *325,* pl. 68
taivana, Motacilla flava, 358
taivanus, Budytes, 358
talisi, Penelopides, 210
Tantalus melanocephalus, 22
Tantalus variegatus, 85
tantilla, Riparia chinensis, 232
    Riparia paludicola, 232
Tanygnathus burbidgii, 148
Tanygnathus everetti, 148
Tanygnathus freeri, 148
Tanygnathus lucionensis horrisonus, 142
Tanygnathus lucionensis hybridus, 143, 143
Tanygnathus lucionensis koikei, 143
Tanygnathus lucionensis lucionensis, 143

475

Tanygnathus lucionensis moro, 143
Tanygnathus lucionensis nigrorum, 143
Tanygnathus lucionensis paraguenus, 143
Tanygnathus lucionensis salvadorii, *142*
Tanygnathus lucionensis siquijorensis, 143
Tanygnathus megalorynchos megalorynchos, *143*
Tanygnathus salvadorii, 142
Tanygnathus sumatranus burbidgii, *148*
Tanygnathus sumatranus duponti, *148*, 148
Tanygnathus sumatranus everetti, *148*
Tanygnathus sumatranus freeri, *148*
Tattler, Gray-tailed, *93*, pl. 22
Tchitrea rufa, 349
Teal, Common, 27, pl. 7
    Cotton, *34*, pl. 8
    Garganey, *30*, pl. 8
telephonus, Cuculus, 155
    Cuculus canorus, *155*
temminckii, Calidris, *101*
    Kurukuru, 123
    Ptilinopus superbus, *123*
    Tringa, 101
tenuirostris, Anous, 114
    Calidris, *100*
    Macropygia, 131, 132
    Macropygia phasianella, *131*
    Totanus, 100
Tererolaema leclancheri, 122
Tern, Black-billed Common, *110*, pl. 27
    Black-naped, *110*, pl. 26
    Brown-winged, *111*, pl. 27
    Caspian, *105*, pl. 26
    Chinese Crested, *114*, pl. 27
    Crested, *111*, pl. 27
    Gull-billed, *105*, pl. 26
    Little, *110*, pl. 26
    Roseate, *110*, pl. 27
    Sooty, *111*, pl. 27
    Whiskered, *105*, pl. 26
    White-winged Black, *104*, pl. 26
TERNS, *104-105*, *110-111*, *114*
Terpsiphone atrocaudata periophthalmica, *350*
Terpsiphone cinnamomea cinnamomea, *349*
Terpsiphone cinnamomea unirufa, *349*
Terpsiphone cyanescens, *350*
Terpsiphone nigra, 350
Tersiphone unirufa, 349
Tersiphone unirufa ramosi, 349
tertius, Lanius validirostris, *364*, 364
Tetrao pintadeanus, 55
Thalasseus bergii halodramus, 111
theresae, Nectarinia sperata, *374*, 374
Thick-knee, Reef, *103*, pl. 25
THICK-KNEES, *103*
thomassoni, Merula, 301
    Turdus poliocephalus, *301*
thompsoni, Pitta erythrogaster, *225*, 225
Threskiornis aethiopica melanocephala, 22

THRESKIORNITHIDAE, *22-23*
Thriponax hargitti, 218
Thriponax javensis confusus, 217
Thriponax javensis var. nov. *suluensis*, 219
Thriponax mindorensis, 218
Thriponax multilunatus, *218*
Thriponax pectoralis, 218
Thriponax philippensis, 218
Thrush, Ashy Ground, *300*, pl. 63
    Blue Rock, *297*, pl. 63
    Dusky, *303*, pl. 64
    Dyal, *294*, pl. 62
    Golden Ground, *300*, pl. 63
    Island, *301*, pl. 64
    Japanese Brown, *302*, pl. 64
    Kuhl's Ground, *297*, pl. 63
    Pale, *302*, pl. 64
    Sunda Ground; *300*, pl. 63
THRUSHES, *290-291*, *294-297*, *300-303*
ticaensis, Penelopides panini, *211*, 211
Tiga everetti, 216
tigrina, Columba, 133
    Streptopelia chinensis, *133*
tigrinus, Lanius, *360*, 360
TIMALIIDAE, *262-269*, *276*
timoriensis, Megalurus, *310*, 310
tinnabulans, Calamanthella, 311
    Cisticola juncidis, *311*
Tinnunculus, Falco, 53
tiphia, Aegithina, *286*, 286
Tit-babbler, Brown, *269*, pl. 58
    Gray-faced, *268*, pl. 58
    Miniature, *276*, pl. 58
TITMICE, *254-257*
Titmouse, Elegant, *254*, pl. 55
    Palawan, *256*, pl. 55
    White-fronted, *256*, pl. 55
tobata [sic], *Tringa*, 102
todayensis, Aplonis minor, *364*
    Lamprocorax, 364
torquatus, Rallus, *67*, 67
    Rallus torquatus, 67
totanus, Totanus, 88
    Tringa, 88
Totanus acuminatus, 101
Totanus brevipes, 93
Totanus guttifer, 89
Totanus stagnatilis, 89
Totanus tenuirostris, 100
Totanus totanus eurhinus, 88
tranquebarica, Streptopelia, *132*
Tree-babbler, Black-crowned, *265*, pl. 57
    Negros, *268*, pl. 58
    Palawan, *268*, pl. 58
    Pygmy, *265*, pl. 57
    Red-headed, *263*, pl. 56
    Rough-templed, *267*, pl. 57
    Striped, *267*, pl. 58

Whitehead's, *267*, pl. 57
TREE SWIFTS, *189*
Treron curvirostra erimacra, 115, 115
Treron formosae filipina, 114, 114
Treron formosae mcgregorii, 115
Treron pompadora amadoni, 115, 115
Treron pompadora axillaris, 115
Treron pompadora canescens, 118, 118
Treron pompadora everetti, 118
Treron vernans vernans, 118
Trichastoma cinereiceps, 262
Trichoglossus johnstoniae johnstoniae, 139
Trichoglossus johnstoniae pistra, 140, 140
Trichostoma rufifrons, 263
trigonostigma, Dicaeum, 394, 395, 396, 396
Triller, Black and White, *239*, pl. 52
        Pied, *240*, pl. 52
Tringa canutus, 95
Tringa chirurgus, 76
Tringa ferruginea, 101
Tringa glareola, 92, 92
Tringa guttifera, 89
Tringa hypoleucos, 92, 92
Tringa incanas brevipes, 93
Tringa interpes, 93
Tringa nebularia, 89
Tringa ochrophus, 92, 92
Tringa pugnax, 102
Tringa squatarola, 77
Tringa stagnatilis, 89
Tringa subminuta, 100
Tringa temminckii, 101
Tringa tobata [sic], 102
Tringa totanus eurhina, 88
trinitatis, Muscicapa hyperytha, 331
trivirgatus, Accipiter, 46, 46
        Phylloscopus, 317, 318, 318, *319*, 319
trochilus, Cinnyris sperata, 373
troglodytes, Collocalia, 186, 186
Trogon, Philippine, *189*, pl. 43
Trogon ardens, 189
TROGONIDAE, *189-190*
TROGONS, *189-190*
Tropicbird, White-tailed, *3*
TROPICBIRDS, *3*
Trynga alba, 100
Trynga ruficollis, 100
tsubame, Collocalia whiteheadi, 183
TURDIDAE, *290-291, 294-297, 300-303*
turdina, Salicaria, 317
Turdus atriceps, 276
Turdus aureus, 300
Turdus chrysolaus, 302
Turdus chrysolaus chrysolaus, 302
Turdus interpes, 297
Turdus luzoniensis, 295
Turdus mindanensis, 295
Turdus mindorensis, 301

Turdus moluccensis, 226
Turdus nigrorum, 301
Turdus obscurus, 303, 303
Turdus pallidus, 302, 302
Turdus philippensis, 297
(Turdus) philippinus, 279
Turdus poliocephalus katanglad, 302, 302
Turdus poliocephalus kelleri, 302
Turdus poliocephalus malindangensis, 301
Turdus poliocephalus mayonensis, 301
Turdus poliocephalus mindorensis, 301
Turdus poliocephalus nigrorum, 301
Turdus poliocephalus thomassoni, 301
Turdus sordida, 225
TURNICIDAE, *57-59, 66*
Turnix celestinoi, 58
Turnix haynaldi, 59
Turnix nigrescens, 59
Turnix ocellata benguetensis, 66, 66
Turnix ocellata ocellata, 59
Turnix suluensis, 58
Turnix suscitator fasciata, 59
Turnix suscitator nigrescens, 59
Turnix sylvatica celestinoi, 58
Turnix sylvatica masaaki, 58, 58
Turnix sylvatica suluensis, 58
Turnix sylvatica whiteheadi, 57
Turnix whiteheadi, 57
Turnix worcesteri, 58, 58
Turnstone, *93*, pl. 22
tweeddalei, Irena, 287
        Irena puella, 287
        Megalurus, 310
        Megalurus timoriensis, 310
Tyto capensis amauronota, 166
TYTONIDAE, *166-167*

U

unicolor, Bradypterus caudatus, 309
        Collocalia, 183
        Pseudotharrhaleus, 309
unirufa, Terpsiphone cinnamomea, 349
        Tersiphone, 349
unirufus, Centropus, 163, 163
        Pyrrhocentor, 163
Upupa epops (?) *longirostris, 207*
Upupa longirostris, 207
UPUPIDAE, *207*
urostictus, Brachypus, 276
        Poliolophus, 277
        Pycnonotus, 276, 277, 277
        Pycnonotus urostictus, 276

V

validirostris, Dendrocopos maculatus, 219
        Lanius, 361, 361, *364*, 364
        Lanius validirostris, 361

validirostris (cont.)
    Picus, 219
Vanellus cinereus, 77
vanikorensis, Collocalia, 183
vargasi, Ceyx erithacus, 199
variegatus, Numenius variegatus, 85
    Tantalus, 85
variolosus, Cacomantis, 158, 158
vegae, Larus argentatus, 104
velutinus, Surniculus, 159
    Surniculus lugubris, 159
veredus, Charadrius, 84, 84
vernans, Columba, 118
    Dendrophassa, 118
    Treron, 118
    Treron vernans, 118
verreauxii, Alcedo, 191
    Alcedo meninting, 191
verticalis, Prioniturus, 142
    Prioniturus montanus, 142
vestita, Collocalia, 183
violacea, Motacilla, 365
virescens, Ardea (Butorides), 18
virgatus, Accipiter, 43, 43
virgicapitus, Ceyx goodfellowi, 198
viridicollis, Orthotomus cucullatus, 321, 321
viridifacies, Erythrura, 410, 410
viridis, Centropus, 162, 163
    Centropus viridis, 162
    Cuculus, 162
    Merops, 206
viridissimum, Dicaeum bicolor, 389, 389
visayanus, Pardaliparus elegans, 255
    Parus elegans, 255
Volvocivora mindanensis, 238
vulcani, Zosterops montana, 405
    Zosterops whiteheadi, 405
vulgaris, Coturnix, 56

W

Wagtail, Forest, *355,* pl. 74
    Gray, *358,* pl. 74
    Pied, *358,* pl. 74
    Yellow, *355,* pl. 74
waldeni, Aceros leucocephalus, 211
    Craniorrhinus [sic], 211
Warbler, Arctic Willow, *320,* pl. 67
    Asiatic Grasshopper, *316,* pl. 66
    Bush-, *303,* pl. 65
    Common Fantail, *311,* pl. 67
    Dubois' Leaf, *319,* pl. 67
    Golden-headed Fantail, *311,* pl. 67
    Gray's Grasshopper, *316,* pl. 66
    Great Reed, *317,* pl. 66
    Long-tailed Ground, *309,* pl. 65
    Mountain Bush-, *308,* pl. 65
    Mountain Leaf, *317,* pl. 67
    Philippine Leaf, *319,* pl. 67

Rufous-capped Canegrass, *310,* pl. 66
    Russet Scrub, *308,* pl. 65
    Speckled Reed, *317,* pl. 66
    Streaked Grasshopper, *316,* pl. 66
    Striated Canegrass, *309,* pl. 66
    Yellow-breasted Flycatcher, *320,* pl. 67
    Yellow-breasted Wren-, *303,* pl. 65
WARBLERS, OLD WORLD, *303, 308-311, 316-321, 324-326*
Watercock, 75, pl. 18
watermanni, Ficedula, 338
    Ficedula westermanni, 338
    Muscicapa, 338
    Muscicapula, 338
waterstradti, Prioniturus, 141
    Prioniturus montanus, 141
WAXBILLS, *409-411, 414-415*
WEAVERBIRDS, *409*
Wheatear, *297,* pl. 63
Whimbrel, *85,* pl. 21
Whistler, White-bellied, *350,* pl. 73
    Yellow-bellied, *354,* pl. 73
Whistling-duck, Spotted, *26,* pl. 7
    Wandering, *26,* pl. 7
White-eye, Cinnamon, *408,* pl. 83
    Everett's, *405,* pl. 83
    Goodfellow's, *408,* pl. 83
    Mountain, *404,* pl. 83
    Philippine, *399,* pl. 83
    Yellow, *406,* pl. 83
WHITE-EYES, *399, 404-408*
whiteheadi, Cinnyris, 374
    Collocalia, 182, 183
    Collocalia brevirostris, 182
    Dicaeum haematostictum, 394
    Dicrurus leucophaeus, 244
    Hyloterpe, 351
    Prioniturus discurus, 141, 141
    Scops, 168
    Stachyris, 267, 267
    Syrnium, 176
    Turnix, 57
    Turnix sylvatica, 57
    Zosterops, 404, 405
    Zosterops montana, 404
    Zosterornis, 267
Widgeon, European, *30,* pl. 8
wiepkeni, Strix seloputo, 176
    Syrnium, 176
wiglesworthi, Anthreptes malacensis, 372, 372
winchelli, Halcyon, 202, 202, 203, 203
    Halcyon winchelli, 202
    Hyloterpe, 351
    Pachycephala cinerea, 351
wolfei, Alauda arvensis, 227
    Alauda gulgula, 227
Woodcock, *95,* pl. 23
woodi, Cyrtostomus jugularis, 378

478

Leonardina, 262, 262
Macronous gularis, 268
Mixornis, 268
Nectarinia jugularis, 378
Woodpecker, Crimson-backed, *220*, pl. 48
Great Slaty, *216*, pl. 48
Pygmy, *219*, pl. 48
Sooty, *217*, pl. 48
Three-toed, *216*, pl. 48
White-bellied Black, *217*, pl. 48
WOODPECKERS, *216-221*
Wood-swallow, White-breasted, *360*, pl. 75
WOOD-SWALLOWS, *360*
worcesteri, Anous tenuirostris, 114
Chibia, 248
Loriculus, 150
Loriculus philippensis, *150*
Micranous, 114
Turnix, *58*, 58
Wren-babbler, Luzon, *264*, pl. 56
Yellow-breasted, *303*, pl. 65

X

xanthocephalus, Chrysocolaptes, 221
Chrysocolaptes lucidus, 221
xanthodryas, Phyllopneuste, 320
Phylloscopus borealis, 320
Xantholaema intermedia, 216
Xantholestes panayensis, 347
xanthonotus, Oriolus, 248, 249, 249, *250*, 250
xanthopygia, Cryptolopha, 320
xanthopygium, Dicaeum, 394
Dicaeum trigonostigma, 394
xanthopygius, Seicercus montis, 320
xanthorhynchus, Chalcites, 159
Chrysococcyx, 159
Chrysococcyx xanthorhynchus, *159*
Xenus cinereus, 93

Y

yairocho, Pitta erythrogastra, 224
yamamurae, Oriolus chinensis, 250
Yungipicus basilanicus, 219
Yungipicus leytensis, 219
Yungipicus siasiensis, 220
yunnanensis, Anthus hodgsoni, 359
Anthus maculatus, 359

Z

zamboanga, Rhabdornis inornatus, 262
Rhinomyias ruficauda, *329*, 329
Sitta frontalis, *258*, 258
Zeocephus cinnamomeus, 349
Zeocephus cyanescens, 350
zimmeri, Culicicapa heliathea, *347*, 347
zimmermanni, Sterna, *114*, 114

Zonophaps poliocephala nobilis, 130
zonorhyncha, Anas, 27
Anas poecilorhyncha, 27
Zoothera andromedae, 300
Zoothera cinerea, 300
Zoothera dauma aurea, 300
Zoothera interpres interpres, 297
ZOSTEROPIDAE, *399, 404-408*
Zosterops aureiloris, 407
Zosterops basilanica, 405
Zosterops batanis, 399
Zosterops boholensis, 405
Zosterops everetti, 406
Zosterops everetti basilanica, 405
Zosterops everetti boholensis, 405
Zosterops everetti everetti, 406
Zosterops everetti mandibularis, 406, 406
Zosterops everetti siquijorensis, 406
Zosterops flavissima, 407
Zosterops forbesi, 405
Zosterops goodfellowi, 408
Zosterops goodfellowi malindangensis, 408
Zosterops halconensis, 404
Zosterops laeta, 405
Zosterops luzonica, 406
Zosterops meyeni, 399
Zosterops meyeni batanis, 399
Zosterops meyeni meyeni, 399
Zosterops meyleri, 407
Zosterops montana diuatae, 405, 405
Zosterops montana finitima, 404
Zosterops montana gilli, 404, 404
Zosterops montana halconensis, 404
Zosterops montana parkesi, 404, 404
Zosterops montana pectoralis, 404, 404
Zosterops montana vulcani, 405
Zosterops montana whiteheadi, 404
Zosterops nigrorum, 407
Zosterops nigrorum aureiloris, 407
Zosterops nigrorum catarmanensis, 408, 408
Zosterops nigrorum luzonica, 406
Zosterops nigrorum meyleri, 407
Zosterops nigrorum mindorensis, 407, 407
Zosterops nigrorum nigrorum, 407
Zosterops nigrorum richmondi, 407
Zosterops nigrorum sierramadrensis, 407
Zosterops richmondi, 407
Zosterops siquijorensis, 406
Zosterops whiteheadi, 404
Zosterops whiteheadi vulcani, 405
Zosterornis affinis, 266
Zosterornis dennistouni, 266
Zosterornis pygmaeus, 265
Zosterornis striatus, 267
Zosterornis whiteheadi, 267

Publication date:
December 30, 1971

480